KU-371-491

Kinetics of Chemical Change
in Solution

THE MACMILLAN COMPANY
NEW YORK · BOSTON · CHICAGO · DALLAS
ATLANTA · SAN FRANCISCO

MACMILLAN AND CO., Limited
LONDON · BOMBAY · CALCUTTA · MADRAS
MELBOURNE

THE MACMILLAN COMPANY
OF CANADA, Limited
TORONTO

KINETICS OF
CHEMICAL CHANGE
IN SOLUTION

By EDWARD S. AMIS

FORMERLY ASSOCIATE PROFESSOR OF CHEMISTRY, LOUISI-
ANA STATE UNIVERSITY; ALSO SENIOR RESEARCH CHEMIST,
CARBIDE AND CARBON CHEMICALS CORPORATION, OAK
RIDGE, TENN. AT PRESENT PROFESSOR OF CHEMISTRY,
UNIVERSITY OF ARKANSAS

THE MACMILLAN COMPANY

NEW YORK: *1949*

COPYRIGHT, 1949, BY THE MACMILLAN COMPANY

All rights reserved — no part of this book may be reproduced in any form without permission in writing from the publisher, except by a reviewer who wishes to quote brief passages in connection with a review written for inclusion in magazine or newspaper.

PRINTED IN THE UNITED STATES OF AMERICA

"The Catalytic Isomerization of Paraffin Hydrocarbons III. The Course of the Reaction," by Julius D. Heldman. *J. Am. Chem. Soc.*, **66**, 1789 (1944). Copyright, 1944, by the American Chemical Society.

"The Dielectric Constant of Polar Liquids," by J. Norton Wilson. *Chem. Rev.*, **25**, 377 (1939). Copyright, 1939, by The Williams and Wilkins Co., Baltimore, Md.

"The Influence of Dipole-Dipole Coupling on the Specific Heat and Susceptibility of a Paramagnetic Salt," by J. H. Van Vleck. *J. Chem. Phys.*, **5**, 320 (1937). Published by the American Institute of Physics, Inc. (1937).

"Solid Catalysis and Reaction Rates," by O. A. Hougen and K. M. Watson. *Ind. Eng. Chem.*, **35**, 529 (1943). Copyright, 1943, by the American Chemical Society.

"The Catalytic Decomposition of Sodium Hypochlorite Solutions," by John R. Lewis. *J. Phys. Chem.*, **32**, 1808 (1928). Copyright, 1928, by The Williams and Wilkins Co., Baltimore, Md. (See Fig. 9, p. 324.)

"The Rate of Solution of Magnesium in Acids," by Martin Kilpatrick and J. Henry Rushton. *J. Phys. Chem.*, **38**, 269 (1934). Copyright, 1934, by The Williams and Wilkins Co., Baltimore, Md. (See Fig. 8, p. 317.)

"Reaction Velocity in Ionic Solutions, " by Victor K. LaMer. *Chem. Rev.*, **10**, 179 (1932). Copyright, 1932, by The Williams and Wilkins Co., Baltimore, Md. (See Fig. 1, p. 75.)

"The Activated Complex and the Absolute Rate of Chemical Reactions," by Henry Eyring. *Chem. Rev.*, **17**, 65 (1935). Copyright, 1935, by The Williams and Wilkins Co., Baltimore, Md. (See Fig. 9, p. 138.)

"The Velocity of Ionic Reactions," by J. N. Brönsted and Robert Livingston. *J. Am. Chem. Soc.*, **49**, 435 (1927). Copyright, 1927, by the American Chemical Society. (See Fig. 2, p. 8.)

"Contribution to the Theory of Acid and Basic Catalysis. The Mutarotation of Glucose," by J. N. Brönsted and E. A. Guggenheim. *J. Am. Chem. Soc.*, **49**, 2554 (1927). Copyright, 1927, by the American Chemical Society. (See Fig. 1, p. 249.)

"The Rate of Reaction of Certain Alcohols with Para-nitrobenzoyl Chloride in Anhydrous Ether Solutions," by Avery Allen Ashdown. *J. Am. Chem. Soc.*, **52**, 268 (1930). Copyright, 1930, by the American Chemical Society. (See Fig. 3, p. 9.)

"The Effect of Structure upon the Reactions of Organic Compounds. Benzene Derivatives," by Louis P. Hammett. *J. Am. Chem. Soc.*, **59**, 96 (1937). Copyright, 1937, by the American Chemical Society. (See Fig. 2, p. 251.)

"The Kinetics of the Decompositions of the Trinitrobenzoates in Ethyl Alcohol," by Frank H. Verhoek. *J. Am. Chem. Soc.*, **61**, 186 (1939). Copyright, 1939, by the American Chemical Society. (See Figs. 1, 2, pp. 185, 187.)

"The Activity Coefficient of Ions in Very Dilute Solutions," by J. N. Brönsted and Victor K. LaMer. *J. Am. Chem. Soc.*, **46**, 555 (1924). Copyright, 1924, by the American Chemical Society. (See Figs. 1, 2, 3, pp. 26, 27, 28.)

"Absolute Rates of Four-Atom Reactions," by William Altar and Henry Eyring. *J. Chem. Phys.*, **4**, 661 (1936). Published by the American Institute of Physics, Inc. (See Figs. 6, 7, pp. 135, 136.)

"The Absolute Rate of Homogeneous Atomic Reactions," by Henry Eyring, Harold Gerschinowitz, and Cheng E. Sun, *J. Chem. Phys.*, **3**, 786 (1935). Published by the American Institute of Physics, Inc. (See Fig. 3, p. 130.)

"Some Quantum-Mechanical Considerations in the Theory of Reactions Involving an Activation Energy," by J. O. Hirschfelder and E. Wigner. *J. Chem. Phys.*, **7**, 616 (1939). Published by the American Institute of Physics, Inc. (See Fig. 10, p. 141.)

"Solvent Effects on the Kinetics of Ionic Reactions and the Choice of the Concentration Scale," by Hubert G. Davis and Victor K. LaMer. *J. Chem. Phys.*, **10**, 585 (1942). Published by the American Institute of Physics, Inc. (See Figs. 3, 4, pp. 195, 196.)

"The Effects of Solvents on Reaction Rates," by Keith J. Laidler and Henry Eyring. *Ann. New York Acad. Sci.*, **39**, 303 (1940). Published by The New York Academy of Sciences. (See Figs. 2, 6, 7, 8, 3, pp. 124, 174, 176, 177, 264.)

"Measurement of Adsorption at the Air-Water Interface by the Microtome Method," by James W. McBain and Robert C. Swain. *Proc. Roy. Soc.*, **154**A, 608 (1936). (See Figs. 1, 2, pp. 273, 274.)

"Electron Transfer Spectra and their Photochemical Effects," by Eugene Rabinowitch. *Rev. Modern Phys.*, **14**, 112 (1942). Published by the American Institute of Physics, Inc. (See Figs. 2, 3, pp. 231, 233.)

"The Nature of Active Carbon," by John W. Hassler and William E. McMinn, *Ind. Eng. Chem.* **37**, 645 (1945). Copyright, 1945, by the American Chemical Society. (See Figs. 6, 7, pp. 301, 303.)

To my father and mother, Jack and Artie Amis

Preface

The plan of this book is to give a student of kinetics a thorough training in the subject of rate processes in solution. The first chapter is to acquaint him with concepts of the order of reactions, the determination of the order of a reaction, some of the complexities which arise, and the basic equation of Arrhenius. It is then made clear that in order to comprehend the further development of kinetic theory of reactions in solution, certain fundamental concepts must be arrived at and understood. Therefore the next two chapters take up the theory of activity coefficients of ions in solution and the theories of dielectric constants of liquids and polar moments of molecules. From these fundamental concepts and the idea of an intermediate complex the Brönsted-Christiansen-Scatchard equation, the effect of changing ionic strength, and the rate of reaction between ions and dipolar molecules are derived in Chapters IV and VIII.

In Chapters V and VI the theory of temperature coefficients is taken up. In Chapter V energy of activation arising from the ionic atmosphere, the coulombic energy of activation, and the energy of activation in constant composition and isodielectric media are discussed and calculated. Influence of nonelectrostatic forces upon temperature coefficients is determined. In Chapter VI the Arrhenius frequency factor is discussed as to its components. The entropy of activation is developed and the influences of ionic atmosphere and of the dielectric constant of the solvent on the entropy of activation are formulated. The entropy of activation is shown to be the controlling factor in determining the influence of structure upon reaction rates. The difference of the frequency factor in isocomposition and isodielectric solvents is developed.

Chapter VII takes up theoretical and semiempirical calculation of activation energies. It also includes Eyring's theory of absolute reaction rates.

In Chapter IX the influence of the solvent upon reaction rates is summarized. Methods of determining whether these effects are those predicted by electrostatics are discussed and evaluated. Some cases of specific solvent effects are illustrated. The choice of concentration units is considered.

Chapter X deals with photochemistry and chain reactions, Chapter XI with homogeneous catalysis, and Chapter XII with heterogeneous catalysis. Thus are completed the major subjects to be considered when dealing with rate processes in solution.

In many cases complete mathematical treatment of a subject is presented to acquaint the student with methods and procedures. When full mathematical formulation is not given there is no attempt to make the necessary steps appear easy by using the well-worn phrases "it is obvious," "it can readily be shown" and "it is easily seen."

The most difficult chapters perhaps are Chapters II, III, VII and VIII. Chapters II and III may be omitted without seriously impairing the continuity of the treatment, provided the results of the calculations presented in these chapters are accepted on faith. For a thorough grasp of the kinetics of rate processes in solution, however, the matter presented in these chapters is fundamental.

The student who masters this book will have the fundamentals of kinetics of reactions in solution, both theoretical and applied, well in hand. He will also know much about activity coefficients of ions, electrostatic and nonelectrostatic forces between ions and between ions and molecules in solution, polar moments in solution, dielectric constants of liquids, and also about many of the fundamentals of gaseous kinetic processes.

The plan is to make the book lucid and readable, but also thorough. It is planned to design a text and at the same time make the contents such that the book will be a worthwhile addition to the bookshelf of any chemist who deals at all with kinetics, the Debye-Hückel theory, solvent effects upon solutes and the theory of liquid dielectrics.

The author wishes to thank Dr. George Jaffé for his valuable criticisms of many chapters in this book and for his collaboration in the writing of Chapter III. Thanks are also due to Dr. Selmer W. Peterson for his criticisms of Chapter II. To the Research Council of Louisiana State University the author is deeply grateful for a grant-in-aid which made the writing of this book possible.

Table of contents

Table of contents

CHAPTER I

Introduction

The law of mass action and reaction rate

In the derivation of the law of mass action, Guldberg and Waage in 1867 indicated the influence of concentration of reactants upon the rate of chemical change. This law states that the rate of a chemical reaction at any specified time is proportional to the effective molecular concentrations of the reactants present at that time. Thus for the general reaction

$$A + B + \cdots \longrightarrow L + M + \cdots$$

the rate, r, of the reaction is

$$r \propto C_A C_B \cdots \tag{1.1}$$

or

$$r = k' C_A C_B \cdots \tag{1.2}$$

where k' is the specific rate constant. For the case where more than one molecule of a reactant is involved in the reaction, the concentration of that reactant must be raised to the power represented by the coefficient of that reactant in the chemical equation depicting the reaction. Thus for the reaction

$$aA + bB + \cdots \longrightarrow lL + mM + \cdots$$

$$r \propto C_A^a C_B^b \tag{1.3}$$

$$r = k' C_A^a C_B^b \tag{1.4}$$

Sometimes the simplest stoichiometrical equation which can be written for reactants going to products does not represent the true nature of the kinetic process, and in this case the rate equation must be written to represent the rate-governing step in the rate process. Thus Busse and Daniels (*J. Am. Chem. Soc.*, **49**, 1257, 1927) show that while the decomposition of N_2O_5 depends only on the concentration of N_2O_5 the over-all reaction is represented by the equation

$$2N_2O_5 \longrightarrow 4NO_2 + O_2$$

1

The rate would seem to be dependent upon the square of the concentration of the N_2O_5, thus

$$r = k'C_{N_2O_5}^2 \tag{1.5}$$

However if the mechanism is written as given by these authors

$$
\begin{array}{lll}
(1) & N_2O_5 \longrightarrow NO + NO_2 + O_2 & \text{(slow)} \\
(2) & \underline{NO + N_2O_5 \longrightarrow 3NO_2} & \text{(fast)} \\
 & 2N_2O_5 \longrightarrow 4NO_2 + O_2 &
\end{array}
$$

then, since step (1) is the slow and, therefore, the rate-determining step, the rate is given by

$$r = k'C_{N_2O_5} \tag{1.6}$$

First-order reactions

The order of a reaction is determined by the dependence of the rate of chemical change upon the concentrations of reactants and hence by the mathematical equation used in the calculation of the rate. The mechanism of a reaction on the other hand depends on the number of molecules involved in a chemical transformation. For example, two types of reactant molecules may have to participate in a chemical change, but one of the types may be present in large excess or it may play the part of a catalyst. Its contribution to the rate will be a constant factor. The velocity of the reaction will then be dependent only upon the concentration of the other reacting substance. Whether one or more substances are reacting, if the rate of reaction is directly proportional to the concentration of one reacting substance, then the reaction is first-order. The mechanisms of reactions will be discussed later.

Thus the decomposition of nitrogen pentoxide both in the gaseous phase (Daniels and Johnston, *J. Am. Chem. Soc.*, **43**, 53, 1921) and in solution (Eyring and Daniels, *J. Am. Chem. Soc.*, **52**, 1472, 1929) was shown to be first-order. The first step in the mechanism given above involving only nitrogen pentoxide concentration to the first power meets the requirements of the definition of the first-order reaction. The rate equation can be written

$$\frac{-dC_{N_2O_5}}{dt} = k'C_{N_2O_5} \tag{1.7}$$

or

$$-\int \frac{dC_{N_2O_5}}{C_{N_2O_5}} = k'\int dt \tag{1.8}$$

and

$$-\ln C_{N_2O_5} = k't + \text{constant} \tag{1.9}$$

But for this reaction at constant volume of reacting solution

$$C_{N_2O_5} = K(V_\infty - V_t) \qquad (1.10)$$

where V_∞ is the total volume of oxygen liberated, V_t is the volume of oxygen liberated in time t, and K is a constant. Hence

$$-\ln(V_\infty - V_t) = k't + \text{constant} \qquad (1.11)$$

where the integration constant in Eq. (1.11) is greater than that in Eq. (1.9) by the $\ln K$.

If $-\ln(V_\infty - V_t)$ is plotted against t, a straight line results and the slope of this line gives k'.

If Eq. (1.8) is integrated between limits we have

$$\int_{C_{N_2O_5(1)}}^{C_{N_2O_5(2)}} \frac{dC_{N_2O_5}}{C_{N_2O_5}} = k' \int_{t_1}^{t_2} dt \qquad (1.12)$$

$$\ln \frac{C_{N_2O_5(1)}}{C_{N_2O_5(2)}} = k'(t_2 - t_1) \qquad (1.13)$$

or

$$k' = \frac{2.303}{t_2 - t_1} \log \frac{V_\infty - V_1}{V_\infty - V_2} \qquad (1.14)$$

In this calculation k' is obtained by inserting the values of t_1 and t_2, and the corresponding values of $(V_\infty - V_1)$ and $(V_\infty - V_2)$ into Eq. (1.14), and solving for k'. The constancy of k' as calculated for the decomposition of nitrogen pentoxide of an initial concentration of 5.33 moles per liter in carbon tetrachloride at 45° C is illustrated by the data of Eyring and Daniels given in Table I.

TABLE I Decomposition rate of nitrogen pentoxide in carbon tetrachloride at 45° C

Time (sec.)	cc. of O_2 remaining	$k' \times 10^4$ (sec.$^{-1}$)
0	32.60	—
82	30.79	6.97
162	29.19	6.67
409	24.82	6.57
604	20.59	6.37
1129	14.49	6.67
1721	9.60	6.95
1929	8.30	6.99
3399	3.27	6.69

The methods illustrated in the decomposition of N_2O_5 are general in the case of first-order reactions.

For such first-order reactions the rate should be independent of the initial concentration of the reactant. Actually in the case of the nitrogen pentoxide reaction it was found that the rate was somewhat greater in concentrated than in dilute solutions, though the first-order nature of the reaction was maintained throughout the whole course of the reaction irrespective of the initial concentration. This concentration effect was explained by assuming the decomposition products N_2O_4 and NO_2 to be as effective as the original N_2O_5 molecules in maintaining the rate. This they do probably by maintaining the same collision rate of high energy molecules with reactant N_2O_5 molecules as do N_2O_5 molecules themselves. Thus a corresponding rate of activation of reactant N_2O_5 molecules is produced even after some N_2O_5 decomposes to NO_2 and N_2O_4.

Second-order reactions

If the rate of a reaction is proportional to the square of the concentration of an only reacting substance, or to the product of the concentrations of two reacting substances, the reaction is second-order. Thus in the hypothetical second-order reactions

$$2A \longrightarrow L + M$$

and

$$A + B \longrightarrow L + M$$

we have in the second case

$$\frac{-dC_A}{dt} = \frac{-dC_B}{dt} = k'C_AC_B \tag{1.15}$$

If the initial concentrations of A and B are respectively a and b moles per liter and if x moles of A (and, therefore, of B) have reacted in time t then

$$\frac{dx}{dt} = k'(a - x)(b - x) \tag{1.16}$$

In the simplest case $a = b$ and $a - x = b - x$, then

$$\frac{dx}{(a - x)^2} = k' \, dt \tag{1.17}$$

and

$$\frac{1}{a - x} = k't + \text{constant} \tag{1.18}$$

or integrating between limits

$$\int_0^x \frac{dx}{(a-x)^2} = k' \int_0^t dt \qquad (1.19)$$

yields

$$k' = \frac{x}{ta(a-x)} \qquad (1.20)$$

Eq. (1.15) to (1.20) would hold also for the first case where two like molecules react.

Integrating between limits where $a \neq b$ we have

$$\int_0^x \frac{dx}{(a-x)(b-x)} = k' \int_0^t dt \qquad (1.21)$$

and by the method of rational fractions let

$$\frac{1}{(a-x)(b-x)} = \frac{G}{(a-x)} + \frac{H}{(b-x)} \qquad (1.22)$$

where G and H are constants and are given by

$$G = \frac{1}{b-a} \qquad (1.23)$$

and

$$H = \frac{1}{a-b} \qquad (1.24)$$

Therefore

$$\int_0^x \frac{G\,dx}{a-x} + \int_0^x \frac{H\,dx}{b-x} = k' \int_0^t dt \qquad (1.25)$$

Substituting the values of G and H given by Eq. (1.23) and (1.24), inserting limits, and solving for k', we obtain

$$k' = \frac{1}{(a-b)t} \ln \frac{b(a-x)}{a(b-x)} \qquad (1.26)$$

or

$$k' = \frac{2.303}{(a-b)t} \log \frac{b(a-x)}{a(b-x)} \qquad (1.27)$$

or

$$\log \frac{(a-x)}{(b-x)} = \frac{(a-b)k't}{2.303} - \log \frac{b}{a} \qquad (1.28)$$

According to Eq. (1.18) a plot of the reciprocal of the concentration of one of two reactants present in equal concentrations versus time should give a straight line.

In Table II are the data of Walker (*Proc. Roy. Soc.*, A, **78**, 157, 1906) for the bimolecular reaction

$$CH_3COOCH_3 + OH^- \longrightarrow CH_3CO_2^- + CH_3OH$$

For these data $a = b = 0.0100N$. The values of k' were obtained using Eq. (1.20). The constancy of k' shows that the reaction is strictly second-order.

TABLE II   The specific rate constant for the saponification of methyl acetate by caustic soda

t (min.)	x	$a - x$	$\dfrac{1}{t}\dfrac{x}{a(a-x)} = k'$ (l/mol. min.)
0	0	0.0100	
3	0.00260	.00740	11.7
4	.00317	.00683	11.6
5	.00366	.00634	11.5
6	.00411	.00589	11.6
7	.00450	.00550	11.7
8	.00481	.00519	11.6
10	.00536	.00464	11.5
12	.00584	.00416	11.7
15	.00637	.00363	11.7
18	.00681	.00319	11.8
21	.00712	.00288	11.8
25	.00746	.00254	11.8
	1.000		mean 11.8

In Fig. 1 is a plot of $\dfrac{1}{a-x}$ versus t. The plot of the data is a straight line as theory requires. The slope of the line gives k'.

From Eq. (1.28) when the concentrations of the two reactants are not initially the same, a plot of $\log \dfrac{(a-x)}{(b-x)}$ as ordinates versus time as abscissas gives a straight line for second-order reactions. The slope of this line multiplied by $\dfrac{2.303}{a-b}$ yields k'. Eq. (1.27) can also be used to calculate k'. Brönsted and Livingston (*J. Am. Chem. Soc.*, **49**, 435, 1927) studied the second-order reaction

$$(CoBr(NH_3)_5)^{++} + OH^- \longrightarrow (CoOH(NH_3)_5)^{++} + Br^-$$

where $a \neq b$. A plot of $\log \dfrac{(a-x)}{(b-x)}$ versus t is given in Fig. 2. The value of k' was obtained from the slope of the line as explained above.

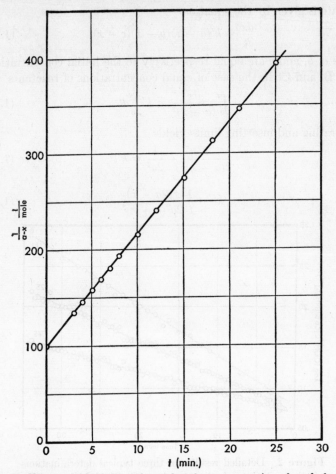

Figure 1 Plot of the reciprocal of the concentration of methyl acetate one of two reactants present in equal concentrations versus time.

Third-order reactions

In third-order reactions the rate is proportional to the product of the concentrations of three reactants. In the hypothetical reaction

$$A + B + C \longrightarrow L + M + N$$

the rate is given by the equation

$$\frac{dx}{dt} = k'(a - x)(b - x)(c - x) \tag{1.29}$$

where a, b, and c are equal respectively to the initial concentrations of A, B, and C. In the case of equal concentrations of reactants

$$\int_0^x \frac{dx}{(a - x)^3} = k' \int_0^t dt \tag{1.30}$$

Integrating and inserting limits yields

$$\frac{1}{2(a - x)^2} - \frac{1}{2a^2} = k't \tag{1.31}$$

or

$$k' = \frac{1}{t} \frac{x(2a - x)}{2a^2(a - x)^2} \tag{1.32}$$

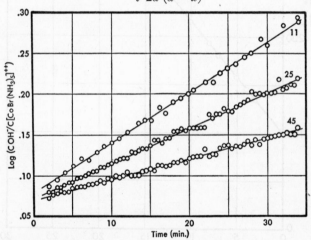

Figure 2   Detailed results for three typical determinations of the velocity of the reaction $[\mathrm{Co\,Br(NH_3)_5}]^{++} + \mathrm{OH^-} \longrightarrow [\mathrm{Co\,OH(NH_3)_5}]^{++} + \mathrm{Br^-}$.

If the reactants are all at different concentrations, Eq. (1.29) can be integrated by the method of rational fractions illustrated in the case of second-order equations. The integration yields

$$k' = \frac{1}{(b - a)(c - a)t} \ln \frac{a}{a - x} + \frac{1}{(a - b)(c - b)t} \ln \frac{b}{b - x}$$
$$+ \frac{1}{(a - c)(b - c)t} \ln \frac{c}{c - x} \tag{1.33}$$

For the case of equal concentration of reactants

$$k't a^2 = \frac{x(2a - x)}{2(a - x)^2} \tag{1.34}$$

and a plot of t as ordinates against the factor on the right of Eq. (1.34) should yield a straight line for third-order reactions. Ashdown (*J. Am. Chem. Soc.*, **52**, 268, 1930) shows that the reaction between para-

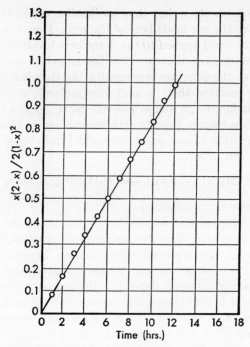

Figure 3 Rate of reaction of n-butyl alcohol with p-nitro-benzoyl chloride calculated as a third order reaction.

nitrobenzoyl chloride and n-butyl alcohol in anhydrous ether solution meets this requirement as is illustrated in Fig. 3. Here a is equal to unity.

In Table III are given Ashdown's data for the reaction between paranitrobenzoyl chloride and n-butyl alcohol. The data are for equal concentrations (in one case molal and in the other one-half molal concentrations) of reactants. The time is in hours. k'^1_3 and $k'^{0.5}_3$

are third-order constants for molal and half-molal concentrations calculated by Eq. (1.32). k'^0_3 is the third-order constant at infinite dilution calculated analytically. The constancy of the values of the velocity constants shows that the reaction is third-order.

Mechanism of chemical reactions

The term *molecularity* rather than *mechanism* would be preferable with respect to the use made here of the term. However, *mechanism* is generally the word applied to the usage here involved. With reference to mechanism, reactions are classified as to how many molecules are included in the equation representing the chemical change. In a unimolecular reaction there is only one molecule involved in the chemical equation, i.e., a single molecule reacts to give one or more molecules. Thus trinitro benzoic acid decomposed in toluene according to the equation (Moelwyn-Hughes and Hinshelwood, *Proc. Roy. Soc.*, A, **131,** 186, 1931).

$$C_6H_2(NO_2)_3COOH \longrightarrow C_6H_3(NO_2)_3 + CO_2$$

and the reaction is unimolecular.

If two particles must come together to cause chemical change, the reaction is bimolecular. This does not mean the reaction rate is necessarily calculated using a second-order equation. In some cases one of two reactants is in large excess or is regenerated in later steps in the reaction. Thus the rate may depend on the concentration of only the reactant present in small amount or permanently altered, and in such a case the reaction would be really bimolecular, sometimes called pseudo-unimolecular, but would be calculated by use of a first-order equation. Thus the inversion of cane sugar involves the collision of sugar molecules with oxonium ions, but the oxonium ion is subsequently regenerated and its concentration remains unchanged. The reaction is pseudo-unimolecular but its rate is calculated from the first-order equation. For the reaction between bromacetate ion and thiosulfate ion, the equation is (LaMer, *J. Am. Chem. Soc.*, **51,** 3341, 1929)

$$BrCH_2COO^- + S_2O_3^{--} \longrightarrow S_2O_3CH_2COO^{--} + Br^-$$

Thus the reaction is bimolecular.

TABLE III n-Butyl alcohol and p-nitrobenzoyl chloride at equal molal concentrations

	MOLAL				HALF-MOLAL		
t	x	$k_3'^1$	$k_3'^0$	t	x	$k_3'^{0.5}$	$k_3'^0$
1	0.717	0.080	0.119	1	0.0266	0.110	0.138
2	.1366	.085	.125	2	.0452	.097	.121
3	.1877	.086	.124	3	.0727	.107	.134
4	.2302	.086	.123	4	.0854	.098	.121
5	.2614	.083	.119	5	.1035	.098	.121
6	.2895	.082	.116	6	.1146	.092	.114
7	.3212	.084	.117	7	.1366	.098	.120
8	.3439	.083	.115	8	.1506	.097	.117
9	.3663	.082	.113	9	.1632	.095	.115
10	.3862	.083	.114	10	.1736	.093	.114
11	.4071	.084	.115	11	.1840	.091	.112
				12	.1963	.091	.112

In termolecular reactions three molecules participate in the reaction. Ashdown (*J. Am. Chem. Soc.*, **52,** 268, 1930) represents the reaction between certain alcohols and paranitrobenzoyl chloride in anhydrous ether solutions by the symbolical equation

$$A + 2B \longrightarrow E + F + B$$

where A represents the paranitrobenzoyl chloride and B represents the alcohol. One molecule of alcohol is regenerated in the process. This equation represents a termolecular reaction involving one molecule of the chloride and two molecules of the alcohol.

Zero-order reactions

Sometimes concentration is held constant, as in the case of a saturated solution in contact with undissolved material. Sometimes also, there may be limiting factors other than concentration which govern a reaction rate. For example the intensity of light in a photochemical reaction or the extent of surface available for adsorption of reactant may be the rate-determining quantity. For these cases where the rate is not determined by the concentration of the reactant (or concentrations of the reactants) the reaction is of zero-order and the rate equation is

$$\frac{dx}{dt} = k' \qquad\qquad (1.35)$$

or

$$x = k't + \text{constant} \qquad\qquad (1.36)$$

and since $x = 0$ when $t = 0$, the constant equals 0, and

$$x = k't \qquad (1.37)$$

Schwab and Rudolph (*Z. physik. Chem.*, **B12,** 427, 1931) found that the hydrogenation of ethyl cinnamate using nickel catalyst was zero-order at normal hydrogen concentrations on the nickel. At smaller concentrations there were deviations from zero-order. Lewis and co-workers (*J. Phys. Chem.*, **32,** 243, 1808, 1928; *ibid.*, **35,** 915, 1931; *ibid.*, **37,** 917, 1933) found that the catalytic decomposition of sodium hypochlorite solutions was in some cases zero-order.

Complex chemical reactions

In many chemical reactions complications arise so that the rate process is not simple. Sometimes there is a reverse reaction in which products react to produce the original reactants. Thus

$$A + B \underset{k_2'}{\overset{k_1'}{\rightleftharpoons}} L + M$$

Such reactions should be avoided in theoretical kinetic studies if the reverse reaction is pronounced at early stages in the process. Provided the reaction between products is negligible over an appreciable change of reactants to products, the forward reaction rate can be measured at the beginning before the reverse process is of such a magnitude as to influence the results. Then if the equilibrium constant, K, is determined, the reverse rate constant, k_2', can be calculated from the relation $k_1'/k_2' = K$, provided the reacting substances are nearly ideal solutes or perfect gases. Thus for the unimolecular reaction

$$A \rightleftharpoons L$$

we have

$$\frac{dx}{dt} = k_1'(a - x) - k_2'x \qquad (1.38)$$

and

$$\int_0^x \frac{dx}{k_1'a - (k_1' + k_2')x} = \int_0^t dt \qquad (1.39)$$

$$k_1' + k_2' = \frac{1}{t} \ln \frac{k_1'a}{k_1'a - (k_1' + k_2')x} \qquad (1.40)$$

At equilibrium $\frac{dx}{dt} = 0$, and if x_e is the equilibrium value of x, we have from Eq. (1.38)

$$\frac{k_1'}{k_2'} = \frac{x_e}{a - x_e} \tag{1.41}$$

$$x_e = \frac{k_1'a}{k_1' + k_2'} \tag{1.42}$$

Substituting the value of a from Eq. (1.42) into Eq. (1.40) we have

$$k_1' + k_2' = \frac{1}{t} \ln \frac{(k_1' + k_2')x_e}{(k_1' + k_2')x_e - (k_1' + k_2')x_e}$$

$$= \frac{1}{t} \ln \frac{x_e}{x_e - x} \tag{1.43}$$

But $\dfrac{x_e}{a - x_e} = K$ for ideal solutes and from Eq. (1.41), $\dfrac{k_1'}{k_2'} = K$. From Eq. (1.41) and (1.43), k_1' and k_2' can be calculated if a, x_e, and x are determined. Similar treatment of other orders of reactions will lead to comparable relationships between k_1', k_2' and K.

In the case of a reverse reaction maintaining a concentration of intermediate complex which then decomposes into products, we may write

$$A + B \underset{k_2'}{\overset{k_1'}{\rightleftharpoons}} A' + B \qquad A' \overset{k_3'}{\longrightarrow} L$$

For these chemical equations

$$\frac{dC_L}{dt} = k_3'C_{A'} \tag{1.44}$$

and

$$\frac{dC_{A'}}{dt} = k_1'C_AC_B - k_2'C_{A'}C_B - k_3'C_{A'} = 0 \tag{1.45}$$

so that

$$\frac{dC_L}{dt} = \frac{k_3'k_1'C_AC_B}{k_3' + k_2'C_B} = \frac{k_1'C_AC_B}{1 + \dfrac{k_2'}{k_3'}C_B} \tag{1.46}$$

For C_B so large that the denominator becomes equal to $(k_2'/k_1')C_B$

$$\frac{dC_L}{dt} = \frac{k_1'}{k_2'}k_3'C_A = Kk_3'C_A = k'C_A \tag{1.47}$$

and the reaction is first-order. For C_B so small that $(k_2'/k_1')C_B$ is negligible in comparison with unity

$$\frac{dC_L}{dt} = k_1'C_AC_B \tag{1.48}$$

Here the rate is second-order. For intermediate concentrations of B (and assuming either that the number of collisions between A molecules is relatively small or that activation of A is brought about only by collision with B), the reaction will be neither strictly first- nor strictly second-order. This is a mathematical picture of the collision theory which pictures the activation of the reacting molecules as being due to collisions between the molecules. The number of collisions is given by gas kinetic theory. The number of molecules activated by collision is dependent upon the velocity of the colliding molecules. Not only can a high velocity molecule collide per unit time with more molecules than can a low velocity molecule, but the high velocity molecule can impart more energy per collision to the other molecule or molecules involved than can a molecule of low energy content. These activated molecules then react to give products, and thus since the number of high velocity molecules increases rapidly with temperature, the temperature coefficients of chemical reactions are generally large.

Consecutive first-order reactions are exemplified by some radioactive disintegrations. Such a reaction can be represented by the equation

$$A \xrightarrow{k_1'} L \xrightarrow{k_2'} M$$

Let a moles of A be present at the initial time and x moles of L be produced after time t. Also let y of those x moles of L decompose during the same time interval to give M. Then

$$\frac{dx}{dt} = k_1'(a - x) \tag{1.49}$$

and

$$\frac{dy}{dt} = k_2'(x - y) \tag{1.50}$$

Integrating and inserting limits Eq. (1.49) becomes

$$\ln \frac{a}{a - x} = k_1't \tag{1.51}$$

and in exponential form Eq. (1.51) can be written

$$\frac{a - x}{a} = e^{-k_1't} \tag{1.52}$$

Substituting the value of x from Eq. (1.52) into Eq. (1.50) we obtain

$$\frac{dy}{dt} + k_2'y = ak_2'(1 - e^{-k_1't}) \tag{1.53}$$

an integrating factor for Eq. (1.53) is $e^{\int p\,dt}$ where $p = k_2'$ and

$$\int p\,dt = \int k_2'\,dt = k_2't \qquad (1.54)$$

therefore

$$e^{\int p\,dt} = e^{k_2't}$$

and

$$ye^{k_2't} = \int e^{k_2't} ak_2'(1 - e^{-k_1't})\,dt$$

$$= ak_2'\int e^{k_2't}\,dt - ak_2'\int e^{(k_2'-k_1')t}\,dt$$

$$= ae^{k_2't} - \frac{ak_2'}{k_2' - k_1'} e^{(k_2'-k_1')t} + C \qquad (1.55)$$

Writing the right-hand side of Eq. (1.55) over the common denominator $k_2' - k_1'$ and dividing through by $e^{k_2't}$ yields

$$y = \frac{ak_2' - ak_1' - ak_2'e^{-k_1't} + ak_1'C_1e^{-k_2't}}{k_2' - k_1'} \qquad (1.56)$$

where $ak_1'C_1 = C(k_2' - k_1')$. Rearranging terms we obtain

$$y = \frac{ak_2'(1 - e^{-k_1't}) - ak_1'(1 - C_1e^{-k_2't})}{k_2' - k_1'} \qquad (1.57)$$

A particular solution for $C_1 = 1$, is

$$y = \frac{ak_2'(1 - e^{-k_1't}) - ak_1'(1 - e^{-k_2't})}{k_2' - k_1'} \qquad (1.58)$$

Thus the amount of M produced in time t is dependent both upon k_1' and k_2'. This illustrates how complicated a mathematical analysis relating amount of product to time elapsed may become.

Methods of determining the order of chemical reactions

The order of a reaction may be determined in one of several ways provided the reaction is not complicated by side reactions, back reactions, simultaneous reactions, consecutive reactions, or other factors which may influence the rate.

If over a considerable range of concentration change with time, substitution of data into the formula for a particular order yields a constant value for k', then the reaction is of that order.

The data under certain conditions can be plotted and the order of the reaction thus determined. For a first-order reaction according to Eq. (1.9) a plot of $\log C$ versus time gives a straight line. A second-order reaction should, if the concentrations of the two reactants are the same, yield a straight line when $1/C$ versus time is plotted (see Eq. (1.18)). If the concentrations of the three reactants are the same, a third-order reaction gives a straight line when $1/C^2$ is plotted against time (see Eq. (1.31)). If a plot of C versus time is a straight line, the reaction is zero-order, as is shown by Eq. (1.36). The dependence of half-life periods on the initial concentration indicates the order of the reaction. In Eq. (1.13) if $t_1 = 0$ and $C_2 = 1/2 C_1$, then $t_{\frac{1}{2}} = \dfrac{\ln 2}{k'}$.

The period of half-life, $t_{\frac{1}{2}}$, for a first-order reaction is, therefore, $\dfrac{\ln 2}{k'}$. For a second-order reaction where $a = b$, we have from Eq. (1.20) that $t_{\frac{1}{2}} = 1/k'a$.

Another way of determining the order is to determine the exponent of each reactant in the rate equation, by doubling the concentrations of these reactants one at a time. Thus

$$\frac{\left(\dfrac{dx}{dt}\right)_{(2C_A)^a C_B^b \cdots}}{\left(\dfrac{dx}{dt}\right)_{C_A^a C_B^b \cdots}} = \frac{k' 2^a C_A^a C_B^b \cdots}{k' C_A^a C_B^b \cdots} = 2^a \tag{1.59}$$

Therefore, if the exponent of A in the rate equation is one, the rate will be doubled by doubling C_A; if the exponent of A is two in the rate equation, the rate will be increased to four times its value by doubling A. The exponent of each reactant can be determined similarly.

By having all the reactants except one present in large excess, the exponent in the rate equation of the one reactant present in small quantities can be determined. Thus the exponent of each reactant is determined and in this way the order of the reaction ascertained.

The Arrhenius equation

An important step in the development of chemical kinetics was the equation proposed by Arrhenius in 1889 to account for the temperature coefficient of reaction rates. This equation is written

$$k' = Ze^{-\Delta E/RT} \tag{1.60}$$

Here k' is the specific reaction rate constant, Z is the Arrhenius frequency factor, ΔE is termed the *heat of activation* or *energy of activation* of the reaction, and the other quantities have their usual significance.

Taking decadic logarithms of either side of Eq. (1.60) we have

$$\log k' = \log Z - \frac{\Delta E}{2.303RT} \tag{1.61}$$

Thus if values of $\log k'$ are plotted as ordinates against the values of $1/T$ as abscissas a straight line is obtained from which ΔE can be calculated by multiplying the slope by $2.303R$. Taking the value of ΔE and substituting in Eq. (1.61) the value for Z can be obtained.

In the differential form Eq. (1.60) becomes (if Z and ΔE are considered constant)

$$\frac{d \ln k'}{dt} = \frac{\Delta E}{RT^2} \tag{1.62}$$

and when this is integrated between limits we have

$$\ln \frac{k_2'}{k_1'} = \frac{\Delta E}{R} \frac{T_2 - T_1}{T_2 T_1} \tag{1.63}$$

Therefore, by substituting two values of k' and the corresponding values of T into Eq. (1.63) we can calculate ΔE.

While ΔE is not independent of temperature (LaMer, *J. Chem. Phys.*, **1**, 289, 1933), it is often assumed to be so in order to simplify theory, and under these conditions from Eq. (1.61), considering $\log Z$ and ΔE constant and taking values of k' at each of two temperatures, we can obtain the equation

$$\log Z = \frac{\Delta(T \log k')}{\Delta T} \tag{1.64}$$

In the Arrhenius equation ΔE represents the energy which a mole of the reactant in the initial state must acquire before it will react to form products.

For bimolecular reactions the frequency factor Z is considered by some authorities to be the frequency of collision z_0 between reacting molecules A and B and as such can be calculated by the kinetic-theory equation.

$$z_0 = 1000\sigma_{A,B}^2 n_A n_B \left[8\pi RT \left(\frac{m_A + m_B}{m_A m_B} \right) \right]^{\frac{1}{2}} \tag{1.65}$$

In this equation m_A and m_B are the masses of the A and B molecules respectively. $\sigma_{A,B}$ is the collision diameter (the sum of the molecular radii) of A and B. R is the gas constant per mole and n_A and n_B are the number of molecules of A and B, respectively, per cubic centimeter. z_0 will be then the number of collisions occurring per liter per second presumably in a gaseous system, though the same collision frequency has been applied to reactions taking place in solutions.

LaMer (*J. Chem. Phys.*, **1**, 289, 1933) integrates the Arrhenius equation in the form

$$\frac{d \ln k'}{dT} = \frac{1}{2T} + \frac{\Delta E}{RT^2} \tag{1.66}$$

which Tolman (*Statistical Mechanics*, New York, The Chemical Catalog Company, Inc., pp. 259–69, 1927) has derived statistically for bimolecular reactions and obtains

$$\ln k' = C + \tfrac{1}{2} \ln T - \frac{\Delta F}{RT} \tag{1.67}$$

where $\Delta F = \Delta E - T \, \Delta S$ gives the temperature dependence of ΔE. He solves for C in Eq. (1.67) by setting $\Delta F = 0$. Under these conditions every collision results in reaction, and k', the specific reaction rate constant, is the same as the collision rate z_0. Hence, $C = \ln z_0 - \tfrac{1}{2} \ln T$. Equation (1.67) emphasizes that there is an entropy of activation as well as an energy of activation.

In unimolecular reactions Z is many times equal to the frequency of vibration of the atoms within the molecule.

CHAPTER II

The Debye-Hückel theory

Fundamental theories in solution kinetics

We have already studied in Chapter I two great steps made toward the interpretation of reaction kinetics. These steps were the statement of the mass action principle and the formulation of the theory of the temperature coefficients of reaction rates. Before we can go further into the kinetics of reactions in solution we must develop the theory of Debye and Hückel (*Physik. Zeits.*, **24,** 185, 1923) for activity coefficients of ions and of electrolytes, and the theories of Debye (*Polar Molecules*, New York, The Chemical Catalog Company, Inc., 1929), Onsager (*J. Am. Chem. Soc.*, **58,** 1486, 1936), Van Vleck (*J. Chem. Phys.*, **5,** 320, 1937), Kirkwood (*J. Chem. Phys.*, **7,** 911, 1939), and Jaffé (*J. Chem. Phys.*, **8,** 879, 1940) concerning polar molecules and liquid dielectrics.

Brönsted (*Z. physik. Chem.*, **102,** 169, 1922) formulated the influence of ion atmospheres upon ionic reaction rates in solution. Brönsted (*ibid.*, **115,** 337, 1925) and Christiansen (*ibid.*, **113,** 35, 1924) applied the theory of Debye and Hückel concerning the ion atmosphere effect upon the activities of ions in solution, to rates of ionic reactions in liquid dielectrics. This was the third great step in chemical kinetic theory as applied to reactions taking place in solution. Scatchard (*Chem. Rev.*, **10,** 220, 1932) made the fourth outstanding contribution to the kinetics of reactions in solution when he developed the effect upon reaction velocities of changing solvent in so far as the solvent can be considered homogeneous and of uniform dielectric constant. A fifth step which applied to kinetics of reactions in general was Eyring's theory of absolute reaction rates (*Z. physik. Chem.*, **12B,** 279, 1931; *J. Chem. Phys.*, **3,** 107, 1935).

Amis and Jaffé (*J. Chem. Phys.*, **10,** 598, 1942) have derived

19

an equation for the rate of reaction between ions and dipolar molecules.

These reaction rate formulas, however, are based on the theories of ionic atmospheres, of polarity of molecules, and of the dielectric constants of solvents.

This chapter will, therefore, deal with the theory of ionic atmospheres and the following chapter will deal with the theories of polarity and dielectrics.

Procedure of Debye and Hückel

Experimentally it was known that the activity coefficients of ion constituents in solutions were less than unity, long before any theoretical explanation was found for the phenomena. Milner (*Phil. Mag.*, [6] **23**, 551, 1912; **25**, 742, 1913) attempted a solution of the problem by assuming attractive and repulsive forces between charged particles; however, it was Debye and Hückel (*Physik. Z.*, **24**, 185, 1923) who most satisfactorily solved the problem of the decrease in the activity of ions due to electrostatic forces among the ions. Debye and Hückel assumed complete dissociation of strong electrolytes and explained their decreased activity in solutions at all concentrations by taking into account the attractive and repulsive forces among the ions. Since like charges attract and unlike charges repel each other, there will be on a time average more ions of unlike than of like sign in the vicinity of any ion. Hence, every ion is considered to be surrounded by an ionic atmosphere of opposite charge. Debye and Hückel's procedure is in essence the combination of the Boltzmann principle which gives the distribution of the ions as a function of their electrical and of their thermal energies with the Poisson equation which relates potential and charge density. In this manner they were able to arrive at an equation which gave the potential arising from the ionic atmosphere and which was, therefore, dependent upon the charge types and the concentrations of all the ions. From this potential the work function (Helmholtz free energy), and hence the activity coefficient of an ith sort of ion surrounded by an ionic atmosphere, could be evaluated. In the following pages the Debye-Hückel expressions for activity coefficients of ions and electrolytes will be derived.

The potential arising from the ionic atmosphere

We shall assume that there are s different species of ions. We shall further let n_i be the number of ions of species i per cubic centimeter and z_i be the valence of each ion of this species. Now since the solution is electrically neutral,

$$\sum_s n_i z_i \epsilon = 0 \tag{2.1}$$

The electrical density ρ from the Boltzmann principle is given by the equation

$$\rho = \epsilon \sum n_i z_i e^{-\frac{z_i \epsilon \psi}{kT}} \tag{2.2}$$

where ψ is the potential, k the Boltzmann gas constant, and ϵ the electronic charge. Eq. (2.2) can be expanded to give

$$\rho = \epsilon \sum n_i z_i \left[1 - \frac{z_i \epsilon \psi}{kT} + \frac{1}{2!} \left(\frac{z_i \epsilon \psi}{kT} \right)^2 - \frac{1}{3!} \left(\frac{z_i \epsilon \psi}{kT} \right)^3 + \cdots \right] \tag{2.3}$$

In the case where the electrical energy $\frac{z_i \epsilon \psi}{2}$ is small compared to the thermal energy kT, as in the case for ions in solution, the higher terms in Eq. (2.3) can be neglected and there remains

$$\rho = \epsilon \sum \left(n_i z_i - n_i z_i^2 \frac{\epsilon \psi}{kT} \right) \tag{2.4}$$

and, since the first term on the right of Eq. (2.4) is zero (see Eq. 2.1), we may write

$$\rho = -\frac{\epsilon^2}{kT} \sum n_i z_i^2 \psi \tag{2.5}$$

Poisson's equation for spherical symmetry relates potential and charge density by the expression

$$\frac{1}{r^2} \frac{d}{dr} \left(r^2 \frac{d\psi}{dr} \right) = -\frac{4\pi}{D} \rho \tag{2.6}$$

Here D is the dielectric constant of the medium, r is the distance from the central ion, and ψ is the potential at that distance. Substitution of the value of ρ from Eq. (2.5) into Eq. (2.6) gives

$$\frac{1}{r^2} \frac{d}{dr} \left(r^2 \frac{d\psi}{dr} \right) = \frac{4\pi \epsilon^2}{DkT} \sum n_i z_i^2 \psi \tag{2.7}$$

Defining $\varkappa$ by the equation

$$\varkappa = \sqrt{\frac{4\pi \epsilon^2}{DkT} \sum n_i z_i^2} \tag{2.8}$$

Eq. (2.7) becomes

$$\frac{1}{r^2}\frac{d}{dr}\left(r^2\frac{d\psi}{dr}\right) = \varkappa^2\psi \tag{2.9}$$

This equation is of the form

$$\frac{\partial^2\psi}{\partial r^2} + P\frac{d\psi}{dr} + Q = 0 \tag{2.10}$$

and can be solved by removal of the first derivative by setting

$$\psi = \psi_1 v \tag{2.11}$$

which yields

$$\frac{d^2v}{dr^2} + P_1\frac{dv}{dr} + Q_1 v = 0 \tag{2.12}$$

where

$$P_1 = P + \frac{2}{\psi_1}\frac{d\psi_1}{dr} \tag{2.13}$$

and

$$Q_1 = \frac{1}{\psi_1}\left(\frac{d^2\psi_1}{dr^2} + P\frac{d\psi_1}{dr} + Q_1\psi\right) \tag{2.14}$$

Any value desired can be assigned to P_1 and Q_1 by a proper choice of ψ_1. Thus for any value of P_1 we must have from Eq. (2.13)

$$\psi_1 = e^{\frac{1}{2}\int(P_1-P)\,dr} \tag{2.15}$$

and thus to eliminate the first derivative from Eq. (2.12), P_1 must be zero and Eq. (2.15) becomes

$$\psi_1 = e^{-\frac{1}{2}\int P\,dr} \tag{2.16}$$

Substituting this value of ψ_1 in Eq. (2.14), Q_1 becomes

$$Q_1 = Q - \frac{1}{2}\frac{dP}{dr} - \frac{1}{4}P^2 \tag{2.17}$$

Therefore differential Eq. (2.10) of the second-order is transformed into a differential equation not containing the first derivative by substituting

$$\psi = ve^{-\frac{1}{2}\int P\,dr} \tag{2.18}$$

and the transformed equation is

$$\frac{d^2v}{dr^2} + Q_1 v = 0 \tag{2.19}$$

From Eq. (2.9), (2.10), and (2.17)

$$Q_1 = -\varkappa^2 - \frac{1}{2}\frac{d}{dr}\left(\frac{2}{r}\right) - \frac{1}{4}\left(\frac{2}{r}\right)^2 = -\varkappa^2 \tag{2.20}$$

Hence Eq. (2.19) becomes

$$\frac{d^2v}{dr^2} - \varkappa^2 v = 0 \tag{2.21}$$

The corresponding auxiliary equation is

$$D^2 - \varkappa^2 = 0 \tag{2.22}$$

Hence the solution of Eq. (2.21) is

$$v = C_1 e^{-\varkappa r} + C_2 e^{\varkappa r} \tag{2.23}$$

From Eq. (2.9), (2.10), and (2.18)

$$\psi = v e^{-\frac{1}{2}\int P\, dr} = v e^{-\frac{1}{2}\int (2/r)\, dr} = v/r \tag{2.24}$$

and from Eq. (2.23) and (2.24),

$$\psi = \frac{C_1 e^{-\varkappa r}}{r} + \frac{C_2 e^{\varkappa r}}{r} \tag{2.25}$$

Now we may choose $\psi = 0$, when $r = \infty$ and since as r increases $\dfrac{e^{\varkappa r}}{r}$ becomes indefinitely large, C_2 must be zero. Then

$$\psi = \frac{C_1 e^{-\varkappa r}}{r} \tag{2.26}$$

To evaluate C_1 we proceed as follows. The charge on the central ion must be equal and opposite in sign to the charge of the surrounding atmosphere. Therefore

$$-z_i \epsilon = \int_{a_i}^{\infty} 4\pi r^2 \rho \, dr \tag{2.27}$$

Here a_i is the distance of closest approach of an ion to the central ion. But from Eq. (2.5), (2.8), and (2.26),

$$4\pi\rho = \frac{-D\varkappa^2 C_1 e^{-\varkappa r}}{r} \tag{2.28}$$

and Eq. (2.27) therefore becomes

$$z_i \epsilon = \int_{a_i}^{\infty} C_1 D\varkappa^2 r e^{-\varkappa r} \, dr \tag{2.29}$$

Letting $u = r$ and $dv = e^{-\varkappa r} \, dr$, and integrating by parts yields

$$z_i \epsilon = C_1 D e^{-\varkappa a_i}(\varkappa a_i + 1) \tag{2.30}$$

Whence

$$C_1 = \frac{z_i \epsilon}{D} \frac{e^{\varkappa a_i}}{1 + \varkappa a_i} \tag{2.31}$$

and substituting this value of C_1 into Eq. (2.26) gives for the value of ψ,

$$\psi = \frac{z_i\epsilon}{Dr} \frac{e^{\varkappa(a_i-r)}}{1 + \varkappa a_i} \qquad (2.32)$$

If the distance r from the central ion at which the potential is being measured is the distance of closest approach, then $r = a_i$, and Eq. (2.32) becomes

$$\psi_{a_i} = \frac{z_i\epsilon}{Da_i} \frac{1}{1 + \varkappa a_i} = \frac{z_i\epsilon}{Da_i} - \frac{z_i\epsilon}{D} \frac{\varkappa}{1 + \varkappa a_i} \qquad (2.33)$$

Therefore the total potential consists of two parts: that due to the central ion itself, which is given by

$$\psi_0 = \frac{z_i\epsilon}{Da_i} \qquad (2.34)$$

and is independent of concentration, and that due to the atmosphere, namely

$$\psi_i = -\frac{z_i\epsilon}{D} \frac{\varkappa}{1 + \varkappa a_i} \qquad (2.35)$$

which is a function of the concentration of the ions in the solution.

The activity coefficient of an ion

For a single ion the work function (Helmholtz free energy) due to interionic attraction is equal to the electrical energy required to charge the ion in the presence of the ionic atmosphere. Hence

$$F = kT \ln f_i = \int_0^{z_i\epsilon} \psi_i d(z_i\epsilon) \qquad (2.36)$$

Here f_i is the activity coefficient of an ion of the ith species. From Eq. (2.35) and (2.36)

$$kT \ln f_i = \int_0^{z_i\epsilon} -\frac{z_i\epsilon}{D} \frac{\varkappa}{1 + \varkappa a_i} d(z_i\epsilon)$$

$$= -\frac{z_i^2\epsilon^2}{2D} \frac{\varkappa}{1 + \varkappa a_i} \qquad (2.37)$$

Lewis and Randall define the ionic strength μ of a solution by the equation

$$\mu = \tfrac{1}{2} \sum C_i z_i^2 \qquad (2.38)$$

and from Eq. (2.37) and (2.38)

$$-\ln f_i = \frac{z_i^2 A \sqrt{\mu}}{1 + \beta a_i \sqrt{\mu}} \qquad (2.39)$$

where

$$A = \frac{\epsilon^3}{DkT} \sqrt{\frac{2\pi N}{1000DkT}} \tag{2.40}$$

and

$$\beta = \sqrt{\frac{8\pi n\epsilon^2}{1000DkT}} \tag{2.41}$$

The activity coefficient of an electrolyte

The activity coefficient of a binary electrolyte is

$$f_\pm^\nu = f_+^{\nu^+} f_-^{\nu^-} \tag{2.42}$$

In this equation ν, ν^+, and ν^- are the total number, the number of positive ions, and the number of negative ions per molecule of electrolyte, and since $\nu = \nu^+ + \nu^-$, we can write from Eq. (2.39) and (2.42)

$$-\nu \ln f_\pm = \frac{(\nu^+ z_+^2 + \nu^- z_-^2)A\sqrt{\mu}}{1 + \beta a_i \sqrt{\mu}} \tag{2.43}$$

But, since the solution is electrically neutral

$$\nu^+ z_+ = \nu^- z_- \tag{2.44}$$

Hence

$$-\nu \ln f_\pm = (\nu^- z_- z_- + \nu^+ z_+ z_-) \frac{A\sqrt{\mu}}{1 + \beta a_i \sqrt{\mu}} \tag{2.45}$$

and

$$-\ln f_\pm = \frac{z_+ z_- A\sqrt{\mu}}{1 + \beta a_i \sqrt{\mu}} \tag{2.46}$$

For very dilute solutions $\beta a_i \sqrt{\mu}$ can be neglected with respect to unity and the Debye-Hückel limiting law can be written

$$-\ln f_\pm = z_+ z_- A\sqrt{\mu} \tag{2.47}$$

Van Rysselberghe (*J. Am. Chem. Soc.*, **65,** 1249, 1943), using fundamental constants listed by Birge (*Rev. Mod. Phys.*, **13,** 233, 1941) and the dielectric constant of water at 25° C. determined by Wyman (*Phys. Rev.*, **35,** 623, 1930), gives the general values of A and β as

$$A = \frac{0.5091}{(dt)^{\frac{3}{2}}} \tag{2.48}$$

and

$$\beta = \frac{0.3286 \times 10^8}{(dt)^{\frac{1}{2}}} \tag{2.49}$$

when decadic logarithms are used and where $d = D/78.54$ and $t = T/298.16$. Therefore at 25° C. Eq. (2.46) becomes

$$-\log f_{\pm} = \frac{0.5091z_{+}z_{-}\sqrt{\mu}}{1 + 0.3286a_i\sqrt{\mu}} \qquad (2.50)$$

and the limiting law Eq. (2.47) can be written

$$-\log f_{\pm} = 0.5091z_{+}z_{-}\sqrt{\mu} \qquad (2.51)$$

Manov, Bates, Hamer and Acree (*J. Am. Chem. Soc.*, **65,** 1765, 1943) list values of A and β for water over the temperature range from 0° C. to 100° C.

Testing the theory

Brönsted and LaMer (*J. Am. Chem. Soc.*, **46,** 555, 1924) checked Eq. (2.51) by determining $-\log f_{\pm}$ from solubility data for uni-univalent,

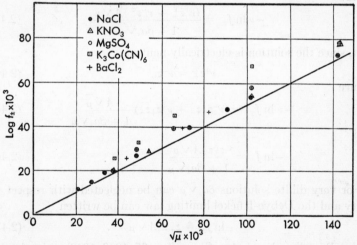

Figure 1 The relation of the activity coefficient f to the ionic strength μ for the uni-univalent salt, oxalotetramminecobalto-diammino-dinitro-oxalo cobaltiate (oxalo-nitro) in the presence of various solvent salts. The heavy line is the theoretical curve.

uni-bivalent, and tri-univalent salts for various ionic strengths. The relationship between solubilities and activity coefficients is given by these authors as

$$\log \frac{f_{\pm}^0}{f_{\pm}} = \log \frac{s}{s^0} \qquad (2.52)$$

where $f_\pm^0$ is the activity coefficient of the binary salt in a saturated solution in pure water, $f_\pm$ is the activity coefficient of the salt in a saturated solution in the presence of other salts of various concentrations, s^0 is the concentration of the salt in saturated solution in pure water, and s is the saturated concentration of the salt in solutions of other salts of various concentrations. By determining solubilities of the salt in pure water and in solutions of other salts of different concentrations, the activity coefficients of the desired salt in the various solutions can be calculated. From Eq. (2.51) the slope of the line obtained by plotting $\log f_\pm$ versus $\sqrt{\mu}$ should be about 0.51, 1.02, and

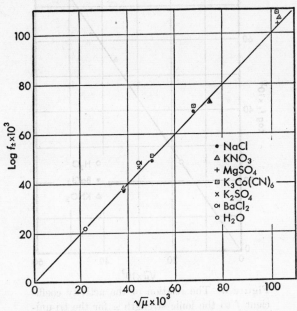

Figure 2 The relation between the activity coefficient f and the ionic strength μ for the uni-bivalent salt, oxalo-dithionato in the presence of solvent salts of various types. The heavy line is the theoretical curve.

1.53 for uni-univalent, uni-bivalent, and uni-trivalent salts, respectively. Plots of such data for the uni-univalent salt, oxalotetramminecobalt-diammino-dinitrooxalo cobaltiate [Co(NH$_3$)$_4$C$_2$O$_4$] [Co(NH$_3$)$_2$(NO$_2$)$_2$C$_2$O$_4$], the uni-bivalent salt, oxalotetramminecobalto dithionate, [Co(NH$_3$)$_4$C$_2$O$_4$]$_2$ [S$_2$O$_6$], and the tri-univalent salt, luteo-diamminodinitrooxalo cobaltiate, $[Co(NH_3)_6][Co(NH_3)_2(NO_2)_2C_2O_4]_3$, are given in Figs. 1, 2, and 3, respectively. The solid lines in these figures are the theoretical curves required by Eq. (2.51). The circles, triangles, etc. represent the data. These data for sparingly soluble electrolytes in the presence of other electrolytes of various valence types for concentrations extending from $0.0000M$ to $0.0200M$ verify the limiting law as expressed by Eq. (2.51) as well as could be expected.

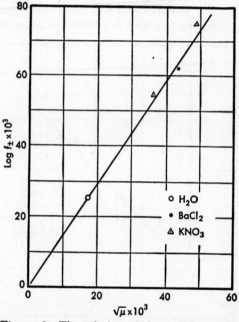

Figure 3 The relation of the activity coefficient f to the ionic strength μ for the tri-univalent salt, luteo-diamminodinitrooxalo cobaltiate in the presence of various solvent salts. The heavy line is the theoretical curve.

Inclusion of higher terms

When higher terms are used in the expansion for Eq. (2.3) an equation of the form

$$-\ln f_\pm = \frac{z_+ z_- A \sqrt{\mu}}{1 + \beta a_i \sqrt{\mu}} + \text{higher terms} \tag{2.53}$$

is obtained. Hückel (*Physik. Z.*, **26,** 83, 1925) proposes the formula

$$-\ln f_\pm = \frac{z_+z_- A\sqrt{\mu}}{1 + \beta a_i \sqrt{\mu}} + c\mu \qquad (2.54)$$

where the semiempirical constant c takes into account the variation of the dielectric constant of the solution with concentration. Van Rysselberghe (*J. Am. Chem. Soc.*, **65,** 1249, 1943) writes:

$$-\log f_\pm = \frac{0.5091 z_+ z_- \sqrt{\mu}}{1 + 0.3286 a_i \sqrt{\mu}} + \log (1 + 0.018 \Sigma m_i) \qquad (2.55)$$

Gronwall, LaMer, and Sandved (*Physik. Z.*, **29,** 358, 1928) expand the expression for ρ given by Eq. (2.2) and retain further terms in the series. They arrive at the equation for symmetrical valence types of salts which, while complex, nevertheless is a definite improvement on the simple Debye formula for predicting activity coefficients in more concentrated solutions. LaMer, Gronwall, and Grieff (*J. Phys. Chem.*, **35,** 2245, 1931) have worked out a similar equation for unsymmetrical electrolytes. The use of these complex equations has been facilitated by their originators working out and recording the values of the complicated concentration terms over a wide range of concentrations.

Criticisms of the Debye-Hückel theory

The Debye-Hückel theory for strong electrolytes is empirically successful and has been developed and applied in great detail on many types of measurements upon solutions of salts, strong acids, and strong bases. There are valid criticisms of the theory, however. For a brief summary of these criticisms the reader is referred to MacInnes, *The Principles of Electrochemistry*, New York, Reinhold Publishing Corporation, 1939, pp. 148–151.

of the dielectric constant of the solution with concentration, etc.

CHAPTER III

Liquid dielectrics and polar moments

It was previously pointed out that in order to understand the kinetics of a reaction in solution one must have some knowledge of the theories of dielectrics and polar moments. Thus the forces between reactants are altered and their rates of reactions modified depending upon the medium in which the reactants are immersed. The greatest physical effect which a solvent exerts upon reactants immersed in it is the modification of the electrostatic forces among the reactant particles through the dielectric constant influence of the medium. These electrostatic forces affect markedly the ability of reactant particles to contact each other. Aside from the dielectric constant of the solvent, these electrostatic forces are influenced largely by the nature and magnitude of charge on the reactant particles. Thus ion-ion forces are relatively large for the same medium and concentration, and ion-ion forces between highly charged ions are greater under like conditions of dielectric constant and concentration than those between ions bearing smaller charges. This is evident from Coulomb's law. Next in order of magnitude are ion-dipole forces which again depend on dielectric constant and concentration, i.e., distance between the types of particles. The nature of the dipole, e.g., the magnitude of the moment and the ease and extent to which the particle can be polarized to produce an induced moment, has a direct bearing on the degree of the ion-dipole interaction, as does also the magnitude of charge on the ion. Again there are the various types of dipole-dipole forces which though small are significant. These effects are likewise influenced by the dielectric constants of the solvent as well as by the values and natures of the moments concerned.

Thus in kinetics of reactions in solution it is necessary to have a grasp of dielectric theory and of the theory of polar moments. This chapter deals with these with the intention of laying a sufficient

30

foundation so that the reader will grasp understandingly their application to kinetic processes in solution.

The dielectric constant of a medium has its origin in the electric moments whether permanent or induced, possessed by the atoms or molecules of the medium. Suppose two charges ϵ and $-\epsilon$, equal in magnitude but opposite in sign, are present in an atom or molecule and are separated by a distance l. The dipole moment of the atom or molecule is ϵl. There are two such moments found in molecules, the permanent moments and the moments induced by the distortion of the molecule due to an applied electric field. An applied field may also induce moments in an atomic substance. In the case of molecules the induced moment may be due to electronic or atomic distortions or both, while in atoms there is a displacement of electrons relative to the nucleus, i.e., electronic distortion.

An induced moment may be calculated from the polarizability α_0 and the strength F of the uniform electric field inducing the moment using the relationship

$$m = \alpha_0 F \tag{3.1}$$

provided α_0 is known from some other set of data. Now α_0 is generally calculated from dielectric constant measurements and using the Clausius-Mosotti equation. This equation will now be derived.

The Clausius-Mosotti equation

In classical theory three vectors describing the behavior in the interior of a polarized medium are introduced: the electric intensity E, the polarization D', and the actual force on a unit pole F. They can be defined in the following way. The electric intensity is the force acting on a unit charge placed in a cylinder of relatively great length compared with its cross section. The cylinder must be bored in the insulator so as to have its axis in the direction of the lines of force. The electric intensity is represented in Fig. 1. If the cavity in the insulator is bounded on two sides by parallel planes perpendicular to the lines of force, and if the distance between the two planes is small compared to their linear dimensions, a unit charge placed between these planes will be acted upon by a force called the *electric displacement D'*. This situation is illustrated in Fig. 2. Now D' is related to E by the expression

$$D' = E + 4\pi I \tag{3.2}$$

which is general, and in which I is the induced moment per unit volume of insulator.

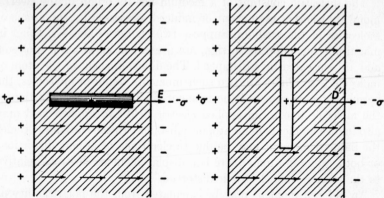

Figure 1 Illustrating the electric intensity E.

Figure 2 Illustrating the electric displacement D'.

If m is the induced moment per molecule and if there are n' molecules per unit volume, then I is given by

$$I = n'm \tag{3.3}$$

Maxwell further related D' and E by the equation

$$D' = DE \tag{3.4}$$

It is now required to find the actual force F at the location of the particle. An exact calculation of this force F requires a complicated averaging process. However, Lorentz has introduced an approximate method of calculating it by using a spherical cavity. A relationship among F, D', and E which will permit the calculation of the dielectric constant D in terms of molar polarizability, α_0, must also be found. If the particle bearing unit positive charge is placed in a spherical cavity in a dielectric medium between two plates, the actual force F at the location of the molecule can be represented as in Fig. 3. The spherical cavity must be large relative to the particle but small in comparison to the distance between the plates. The actual force F acting on the particle will then be $4\pi\sigma$, that is, the force due to the surface density of charge on the plates, minus $4\pi I$, the force due to the charges induced on the dielectric material at its juncture with the plates, and plus $\frac{4}{3}\pi I$ resulting from the charge induced on the surface of the spherical cavity. Now according to electrostatic theory, we have

$$4\pi\sigma = D' \tag{3.5}$$

and hence

$$F = D' - 4\pi I + \tfrac{4}{3}\pi I \tag{3.6}$$

In this derivation the force due to the polarized material which had to be removed to create the cavity has been disregarded. This is legitimate in the case of cubical crystals or of nonassociated liquids with random distribution, but is only approximately true in other cases. Substituting the value of D' from Eq. (3.2) and (3.4) into Eq. (3.6) gives

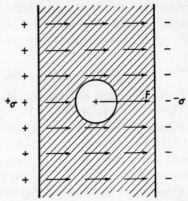

$$F = E + \frac{4}{3}\pi I = \frac{D+2}{3}E \tag{3.7}$$

From Eq. (3.1) and (3.3)

$$I = n'm = n'\alpha_0 F \tag{3.8}$$

and substituting the value of F from Eq. (3.7) into Eq. (3.8) gives

$$I = n'\alpha_0(E + \tfrac{4}{3}\pi I) \tag{3.9}$$

Figure 3 Illustrating the actual force acting on a particle when the Clausius-Mosotti relation holds.

Solving Eq. (3.2) for I and substituting this value into Eq. (3.9) yields

$$\frac{D'-E}{D'+2E} = \frac{4\pi}{3}n'\alpha_0 \tag{3.10}$$

and from this equation and Eq. (3.4) we obtain the dielectric constant D in terms of the molecular polarizability α_0. The expression is

$$\frac{D-1}{D+2} = \frac{4\pi}{3}n'\alpha_0 \tag{3.11}$$

For a dielectric medium of density ρ and molecular weight M, the number of molecules n' per unit volume is $N\rho/M$ where N is Avogadro's number. Substituting this value of n' in Eq. (3.11) yields

$$\frac{D-1}{D+2}\frac{M}{\rho} = \frac{4}{3}\pi N\alpha_0 = P \tag{3.12}$$

where P is the molar polarization. This equation is generally called the Clausius-Mosotti equation. Thus by knowing M, ρ, and D, either

α_0 or P may be calculated using Eq. (3.12). Knowing α_0 and the field strength, the induced moment m may be obtained from Eq. (3.1).

The Clausius-Mosotti equation is not exact since the assumption that the actual force may be identified with the force on a unit charge at the center of a spherical cavity is only an approximation. The above derivation is the classical one of H. A. Lorentz in the form it was given by Debye. Kirkwood (*J. Chem. Phys.*, **4,** 592, 1936) has shown by statistical methods that the equation is a limiting form of a more general expression and is strictly valid only at zero density, however, it is perhaps fairly accurate for an attenuated gas.

The Lorentz-Lorenz equation

Now D is a pure number and M/ρ corresponds to the molar volume. Therefore P as given by Eq. (3.12) is proportional to the molar volume of the dielectric material. Since we have derived the value of the molar polarization P using static methods which make the electric forces independent of temperature, then P should be uninfluenced by temperature. This is true only for those nonpolar substances whose molecules are not permanent dipoles. For these substances Maxwell's relation between the dielectric constant D and index of refraction n

$$D = n^2 \tag{3.13}$$

holds for sufficiently long wave lengths. In this equation n is the refractive index of a substance of dielectric constant D. Writing n^2 for D in Eq. (3.12) we obtain an expression for the molar refraction R which is

$$\frac{n^2 - 1}{n^2 + 2} \frac{M}{\rho} = \frac{4}{3} \pi N \alpha_0 = R \tag{3.14}$$

This is the Lorentz-Lorenz equation. The molar refraction thus calculated is found to agree with molar polarization P given by Eq. (3.12) in many cases even when P is found for long electric waves and n is measured for visible light. Thus Maxwell's relationship between the dielectric constant D and the refractive index n is found to apply in the regions of the visible spectrum when the dielectric material involved has only induced polarity. On the other hand, some media have a polarization arising from the orientation of permanent dipoles in an electric field. This polarization will be dependent upon temperature since the power of a given field to orientate a given moment will depend upon the thermal energy of the dipole. This dependence of polarization upon temperature was worked out by Debye whose ideas were based on the dependence of paramagnetism upon temperature, solved by Langevin. It is logical, therefore, before taking up Debye's theory of total molar polarization, to investigate Langevin's work on paramagnetism.

Langevin's theory of the dependence of paramagnetism upon temperature

Langevin considered each paramagnetic molecule as behaving like a small magnet with a definite moment. There are two forces influencing such a molecule in the presence of an applied external field. The field is acting on the molecular magnet, tending to cause it to orientate itself parallel to the direction of the applied field, while an opposing influence due to the thermal motion of the molecules tends to cause a random orientation. Langevin considered the mean moment m of gaseous molecules in the direction of an external magnetic field whose strength is not too large. The potential energy u of the paramagnetic molecule is given by

$$u = -(\mu \cdot F) \tag{3.15}$$

where μ is the electric moment of the molecule.

In the absence of a field, the moments of the molecules will be randomly distributed in all directions. However, in the presence of magnetic field of intensity F, the number pointing in a given direction is proportional to the solid angle $d\Omega$ and according to the Boltzmann law is given by the expression

$$Ae^{-\frac{u}{kT}} d\Omega \tag{3.16}$$

where A is a proportionality constant.

Let θ be the angle between μ and F, then

$$u = -\mu F \cos \theta \tag{3.17}$$

since a molecule pointing in the direction $d\Omega$ will have a component in the direction of the field equal to $\mu \cos \theta$ (see Fig. 4). The average moment m in the direction of the field of one molecule is given by the sum in the direction of the field of the moments of all the molecules, divided by the total number of molecules. The equation is

$$\overline{m} = \frac{\int Ae^{\frac{\mu F}{kT}\cos \theta} \mu \cos \theta \, d\Omega}{\int Ae^{\frac{\mu F}{kT}\cos \theta} \, d\Omega} \tag{3.18}$$

Since the solid angle of a cone is measured by the area which the cone cuts out of a unit sphere constructed about the apex of the cone, and since the direction of all moments forming an angle between θ

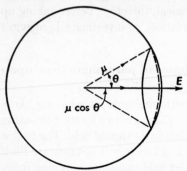

and $\theta + d\theta$ with the direction of the field will constitute a volume cut out from a unit sphere by two coaxial cones with coinciding apexes, therefore, we have (see Fig. 5)

$$d\Omega = \Omega_2 - \Omega_1 \qquad (3.19)$$

Now the area $d\Omega$ on the unit sphere can be found as follows. The radius r' of the circle cut out by the smaller cone on the unit sphere is

Figure 4   Orientation of a moment in an electric field.

$$r' = \sin \theta \qquad (3.20)$$

and the circumference of the circle is then $2\pi \sin \theta$. Therefore the area of the unit sphere which is a measure of $d\Omega$ is given by the length $2\pi \sin \theta$ of the area times its width $d\theta$, i.e.,

$$d\Omega = 2\pi \sin \theta \, d\theta \qquad (3.21)$$

Substituting this value of $d\Omega$ into Eq. (3.18) and letting

$$x = \frac{\mu F}{kT} \qquad (3.22)$$

and

$$\epsilon = \cos \theta \qquad (3.23)$$

we can write

$$\frac{\overline{m}}{\mu} = \frac{\int_{-1}^{+1} e^{x\epsilon} \epsilon \, d\epsilon}{\int_{-1}^{+1} e^{x\epsilon} d\epsilon} \qquad (3.24)$$

Now if u is set equal to ϵ, and dv to $e^{x\epsilon} \, d\epsilon$, and Eq. (3.24) is integrated by parts, we obtain

$$\frac{\overline{m}}{\mu} = \frac{e^x + e^{-x}}{e^x - e^{-x}} - \frac{1}{x} = \operatorname{cotgh} x - \frac{1}{x} \qquad (3.25)$$

This is the equation for the Langevin magnetization as derived by Debye.

For x small we can obtain by expansion

$$\frac{\overline{m}}{\mu} = \frac{x}{3} - \frac{x^3}{45} \qquad (3.26)$$

and for x large

$$\frac{\overline{m}}{\mu} = 1 - \frac{1}{x} + 2e^{-2x} \qquad (3.27)$$

From Eq. (3.26) we can write by neglecting x^3 and substituting the value of x

$$\overline{m} = \frac{\mu^2 F}{3kT} \qquad (3.28)$$

as the mean moment of a gaseous molecule in the direction of the external magnetic field.

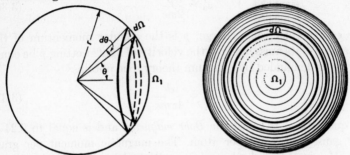

Figure 5 Illustrating how a solid angle is measured.

The molar susceptibility χ_M can be found from the equation

$$\frac{MI}{\rho} = \chi_M F \qquad (3.29)$$

where M is the molecular weight, I is the magnetic moment, in the direction of the applied field per unit volume, and ρ is the density. The molar volume V is given by

$$\frac{M}{\rho} = V \qquad (3.30)$$

and

$$\frac{MI}{\rho} = VI = N\overline{m} \qquad (3.31)$$

Therefore, from Eq. (3.29) and (3.31)

$$\chi_M = \frac{N\overline{m}}{F} \qquad (3.32)$$

Hence from Eq. (3.28) and (3.32)

$$\chi_M = \frac{N\mu^2}{3kT} \qquad (3.33)$$

or

$$\mu = \sqrt{\frac{3kT\chi_M}{N}} \tag{3.34}$$

But the effective moment per mol M_μ is $N\mu$, and from Eq. (3.34) is given by

$$M_\mu = \sqrt{3kNT\chi_M} = \sqrt{3RT\chi_M} \tag{3.35}$$

From classical theory, the magnetic moment μ_0' due to an electron rotating in its orbit is

$$\mu_0' = \frac{\epsilon p}{2mc} \tag{3.36}$$

Here ϵ is the electronic charge, p is the angular momentum of the electron, m is its mass, and c is the velocity of light. Letting p be equal to $h/2\pi$ as demanded by quantum theory, one obtains

$$\mu_0' = \frac{\epsilon h}{4\pi mc} \tag{3.37}$$

The quantity μ_0' is called the *Bohr magneton* and is equal to 9.24×10^{-21} gauss-centimeter per atom. The magnetic moment per gram atom $M_{\mu_0'}$ is obtained when μ_0' is multiplied by Avogadro's number giving $M_{\mu_0'}$ to be 5568 gauss-centimeters.

Therefore, in Eq. (3.35) if R is in ergs and if division by 5568 is performed, M_μ will be in molar Bohr magnetons; thus

$$M_\mu = 2.84\sqrt{\chi_\mu T} \text{ Bohr magnetons} \tag{3.38}$$

Curie's law states that the paramagnetic susceptibility of most paramagnetic substances is inversely proportional to the absolute temperature. Then

$$\chi_M = \frac{C_M}{T} \tag{3.39}$$

where C_M is a constant for each substance, and Eq. (3.38) can be written.

$$M_\mu = 2.84\sqrt{C_M} \text{ Bohr magnetons} \tag{3.40}$$

The *Weiss magneton* is 4.96 Bohr magnetons or 1123.5 gauss-centimeters.

In measuring susceptibility, the sum of the paramagnetic and the diamagnetic susceptibilities is obtained. The latter, however, is small and may be neglected, or if it is desired, allowed for by use of a table of atomic diamagnetic susceptibilities or by making measurements upon a closely related diamagnetic compound. (See Glasstone, *Textbook of Physical Chemistry*, New York, D. Van Nostrand Company, Inc., pages 64–65 and pages 605–606, for the source of the discussion of magnetic moment and magnetic susceptibility.)

Debye's equation for total molar polarization

As has been stated, when considering molar polarization there are two types of molecules which must be considered. For one type of molecule the molar polarization is independent of temperature. A field of intensity F induces a moment m in the molecule by distorting the particle so that there is a separation (the extent of which depends on the polarizability of the particle) of positive and of negative parts within the molecule. This induced moment is given by Eq. (3.1). For the second type of molecule, molar polarization is dependent upon temperature. Not only is there a moment due to distortion which is independent of temperature, but the molecule possesses a permanent moment originating in a separation of positive and negative centers in the molecule even in the absence of an electrical field. The polarization due to the permanent moment depends on the orientation of the moment in the field, and this in turn is dependent not only on the field intensity F but on the thermal energy of the molecules. This latter influence which works in opposition to the orientating effect of the field is determined by the temperature. Thus polarization due to orientation is dependent upon the temperature. Debye (*Polar Molecules*, New York, The Chemical Catalog Company, Inc., 1929) arrived at the average moment in the direction of the field due to orientation in much the same way that Langevin arrived at the average moment (in the direction of the field) of a paramagnetic substance. This average moment is given by Eq. (3.28), if μ now means the permanent electric moment.

Combining Eq. (3.1) and (3.28) gives the total moment of a molecule in the direction of the field of intensity F. The equation is

$$\overline{m} = \left(\alpha_0 + \frac{\mu^2}{3kT}\right) F \tag{3.41}$$

where α_0 is for the distortion effect and $\dfrac{\mu^2}{3kT}$ is for the orientation effect. Thus the total polarizability α is given by

$$\alpha = \alpha_0 + \frac{\mu^2}{3kT} \tag{3.42}$$

and the molar polarization P becomes

$$P = \frac{4}{3} \pi N \alpha = \frac{4}{3} \pi N \alpha_0 + \frac{4}{9} \frac{\pi N \mu^2}{kT} \qquad (3.43)$$

Thus we can write

$$\frac{D-1}{D+2} \frac{M}{\rho} = \frac{4}{3} \pi N \alpha = \frac{4}{3} \pi N \left(\alpha_0 + \frac{\mu^2}{3kT} \right) \qquad (3.44)$$

The molar polarization due to distortion is

$$P_D = \frac{4}{3}\pi N \alpha_0 \qquad (3.45)$$

and can be divided into a part due to electron distortion P_e and a part due to atomic distortion P_a. Then if the molar polarization due to permanent moments is

$$P_\mu = \frac{4}{9} \frac{\pi N \mu^2}{kT} \qquad (3.46)$$

we have the total molar polarization given by

$$P = P_e + P_a + P_\mu \qquad (3.47)$$

For the temperature dependence of polarization Eq. (3.43) may be written

$$P = a + b/T \qquad (3.48)$$

where a and b are constants.

To determine the permanent electric moment of a substance its dielectric constant and density are determined at different temperatures. From these data P is calculated using Eq. (3.12). The values of P are plotted against the reciprocals of the corresponding absolute temperatures. The slope of the resulting straight line is given from Eq. (3.43) and (3.48) by

$$b = \frac{4\pi N \mu^2}{9k} \qquad (3.49)$$

Thus μ is calculable from the slope. The moments so obtained should be of the order of magnitude of 10^{-18} since they are approximately the product of the elementary electronic charge, 4.803×10^{-10} electrostatic unit, and the diameter of a molecule, about 10^{-8} centimeter. This proves to be the case for many substances. Their moments come out to be some small number times 10^{-18}.

Sometimes solutions of a substance in nonpolar solvents such as dioxane and benzene are used to measure electric moments. The molar polarization of a binary solution can be written

$$\frac{D-1}{D+2} \cdot \frac{M_1 N_1 + M_2 N_2}{\rho'} = P_1 N_1 + P_2 N_2 \qquad (3.50)$$

M_1 and N_1 are the molecular weight and mole fraction respectively of component one, and M_2 and N_2 are like quantities respectively for component two; ρ' is the density of the solution, and P_1 and P_2 are the polarizations of the two components. The polarization P_1 of the inert solvent is considered independent of the mole fraction. Deviation from linearity expected from Eq. (3.49) is attributed to P_2. P_2 is measured at several values of N_2 and extrapolated to $N_2 = 0$. This gives the molar polarization of solute molecules in the nonpolar solvent medium. Measurement of P_2 as described above at several different temperatures makes it possible to calculate μ the permanent moment of the solute.

Eq. (3.43) is based upon two assumptions: (a) that the applied field E is small enough so that higher powers than the first of the field may be neglected, and (b) that the effective field acting on a molecule is the Clausius-Mosotti internal field which is $\dfrac{D+2}{3}$ times the applied field E. See Eq. (3.6).

The polarizability and polar moments of gases are satisfactorily accounted for by Eq. (3.43), as are the dielectric properties, by the corresponding equation in terms of dielectric constant, namely,

$$\frac{D-1}{D+2} = \frac{4\pi}{3} \sum_i N_i \left(\alpha_{0i} + \frac{\mu_i^2}{3kT} \right) \qquad (3.51)$$

where the subscript i refers to the ith species of molecule. N_i is the number of molecules of the ith species present per cubic centimeter and the other terms have their usual significance. Eq. (3.51) can be applied to nonpolar liquids and to dilute solutions of polar substances dissolved in nonpolar solvents. Moments fairly consistent with those calculated from dielectric constant measurements on polar gases can be obtained from this equation (modified as in Eq. 3.50) applied to dielectric constant measurements of dilute solutions of dipolar solutes dissolved in nonpolar solvents. However, Müller (*Physik. Z.*, **34**, 688, 1933; *Trans. Faraday Soc.*, **30**, 729, 1934) has shown experimentally that permanent moments determined in this way have values which are systematically dependent upon the dielectric constant of the solvent. Sugden (*Nature*, **133**, 415, 1934) has shown how to extrapolate data on the dielectric constant of a polar solute in a variety of non-polar liquids to dielectric constant unity in order to obtain a true value of the moment of the free polar molecule.

If Eq. (3.51) is solved for the dielectric constant one obtains

$$D = \frac{1 + \dfrac{8\pi}{3} \sum_i N_i \left(\alpha_{0i} + \dfrac{\mu_i}{3kT} \right)}{1 - \dfrac{4\pi}{3} \sum_i N_i \left(\alpha_{0i} + \dfrac{\mu_i}{3kT} \right)} \tag{3.52}$$

The predictions of this equation as well as of the simpler Eq. (3.44) are not in agreement with observation as far as polar liquids are concerned. To see this it is convenient to write Eq. (3.44) in the form given by Van Vleck (*J. Chem. Phys.*, **5**, 556, 1937), namely

$$D - 1 = \frac{3q\phi}{T - q\phi} \tag{3.53}$$

where ϕ is analogous to temperature and is given by the equation

$$\phi = \frac{4\pi N \mu^2}{9k} \tag{3.54}$$

and q has the value

$$q = 1 + \frac{3\alpha_0 kT}{\mu^2} \tag{3.55}$$

From Eq. (3.53) it is seen that for a certain critical value of ϕ corresponding to a temperature about equal to room temperature, the denominator of Eq. (3.53) would become zero and D would become infinite. Eq. (3.52) likewise predicts that D would become infinite near room temperature. This is termed by Van Vleck *the* $\dfrac{4\pi}{3}$ *catastrophe*, since it arises from the term $\dfrac{4\pi P}{3}$ in the Lorentz local field. Without this term the denominator of Eq. (3.53) would be simply T, and hence D would not become infinite at any ordinary temperature. The physical meaning of the $\dfrac{4\pi}{3}$ catastrophe, if it is found, is that there is a critical temperature below which there is the electric analogue of ferromagnetism, that is, saturation, hysteresis, remanence, etc. Actual existence of a critical temperature, analogous to the Curie point, with the consequent above-mentioned anomalous results, is practically unknown except in the case of Rochelle salt.

Wyman's (*J. Am. Chem. Soc.*, **58,** 1482, 1936) experimental work is further evidence against the Lorentz field. From his investigations there results an entirely different dependence of the dielectric constant upon composition than that predicted by the Clausius-Mosotti formula based upon the Lorentz field.

Wilson (*Chem. Rev.*, **25,** 377, 1939) discusses the theory of restricted rotation and Onsager's theory to account for the dielectric properties of free polar liquids. The discussion of these topics will closely follow his treatment.

The theory of restricted rotation

Both Debye (*Physik. Z.*, **36,** 100 and 193, 1935) and Fowler (*Proc. Roy. Soc.* (London), **A149,** 1, 1935) have used the theory of restricted rotation originally suggested by Pauling (*Phys. Rev.*, **36,** 430, 1930) of dipolar molecules to account for the dielectric properties of polar liquids. According to this theory a dipolar molecule in a liquid is not free to rotate but rather oscillates about an axis which slowly changes direction, but over short periods of time may be considered as fixed, due to the arrangement of neighboring molecules. It was assumed that the molecule acquires a potential energy $-U \cos \theta$, when it rotates at an angle θ with the temporary axis about which it oscillates. Further, it was assumed that the Clausius-Mosotti expression for the internal field held in a polar liquid. Based upon the above assumptions it was shown that the term $\mu^2/3kT$ in Eq. (3.51) should be multiplied by a correction factor $[1 - L^2(y)]$ where $L(y)$ is the Langevin function, namely,

$$L(y) = \coth(y) - \frac{1}{y} \qquad (3.56)$$

and

$$y = \frac{U}{kT} \qquad (3.57)$$

Debye used U as a constant and accounted for the difference between gaseous and liquid water with respect to the Kerr effect, molar polarization, and dielectric saturation. There is no method available for calculating the energy U theoretically.

If the theory of restricted rotation is the true explanation of the dielectric properties of liquids, the time for the momentary axis of oscillation to become orientated in the direction of the applied field should be long compared with the period of the field, which for ordinary dielectric constant measurements is 10^{-6} second. Theoretically such a time of orientation has never been substantiated. Wilson concludes that the actual time of orientation may be of the order of the time of relaxation of the dielectric which Debye (*Trans. Faraday Soc.*, **30**, 679, 1934) shows is about 10^{-12} second for most polar liquids.

Van Vleck (*J. Chem. Phys.*, **5**, 556, 1937) believes that cessation of free rotation may account for the discontinuities which occur in the dielectric constants and other properties of certain crystals, for example, hydrogen chloride and hydrogen bromide at 100° K. Van Vleck points out that the hindering of free rotation, however, will not consistently account for the dielectric properties of these substances at higher temperatures.

Müller (*Physik. Z.*, **38**, 498, 1937) shows that the energy U corresponds approximately to $(2/3)CN\mu^2$, where C is the constant of the van Arkel and Snoek (*Physik. Z.*, **33**, 662, 1932; **35**, 187, 1934; *Trans. Faraday Soc.*, **30**, 707, 1934) equation, which is semiempirical and contains the term $CN\mu^2$ introduced to reduce the importance of the dipole orientation term $\mu^2/3kT$. The equation is

$$\frac{D-1}{D+2} = \frac{4\pi N}{3}\left(\alpha_0 + \frac{\mu^2}{3kT + CN\mu^2}\right) \tag{3.58}$$

Except for hydrogen-bonding liquids, the constant C does not vary greatly from one polar liquid to another or from one solvent to another in case of concentrated solutions of a given polar substance in nonpolar solvents. Müller (*loc. cit.*) points out that the values of the constant given by van Arkel and Snoek are really values of $3C/4\pi$. Onsager's theory leads to theoretical values of C which agree approximately with experiment.

Wilson indicates that the above objections to the Debye-Fowler theory of hindered rotation does not exclude restricted rotation in liquids. However, it is pointed out that the Kirkwood extension of the Onsager theory accounts formally for restricted rotation. Kirkwood (*J. Chem. Phys.*, **7**, 911, 1939) indicates that the chief difficulty with the Debye-Fowler theory is its acceptance of the Clausius-Mosotti internal field as valid.

Onsager's theory

Onsager's (*J. Am. Chem. Soc.*, **58**, 1486, 1936) greatest improvement in the theory of liquid dielectrics was the derivation of an alternative expression for the internal field which does not lead to the $4\pi/3$ catastrophe. Upon this expression he based his theory of the dielectric constants of polar liquids. Onsager takes as his molecular model a sphere with radius a and polarizability α related to an *internal refractive index* n by the equation

$$\alpha = \frac{n^2 - 1}{n^2 + 2}\, a^3 \tag{3.59}$$

In an electric field the total moment of the molecule is the vector sum of its permanent and induced dipole moments. Thus

$$m = \mu_0 u + \alpha F \tag{3.60}$$

where u is a unit vector in the direction of the dipole axis. The dipole is a point dipole at the center of a spherical cavity of dielectric constant unity and a radius of the order of a. The sphere is submerged in a homogeneous isotropic continuum of dielectric constant D. For this model the internal field F acting on the dipole is found from classical electrostatic methods to be composed of the reaction field R caused by the polarization of the surrounding medium by the field of the dipole, and the cavity field G caused by the applied field E. R acts parallel to the instantaneous dipole moment m and exists even in the absence of an applied field. G acts parallel to the applied field.

The Onsager molecular model is like that of the Lorentz theory. In the latter theory (as pointed out before, p. 32) a molecule is placed in a sphere whose radius, however, is large compared to that of the molecule. The sphere is again considered to be immersed in a polarized medium. The field acting on the molecular dipole in the cavity is then made up of the resultant of two fields, E_1 and E_2, where E_1 is the field at the point due to the applied field plus the polarization of the molecules outside the sphere, and E_2 is the field due to the molecules inside the sphere except the dipole under consideration. As was pointed out before, for a sufficiently dilute gas E_2 will be zero since there will be no other than the dipole being considered within the sphere. E_2 will likewise be zero if the molecules within the sphere are arranged in a cubic lattice. These two cases yield the Clausius-Mosotti field. The application of the Lorentz equation to dilute solutions of dipoles in nonpolar solvents is, therefore, based upon the assumption that E_2 is negligible and that the Clausius-Mosotti internal field is valid. See Fig. 6 and the accompanying caption for a representation of the Lorentz field versus the Onsager field.

In deriving the Clausius-Mosotti field the polarization of the molecule (the material within the sphere) is assumed to have its average rather than its instantaneous value. The Onsager field is derived for

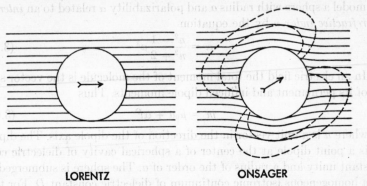

LORENTZ   **ONSAGER**

Figure 6 In the Lorentz method, the field inside the cavity is computed on the assumption that the lines of induction outside the cavity are unmodified by the existence of the latter. With the Onsager model the distribution of these lines is revised by elementary electrostatics to take cognizance of the cavity. The resulting portion of the local field may be called the direct part. In addition, Onsager has a *reaction field* which is shown by dashed lines in the figure and which will arise because the dipole itself will polarize the surrounding medium. The reaction field on a dipole is clearly always parallel to it and has no influence on the latter's orientation. So in dealing with permanent rather than induced polarization, only the direct portion need be considered. In the case of induced polarization, the induced dipoles are all parallel to the field, and the sum of Onsager's direct and reaction fields is identical with the Lorentz expression. From Van Vleck, *J. Chem. Phys.*, **5**, 320 (1937).

the instantaneous orientation of the central molecule. In continuing the presentation of the Onsager theory, we must first derive expressions for the reaction field R and the cavity field G.

From electrostatics, the potential ψ in a region where there are no free charges must satisfy Laplace's equation

$$\Delta^2 \psi = 0 \tag{3.61}$$

The field in any direction x is given by

$$E_x = -\frac{\partial \psi}{\partial x} \tag{3.62}$$

The boundary conditions are: the potential must be a continuous function, and across any interface the normal component of the displacement vector D' must be continuous, where D' is given by Eq. (3.4); also, the potential caused by the presence of polarizable bodies in the region must vanish at least as fast as $1/r$ at large distances. A solution of Laplace's equation which meets the above requirements is a unique solution except for an additive constant. Using spherical polar coordinates, r, θ, ϕ with origin at the center of the cavity, the general solution of Laplace's equation is the sum of spherical harmonics of the form

$$r^{n''} P_{n''}^m (\cos \phi)(A_{n''m} \sin m\phi + B_{n''m} \cos m\phi) \tag{3.63}$$

and

$$r^{-(n''+1)} P_{n''}^m (\cos \theta)(A_{n''m} \sin m\phi + B_{n''m} \cos m\phi) \tag{3.64}$$

where $A_{n''m}$ and $B_{n''m}$ are constants, n'' is integral, and $P_{n''}^m (\cos \theta)$ is an associated Legendre function of order m and degree n''. As far as we are concerned the solutions must be cylindrically symmetric and ϕ need not be specified. Hence, $m = 0$, and we must consider only the simple Legendre functions $P_{n''}^0 (\cos \theta)$ for the formation of possible solutions, e.g. $P_0^0 (\cos \theta) = 1$; $P_1^0 (\cos \theta) = \cos \theta$; $P_2^0 (\cos \theta) = (3 \cos^2 \theta - 1)$. For simple cases inspection will tell which of these functions is likely to fit the boundary conditions.

A homogeneous field E in an isotropic medium of dielectric constant D is modified by introducing a cavity of radius a and dielectric constant unity. Before the cavity is introduced let the unperturbed potential for the field E directed along the polar axis be

$$\psi_0 = -Er \cos \theta \tag{3.65}$$

After the introduction of the cavity let the potential outside the cavity be $\psi_0 + \psi_p$ and the potential inside the cavity be ψ_i. ψ_p is the perturbation potential and must decrease at large distances from the cavity at least as fast as $1/r$. Further, each of these potentials must satisfy Laplace's equation, since outside the cavity

$$\Delta^2(\psi_0 + \psi_p) = 0 = \Delta^2\psi_0 + \Delta^2\psi_p = 0 + \Delta^2\psi_p \tag{3.66}$$

The boundary conditions are

$$(\psi_0 + \psi_p) = \psi_i, \ (r = a) \tag{3.67}$$

$$D \frac{\partial}{\partial r} (\psi_0 + \psi_p) = \frac{\partial \psi_i}{\partial r}, \ (r = a) \tag{3.68}$$

Because of these boundary conditions and the form of ψ_0, a solution is

$$\psi_i = -Br \cos \theta \tag{3.69}$$

$$\psi_p = -\frac{r^2}{A} \cos \theta \tag{3.70}$$

where A and B are constants to be determined. Substituting Eq. (3.65), (3.69), and (3.70) into Eq. (3.67) and (3.68) and letting $r = a$, it is found that the boundary conditions are satisfied if

$$A = \frac{D-1}{2D+1} a^3 E \tag{3.71}$$

and

$$B = \frac{3D}{2D+1} E \tag{3.72}$$

Then the field inside the cavity is from Eq. (3.69) and (3.72)

$$-\frac{\partial}{\partial r} (\psi_i)_{\cos \theta = 1} = B = \frac{3D}{2D+1} E \tag{3.73}$$

and from Eq. (3.62) and (3.73) we have

$$G = -\frac{\partial}{\partial r} (\psi_i)_{\cos \theta = 1} = \frac{3D}{2D+1} E \tag{3.74}$$

The next problem is to find the field when a point-dipole is introduced at the center of the spherical cavity of radius a in a homogeneous isotropic medium of dielectric constant D, when no field is applied. Let the moment m be directed along the polar axis. Let the potential outside the cavity be ψ_e and that inside the cavity be $\psi_0 + \psi_p$, where ψ_0 is the potential which would describe the field of the dipole in a vacuum. Then

$$\psi_0 = \frac{m}{r^2} \cos \theta \tag{3.75}$$

The boundary conditions are

$$\psi_0 + \psi_p = \psi_e, \ (r = a) \tag{3.76}$$

$$\frac{\partial}{\partial r} (\psi_0 + \psi_p) = D \frac{\partial \psi_e}{\partial r}, \ (r = a) \tag{3.77}$$

From the form of ψ_0 and since the potential of the dipole should fall off outside of the cavity as $1/r_2$, a solution is

$$\psi_p = Rr \cos \theta \tag{3.78}$$

$$\psi_e = \frac{C}{r^2} \cos \theta \tag{3.79}$$

Substituting Eq. (3.78) and (3.79) and the value of ψ_0 from Eq. (3.75) into Eq. (3.76) and (3.77), it turns out that the boundary conditions are satisfied by

$$R = -\frac{2(D-1)}{2D+1}\frac{m}{a^3} \tag{3.80}$$

$$C = \frac{3m}{2D+1} \tag{3.81}$$

Therefore from Eq. (3.78) and (3.80)

$$\psi_p = -\frac{2(D-1)}{2D+1}\frac{m}{a^3}r\cos\theta \tag{3.82}$$

and from Eq. (3.75), (3.78), and (3.80), the field F within the cavity in the direction of the axis m, that is, in the direction $\cos\theta = 1$, is

$$-\frac{\partial}{\partial r}(\psi_0 + \psi_p)_{\cos\theta=1} = \frac{2m}{r^3} + \frac{2(D-1)}{2D+1}\frac{m}{a^3} \tag{3.83}$$

The second term on the right of Eq. (3.83) is the reaction field R, which tends to increase the moment of the dipole in the cavity and acts parallel to the axis of the dipole. Therefore its value is

$$R = \frac{2(D-1)}{2D+1}\frac{m}{a^3} \tag{3.84}$$

Now under the influence of the fields R and G the molecule will be polarized so that its moment is given by Eq. (3.60), which since

$$F = R + G \tag{3.85}$$

becomes from Eq. (3.60), (3.74), and (3.84)

$$m = \mu_0 u + \frac{3D}{2D+1}\alpha E + \frac{2(D-1)}{2D+1}\frac{\alpha}{a^3}m \tag{3.86}$$

where u is a unit vector in the direction of the permanent dipole μ_0. Solving Eq. (3.86) for m gives

$$m = \left(\mu_0 u + \frac{3D}{2D+1}\alpha E\right)\bigg/\left(1 - \frac{2(D-1)}{2D+1}\frac{\alpha}{a^3}\right) \tag{3.87}$$

Introducing from Eq. (3.59) $\frac{\alpha}{a^3}$ in terms of *internal dielectric constant* n^2 into Eq. (3.87) gives

$$m = \frac{(n^2+2)(2D+1)}{3(2D+n^2)}\mu_0 u + \frac{D(n^2+2)}{2D+n^2}\alpha E$$

$$= \mu u + \frac{D(n^2+2)}{2D+n^2}\alpha E \tag{3.88}$$

where

$$\mu = \mu_0 \frac{(n^2 + 2)(2D + 1)}{3(2D + n^2)} \tag{3.89}$$

The torque T acting on the dipole is

$$T = (R + G) \times m \tag{3.90}$$

but since R is parallel to m

$$R \times m = 0 \tag{3.91}$$

and

$$T = G \times m = \frac{3D}{2D + 1} E \times \left(\mu u + \frac{D(n^2 + 2)}{2D + n^2} \alpha E \right) \tag{3.92}$$

But $G \times E$ vanishes and only the part parallel to u matters. Thus the last term on the right of Eq. (3.92) disappears and from this equation and Eq. (3.89) we have

$$T = \frac{3D}{2D + 1} \mu E \times u = \frac{D(n^2 + 2)}{2D + n^2} \mu_0 E \sin \theta \tag{3.93}$$

where θ is the angle between E and u. Setting

$$\mu^* = \mu_0 \frac{D(n^2 + 2)}{2D + n^2} \tag{3.94}$$

Eq. (3.93) becomes

$$T = \mu^* E \sin \theta \tag{3.95}$$

The μ^* is the *external* characteristic moment of the molecule as contrasted with the actual electric moment μ of the molecule.

The potential energy U is given by

$$U = -\mu^* E \cos \theta \tag{3.96}$$

and the work of orientation is

$$\frac{\partial U}{\partial \theta} = \mu^* E \sin \theta = T \tag{3.97}$$

From Eq. (3.88) the component of m in the direction of E is

$$m_E = \mu \cos \theta + \frac{D(n^2 + 2)}{2D + n^2} \alpha E \tag{3.98}$$

and in order to determine the average value $\overline{m}_E$ of m_E, it is necessary to determine the average value $\overline{\cos \theta}$ of $\cos \theta$.

According to Boltzmann statistics we have

$$\overline{\cos \theta} = \frac{\int_0^{2\pi} \int_0^{\pi} e^{-U/kT} \cos \theta \sin \theta \, d\theta \, d\phi}{\int_0^{2\pi} \int_0^{\pi} e^{-U/kT} \sin \theta \, d\theta \, d\phi} \tag{3.99}$$

For E small enough that powers of $\dfrac{\mu^* E}{kT}$ higher than the first may be neglected, we obtain from Eq. (3.99)

$$\overline{\cos \theta} = \frac{\mu^* E}{3kT} \tag{3.100}$$

and from Eq. (3.89), (3.94), (3.98), and (3.100)

$$\overline{m}_E = \left[\frac{\mu \mu^*}{3kT} + \frac{D(n^2 + 2)}{2D + n^2} \alpha \right] E$$
$$= \left[\frac{(n^2 + 2)^2 (2D + 1)}{3(2D + n^2)^2} \frac{D\mu_0^2}{3kT} + \frac{D(n^2 + 2)}{2D + n^2} \alpha \right] E \tag{3.101}$$

The polarization per unit volume P is given by

$$P = N\overline{m} \tag{3.102}$$

where N is the number of molecules per unit volume. Assuming that the volume of the liquid equals the sum of the volumes of the molecules, we obtain

$$\tfrac{4}{3} \pi a^3 N = 1 \tag{3.103}$$

From the fundamental electrostatic formula

$$(D - 1)E = 4\pi P \tag{3.104}$$

and Eq. (3.59), (3.102), and (3.103), we have

$$\alpha = \frac{3}{4\pi N} \frac{n^2 - 1}{n^2 + 2} \tag{3.105}$$

and

$$\overline{m}_E = \frac{P}{N} = \frac{D - 1}{4\pi N} E \tag{3.106}$$

Substituting the values of α and $\overline{m}_E$ from Eq. (3.105) and (3.106) into Eq. (3.101), we obtain after simplification an expression which relates the dielectric constant of a pure polar liquid to the permanent moment in vacuo μ_0 of its molecules. The equation is

$$\frac{(D - n^2)(2D + n^2)}{D(n^2 + 2)^2} = \frac{4\pi N}{9kT} \mu_0^2 \tag{3.107}$$

When only a small fraction of the electric susceptibility is derived from molecular orientation, that is, when

$$D - n^2 \ll n^2 \tag{3.108}$$

Eq. (3.107) agrees in the first approximation with the Clausius-Mosotti formula. From Eq. (3.107) we can derive the expression

$$\frac{D-1}{D+2} - \frac{n^2-1}{n^2+2} = \frac{3D(n^2+2)}{(2D+n^2)(D+2)} \cdot \frac{4\pi N \mu_0^2}{9kT} = \frac{4\pi N \mu_0^2}{9kT} f(D, n^2) \tag{3.109}$$

When D is large Eq. (3.107) can be written

$$\frac{2D}{(n^2+2)^2} \sim \frac{4\pi N \mu_0^2}{9kT} \tag{3.110}$$

One of the reasons for this simple limiting law is that μ and μ^* approach limits as D increases.

Onsager (*loc. cit.*) derives an equation which applies to solutions as follows. Consider a solution which contains in unit volume $N_1 \cdots N_i \cdots$ spherical molecules of different species, with radii $a_1 \cdots a_i \cdots$, polarizabilities $\alpha_1 \cdots \alpha_i \cdots$, and dipole moments $\mu_1 \cdots \mu_i \cdots$. The individual refractive indices $n_1 \cdots n_i \cdots$ are given by the relation

$$\alpha_i = \frac{a_i^3(n_i^2 - 1)}{n_i^2 + 2} \tag{3.111}$$

and the volume fractions $\theta_1 \cdots \theta_i \cdots$ are expressed by the equation

$$\theta_i = \tfrac{4}{3}\pi a_i^3 N_i \tag{3.112}$$

The dipole moments will depend on the dielectric constant of the environment according to Eq. (3.89) and (3.94). The moments in vacuo will be denoted by μ_{0i}.

From Eq. (3.101), (3.105), (3.106) and (3.112) it can be shown that

$$D - 1 = 4\pi \sum N_i \left(\frac{D(n_i^2 + 2)}{D + n_i^2} \alpha_i + \frac{\mu_i \mu_i^*}{3kT} \right)$$
$$= \sum \theta_i \frac{3D(n_i^2 - 1)}{n_i^2 + 2D} + 4\pi \sum N_i \frac{\mu_i \mu_i^*}{3kT} \tag{3.113}$$

making use of the identity

$$3D(n_i^2 - 1) = (2D + n_i^2)(D - 1) - (2D + 1)(D - n_i^2) \tag{3.114}$$

we can rearrange Eq. (3.113) in the form

$$\frac{(1 - \sum \theta_i)(D-1) + (2D+1)\sum \theta_i(D - n_i^2)}{2D + n_i^2} = 4\pi \sum N_i \frac{\mu_i \mu_i^*}{3kT} \tag{3.115}$$

and if we assume the entire space occupied by molecules

$$\sum_i \theta_i = 1 \tag{3.116}$$

the first term on the left of Eq. (3.115) vanishes and

$$\frac{\sum_i \theta_i (D - n_i^2) 3D}{2D + n_i^2} = \frac{4\pi \sum_i N_i (\mu_i^*)^2}{3kT} \tag{3.117}$$

Eq. (3.117) is a generalization of Eq. (3.107) to the case of several molecular species. In Eq. (3.115) and (3.116) we have from Eq. (3.89) and (3.94) respectively that

$$\mu_i = \mu_{0i} \frac{(n_i^2 + 2)(2D + 1)}{3(2D + n_i^2)} \tag{3.118}$$

and

$$\mu_i^* = \mu_{0i} \frac{D(n_i^2 + 2)}{2D + n_i^2} \tag{3.119}$$

Criticisms of the Onsager method of calculation

Onsager's method of calculation according to Wilson can give only a rough approximation to the value of the reaction field in actual liquids because:

(a) The molecules were idealized as a sphere containing a single dipole.

(b) The environment of the molecule was treated as a homogeneous continuum.

(c) Dielectric saturation was neglected in considering the effect of strong fields in the vicinity of the dipole.

(d) The radius of the cavity was arbitrarily chosen so as to agree with Eq. (3.103).

(e) The association error due to the formation of aggregates of polar molecules when polar substances are dissolved in nonpolar solvents. These aggregates will not be orientated in the applied field in the same manner as simple dipoles, since each dipole exerts a field which influences the orientation of its neighbors. There are two classes of association: (1) *co-association*, in which the dipoles prefer to orientate head to tail, so that their moments reinforce one another and (2) *contra-association*, in which the dipoles tend to orientate in an antiparallel configuration, i.e., positive end to negative end and negative end to positive end, so that their moments cancel.

In spite of its approximate nature the Onsager theory has the following advantages as listed by Wilson:

(a) The Onsager internal field according to Van Vleck (*J. Chem. Phys.*, **5**, 320, 1937; *ibid.*, **5**, 556, 1937) is more consistent with a statistical mechanical treatment of dipole-dipole coupling than is the Clausius-Mosotti field.

(b) Van Vleck (*loc. cit.*) also has shown that the Onsager theory will also explain the fact that the marked dielectric saturation predicted by the Clausius-Mosotti theory for polar liquids in moderately strong fields does not occur.

In a subsequent section Van Vleck's treatment of the Onsager theory will be discussed more in detail.

Application of Onsager's theory

Böttcher (*Physica*, **5**, 635, 1938) put Eq. (3.107) into the form of the van Arkel and Snoek semiempirical expression Eq. (3.58). The empirical constant C of the van Arkel and Snoek equation is given by

$$C = \frac{4\pi}{3} \frac{2D - 2}{2D + 1} \frac{n^2 + 2}{3} \tag{3.120}$$

Wilson calculates $\frac{3}{4\pi} C$ for pure ethyl bromide from Eq. (3.120) and compares them with experimental values taken from Smythe (*J. Phys. Chem.*, **43**, 131, 1939). The D values for use in Eq. (3.120) were taken from Smyth and Morgan (*J. Am. Chem. Soc.*, **50**, 1547, 1928) and the values of n^2 have been calculated from the value of $P_e + P_a = 21.5$ cubic centimeters. (See Smythe and McAlpine, *J. Chem. Phys.*, **2**, 499, 1934.) Here P_e and P_a are the electronic and atomic polarizabilities, respectively. As seen from Table I the theoretical and experimental values of $\frac{3}{4\pi} C$ agree fairly well in magnitude and change in a similar way with increasing temperature.

Comparison of dipole moments calculated from Eq. (3.107) was made with moments as obtained from dielectric constant measurements on gases, and with those calculated from Eq. (3.51) from dielectric constant measurements of dilute solutions of polar substances in nonpolar solvents taken by Wilson from Böttcher. The n^2 values used in the calculations involving Eq. (3.107) were obtained using the electronic polarizability P_e alone; the latter quantity was obtained by extrapolating the mole refractivity to infinite wave length. The excellency of agreement shown among these values of μ according to Wilson is empirically useful but theoretically surprising and is probably due to a fortuitous cancellation of errors.

Wilson carried out other calculations using both the unmodified Eq. (3.107) and a modified Eq. (3.143) which we are going to establish later, and in which qualitative or perhaps even semiquantitative data were obtained regarding the nature of intermolecular association in polar liquids and solutions. Thus it is found that in liquid diethyl ether, ethyl alcohol, and water there is co-association of the molecules,

TABLE I Comparison of values of $\frac{3}{4\pi} C$ for ethyl bromide

$t° C$	-90	-50	-10	$+30$
$\frac{3}{4\pi} C$ (experimental)	1.49	1.43	1.38	1.32
$\frac{3}{4\pi} C$ (theoretical)	1.36	1.30	1.24	1.18

TABLE II Böttcher's dipole moment values calculated from dielectric constants of liquids

Liquid	Calculated	Gas value	Solution value
Nitrobenzene	4.2	4.2	3.9–4.1
Nitromethane ⌡	3.7	3.4	3.0–3.1
o-Nitrotoluene	3.9	3.6	3.7
Acetone	3.0–3.1	2.8	2.7–2.8
Aniline	1.5	1.5	1.5–1.6
Acetonitrile	3.6	3.9	3.1–3.5
Benzonitrile	3.6–3.7	4.4	3.9
Anisole	1.5	1.2	1.2–1.3
Methyl chloride	1.8	1.8	1.6–1.8
Methyl bromide	1.6	1.8	1.5
Methyl iodide	1.3–1.4	1.6	1.4
Ethyl bromide	1.8–1.9	2.0	1.8–1.9
Bromobenzene	1.5–1.6	1.7	1.5–1.6
Acetic acid	1.3–1.7	1.7	
Water	3.0–3.1	1.8	1.7–2.0
Ethyl alcohol	2.8–3.1	1.7	1.7

so that the effective dipole moment is greater than the moment of the free molecule. In liquid aryl and alkyl monohalides, on the other hand, there is contra-association of the molecules so that the effective moment is less than the moment of the free molecule.

Onsager himself made several applications of his theory; among other things he checked theoretically the Wyman empirical constant in the equation (*J. Am. Chem. Soc.*, **58**, 1482, 1936)

$$P = \frac{D+1}{A} \tag{3.121}$$

where P is the total *polarization* per unit volume and is given by the expression

$$P = \frac{4\pi}{3} \sum N_i \left(\alpha_{0i} + \frac{\mu^2}{3kT} \right) \tag{3.122}$$

(See Eq. 3.51).

The value of A was determined by Wyman from measurements of D together with measurements of μ_0 in the vapor or in dilute solutions in nonpolar solvents. For a great number of liquids Wyman found $A = 8.5$, with a spread given by $A = 6.2$ and 11.

Onsager for D large wrote Eq. (3.107) as

$$\frac{D}{A} = \frac{2D}{(n^2+2)^2} \sim \frac{4\pi N \mu_0^2}{9kT} \tag{3.123}$$

and from this equation

$$A = \frac{(n^2+2)^2}{2} \tag{3.124}$$

Therefore, Wyman's typical $A = 8.5$ corresponds to a refractive index $n = 1.46$ which is very reasonable. The range

$$6.2 < A < 11 \tag{3.125}$$

corresponds to

$$1.275 < n < 1.64 \tag{3.126}$$

which is again reasonable. A comparison with individual refractive indices was not undertaken, since it would hardly be significant without allowance for molecular shape.

Extension of the Lorentz and Onsager theories of the local field

As pointed out previously, both the Lorentz theory and the Onsager theory can represent at best only approximations to the real conditions in dielectrics in spite of their successes, the one in the field of nonpolar and the other in the field of polar media. Both theories are based on pure electrostatics and smooth out the dielectric into a continuum. It is therefore to be expected that modifications of the theories will occur if the molecular structure of the medium is taken into account. Owing to this structure the local field surrounding the molecules will undergo strong changes in space as well as in time, and the observable values of the field will be complicated average values. The changes, *fluctuations* as they are called, may have a variety of sources: the irregularity of configuration and eventual anisotropy of the molecules as far as the instantaneous arrangement is concerned; their translational, rotational, and internal motions as far as changes in time are concerned. Furthermore even the average internal field acting on a molecule when in motion will not be the same as the average field in a fixed point in space.

It is evident that the described fluctuations can be handled only by the methods of statistical mechanics, be it classical or quantum-mechanical, and a considerable amount of work has been devoted to this problem during the last decade. We propose to deal in what follows with some of those investigations which represent partly a molecular foundation, partly an extension of the Lorentz and Onsager theories of the local field.

Keyes and Kirkwood (*Phys. Rev.*, **37**, 202, 1931) and later Kirkwood (*J. Chem. Phys.*, **4**, 592, 1936) have pointed out that fluctuations in the induced moment of a molecule lead to correction terms in the expression of the Lorentz field (Eq. 3.7) and the expressions derived therefrom. Owing to the close approach of molecules in gases during their collisions, the forces which they exert on each other will on the average be stronger than if the molecules were evenly spaced. For this reason these fluctuations are called *translational*, and they are treated by the quoted authors for nonpolar dielectrics. We are referring here to the later treatment of Kirkwood which is more extensive and more exact.

The derivation of Kirkwood consists of two parts, the first being purely electrostatic, the second statistical. The dielectric is treated from the outset as a system of (spherical) molecules, rather than a continuum, and therefore it is unnecessary to employ the artifice of the Lorentz cavity. The molecules are pictured as possessing a polarizability α, and therefore, induced moments. The influence of molecular multiple moments of higher order than the dipole, and the eventual inhomogeneity of the local field within the region occupied by a molecule are neglected. No dependence of the molecular polarizability on the density of the dielectric is taken into account. Under these assumptions, if a mole of substance is considered, there will be N (Avogadro's number) linear equations, correlating the N moments.

$$P_i + \alpha \sum_{\substack{k=1 \\ \neq i}}^{N} T_{ik} \cdot P_k = \alpha \vec{D'} \quad i = 1, 2 \cdots N \quad (3.127)$$

Here the polarization P_i of any molecule i is represented as being caused by the external field (right-hand term) and the action of the $(N - 1)$ other molecules on that particular molecule (the sum). The T_{ik}'s are components of a tensor representing that interaction. A solution of the system Eq. (3.127) in the form of a series in powers of α is obtained

$$P_i = \alpha \left[1 - \alpha \sum_{\substack{k=1 \\ \neq i}}^{N} T_{ik} + \alpha^2 \sum_{\substack{k, l=1 \\ k \neq i, l \neq k}}^{N} T_{ik} \cdot T_{lk} + \cdots \right] D' \quad (3.128)$$

and this represents the electrostatic part of the argument. Now the statistical element is introduced, and this is done by taking the average value of Eq. (3.127). This averaging yields the required value $\overline{P_i}$ in terms of mean values such as $\overline{T_{ik}}$, $\overline{T_{ik} \cdot T_{kl}}$, etc. The latter mean values are calculated by representing the fluid as a classical canonical ensemble. Such procedure introduces the translational fluctuations and the influence of the temperature on them, since the canonical ensemble takes into account all possible configurations and is dependent upon temperature.

The results can be represented in the form of a series of the Clausius-Mosotti expressions

$$\frac{D - 1}{D + 2} V = P_0 \left[1 + \gamma \frac{P_0}{V} - \left(\frac{15}{16} + 2\gamma \right) \left(\frac{P_0}{V} \right)^2 + \cdots \right] \quad (3.129)$$

where V is the molal volume and P_0 the molar polarization. (See Eq. 3.12.)

The quadratic term in P_0/V is usually small in applications so that the influence of the translational fluctuations is then given by the correction factor γ which is defined by

$$\gamma = \frac{P_0}{b} \left(1 + \frac{A}{3bRT} \right) \quad (3.130)$$

under the usual assumptions of a van der Waals equation of state. A and $b = \dfrac{2\pi N a^3}{3}$ are the constants in the latter equation, when written as

$$P = RT(V - b) - \frac{A}{V^2} \tag{3.131}$$

It is thus seen that the fluctuations in the induced molecular moment give rise to small but significant deviations from the Clausius-Mosotti formula. When P_0/V is small, the fluctuations cause a positive deviation from that law. As the density is increased, this deviation becomes smaller and vanishes when V is approximately equal to b, the corresponding density being about twice the ordinary density of the liquid. It is reasonable that translational fluctuations become relatively unimportant not only in solids but also in liquids. However, not much significance is to be attached to the value $V = b$ predicted by the above formula since it is probably necessary to take terms of higher degree in P_0/V into account as liquid dielectrics are approached. The numerical value of γ is about 0.1 for most substances.

If the molecules are treated as being not spherical and possessing optical anisotropy a further correction has to be added to γ. Also it should be mentioned that Van Vleck in an investigation and by a method to be discussed presently (*J. Chem. Phys.*, **5,** 320 and 556, 1937) has extended the analysis so as to include permanent moments. The result, too complicated to be quoted here in extenso, was revised in a later calculation (*J. Chem. Phys.*, **5,** 991, 1937) and reduces in the absence of permanent moments to Kirkwood's formula Eq. (3.130).

The treatment of Van Vleck (*loc. cit.*) goes beyond that of Keyes and Kirkwood in as much as it is dynamic rather than static, including rotations and in addition is based on quantum mechanical principles. It takes into account electrostatic dipole-dipole interactions, exchange forces between atoms, and the crystalline field of a crystal as a whole, being thereby applicable, under suitable restrictions, to solids, liquids, and gases. It owes this generality to its method which is the method of the partition sum, or partition function.

In a later chapter (Chapter VII) we will show the importance of the partition function for the calculation of absolute reaction rates. Its general importance is due to its relation to the free energy F (work function) of a system

$$F = -kT \log Z \tag{3.132}$$

where Z is the partition function. Once it is known it serves to solve a variety of problems, such as calculating the entropy of a system, or the specific heat, or the equation of state, etc.

The partition function is defined as

$$Z = \sum i \exp(-W_i/kT) \tag{3.133}$$

and is calculable if the energy states W_i of the system are entirely known, whether in classical or quantum mechanics. As for the application to our problem, when the partition sum in its dependence on the external field E is known, the polarization I will be given by

$$I = kT \, \partial \ln Z/\partial E \tag{3.134}$$

(See Van Vleck, *Electric and Magnetic Susceptibilities*, Oxford, Clarendon Press, 1932, p. 25.) This involves the determination of the susceptibility as the proportionality factor between I and E for sufficiently low fields. The difficulty of the treatment consists solely in the evaluation of the partition sum itself, and this can usually be carried out only by approximations.

Van Vleck's calculations deal in the first place with the case of paramagnetic substances. However, the analysis is applicable, with suitable simplifications, to dielectrics, and this application is made in the second of the quoted papers, with which alone we are concerned here.

Van Vleck's method of approximation consists in developing the partition function as a series in $1/T$.

$$Z = \sum_i \left[1 - \frac{W_i}{kT} + \frac{1}{2}\left(\frac{W_i}{kT}\right)^2 \cdots \right] \tag{3.135}$$

and is valid, therefore, if the temperature is not too low. Eq. (3.135) may also be written

$$Z = \eta \left[1 - \frac{H_{Av}}{kT} + \frac{(H^2)_{Av}}{2kT} - \frac{(H^3)_{Av}}{6k^3T^3} + \frac{(H^4)_{Av}}{24k^4T^4} - \cdots \right] \tag{3.136}$$

Here η is the total number of states (which need not be known for the determination of susceptibilities) and H_{Av}, $(H^2)_{Av}, \cdots$ are mean values of the Hamiltonian function H, etc., which are to be taken according to the principles of quantum mechanics.

Each member of Eq. (3.136) can be developed as an ascending series in the field E. From considerations of symmetry it can be concluded that there will be no odd powers of E so that

$$Z = Z^0(1 + Z^{(2)}E^2 + \cdots) \tag{3.137}$$

It is the coefficient $Z^{(2)}$ which is required for the determination of susceptibility.

Van Vleck has calculated the average values in Eq. (3.136) to the fourth order in $1/kT$ and his results can be stated succinctly in the following form, as far as the application to polar liquids and solids is concerned.

If a characteristic temperature ϕ is defined as in Eq. (3.54) and a factor q which is characteristic of the relative influence of the induced and permanent moments is given by Eq. (3.55), then Eq. (3.44) can be written in the form given by Eq. (3.53). Since in polar media most of the susceptibility arises from the permanent dipoles, the factor q in Eq. (3.53) can be replaced by unity without serious error. Doing this we see that according to this equation D becomes infinite at the *Curie temperature* $T = \phi$.

Now it was shown by Van Vleck that the statistical method of the partition function leads to the same expression (Eq. 3.53) if terms of the first order in ϕ/T only are considered. Therefore Van Vleck's deductions contain, as he states, the first general kinetic derivation of the Clausius-Mosotti formula showing at the same time that its validity is confined to the limiting case $\phi/T \to 0$.

For liquids and solids however, ϕ and T become comparable and at least the second approximation has to be introduced. This can be done by one of various methods. If one extrapolates the results of the second approximation by a procedure analogous to using a Gaussian distribution of energies in Heisenberg's theory of ferromagnetism, one obtains

$$D - 1 = \frac{3\phi q}{T - \phi q + (9Q\phi^2/16\pi^2 T)} \tag{3.138}$$

and this formula remains "valid when the induced moment is included, provided it is represented by the harmonic oscillator model."

The quantity Q is dimensionless and is defined as

$$Q = 2N^{-2} \sum_j j r_{ij}^{-6} \tag{3.139}$$

where r_{ij} is the distance between the atoms i and j and the summation is to be extended over all atoms j in the crystal. The number Q can be evaluated rigorously for a given lattice arrangement. Thus the values 16.8 and 14.4, respectively, are obtained for simple and face-centered cubic lattices.

If Eq. (3.139) is to be applied to a liquid, this can be done in the usual way by converting the sum into an integral which is to be extended over the whole medium outside a sphere of given radius. Thus

$$Q = 8\pi N^{-1} \int_a^\infty r^{-4} \, dr \tag{3.140}$$

If furthermore a is determined by Eq. (3.103), Q assumes the value

$$2 \left(\frac{4\pi}{3} \right)^2 = 35.1$$

Another way of extrapolating the second approximation is by using the Onsager field which leads, as we have seen, to a formula which avoids, as does Eq. (3.138), the $\frac{4\pi}{3}$ catastrophe. Now it is shown by Van Vleck that his method of developing the partition function leads to a result which agrees to the second approximation in the dipole-dipole interaction with the Onsager formula, one order more than with the Lorentz relation. This result is particularly gratifying since the superiority of Onsager's formula as far as the polar media are concerned was brought out by the discussion in the preceding section. It should be stressed, however, that such agreement is obtained only by giving Q, in a somewhat arbitrary way, the value 35.1 which results from Eq. (3.103). It will be noticed that this value is almost twice as high as in the case of simple and face-centered cubic lattices.

The main results of these calculations which are based on the accurate methods of the partition function is that they do not lead to an infinite value of the dielectric constant as does the Clausius-Mosotti formula. Of course it has been possible to evaluate only the first few terms in Eq. (3.136) but it is questionable, according to Van Vleck, "whether an isotropic dielectric body can ever acquire spontaneous polarization simply by virtue of dipole-dipole coupling." As pointed out previously it is not even necessary to introduce the hypothesis of hindered rotation to do away with the $\frac{4\pi}{3}$ catastrophe.

On the other hand it remains unexplained why the Clausius-Mosotti formula fits the empirical data so exceedingly well in many cases of nonpolar liquids since, again according to Van Vleck, "it is theoretically valid at high densities only for an artificial model of harmonic oscillators which cannot be regarded as an accurate representation of the induced polarization."

The formulation of the problem by Van Vleck which we have discussed in the last section is entirely rigorous. It contains hindered rotation (as a consequence of dipole-dipole interaction) and deviations from the Lorentz field implicitly. However, the actual calculation of the series, Eq. (3.136), is naturally limited to a few terms which are hardly adequate to describe the complex behavior of condensed phases, though the term of the second order (in dipole interaction) already does away with the $\frac{4\pi}{3}$ catastrophe. At the same time it was shown that the rigorous treatment by the method of the partition function agrees to the second order with Onsager's theory. It seems, therefore, reasonable that further developments have taken their starting point from Onsager's theory since this avoids the complications of the method of the partition function. On the other hand, as previously pointed out (p. 53) Onsager's treatment itself represents only a first approximation though a new and fertile one. Some of the objections summarized by Wilson have been met by subsequent investigations.

At first we wish to mention a few generalizations which leave the gist of the method unaltered. Thus Van Vleck has shown in connection with his own work that Onsager's formula can be made to include the action of an electrostatic crystalline field. This can be done (Van Vleck, *loc. cit.*) by substituting in Onsager's results, e.g., Eq. (3.107) for $N\mu_0^2/3kT$ the value of the susceptibility at infinite dipole dilution, i.e., exclusive of dipole-dipole interaction but inclusive of the crystalline.

In a similar formal way Wilson (*loc. cit.*) has introduced the optical anisotropy of polar molecules.

Wilson indicated that optical anisotropy of a polar molecule was of some importance, since the reaction field R is directed along the axis of the instantaneous dipole of the molecule, and this in turn has its principal component along the axis of the permanent dipole. From the Kerr effect and from the depolarization of scattered light in polar gases it is known that the polarizability of a molecule along its dipole axis is in general different from the polarizability averaged over all directions. Wilson accounted for this fact in the following way: He assumed that the forces acting on the dipole are given by Eq. (3.74) and (3.84) and took components A and B of the instantaneous dipole in the directions of E and of the permanent dipole, that is, along the unit vector u. He further assumed that the polarization produced by the forces in the direction of u may be calculated by use of the polarizability α_1 along the dipole axis, while that produced by forces in the direction of E may be calculated by use of the average polarizability α. This is a good approximation, since for fields far from saturation the orientation of the dipole in the field is nearly random. Proceeding as in the derivation of Eq. (3.86) we obtain

$$m = Au + BE = \mu_0 u + \frac{3D}{2D+1} \alpha E + \frac{2(D-1)}{2D+1} \left(A \frac{\alpha_1}{a^3} u + B \frac{\alpha}{a^3} E \right)$$

$$(3.141)$$

Equating coefficients of u and E separately we may solve for A and B, and substituting for a^3 and α by means of Eq. (3.103) and (3.105) and for α_1 by means of an equation in n_1^2 similar to Eq. (3.105), we obtain

$$m = \frac{(2D+1)(n_1^2+2)}{3(2D+n_1^2)} \mu_0 u + \frac{D(n^2+2)}{2D+n^2} \alpha E \qquad (3.142)$$

Proceeding from this point just as in Onsager's original treatment the final result is found to be

$$\frac{D-1}{D} - \frac{3(n^2-1)}{2D+n^2} = \frac{4\pi N}{9kT} \mu_0^2 \frac{(2D+1)(n_1^2+2)^2}{(2D+n_1^2)^2} \qquad (3.143)$$

Wilson points out that a more tedious but a more rigorous treatment in which it is assumed that the polarizability ellipsoid of the molecule has components α_1, α_2, and α_3 to which correspond indices of refraction n_1, n_2, n_3 and that the permanent dipole μ_0 is parallel to α_1, yields an equation similar to (3.143) except that the term

$$\frac{3(n^2-1)}{2D+n^2} \qquad (3.144)$$

becomes

$$\frac{n_1^2-1}{2D+n_1^2} + \frac{n^2-1}{2D+n_2^2} + \frac{n_3^2-1}{2D+n_3^2} \qquad (3.145)$$

However, the correction (3.145) is not significant for polar liquids at usual temperatures where D is large.

Wilson also modifies Onsager's theory for the dielectric properties of polar liquids to take into account the optical anisotropy of polar molecules. For a solution of a single polar solute in a nonpolar solvent this equation is

$$\frac{D-1}{D} = \frac{4\pi N_2}{9kT} \mu_{02}^2 \frac{(n_{21}^2 + 2)^2(2D + 1)}{(2D + n_{21}^2)^2} + \frac{3\theta_2(n_2^2 - 1)}{2D + n_2^2} + \frac{3\theta_1(n_1^2 - 1)}{2D + n_1^2}$$

$$(3.146)$$

Here N_2 is the number of polar molecules per cubic centimeter of solution, θ_2 and θ_1 are the fractions of the total volume occupied by polar solute and nonpolar solvent, respectively, and n_{21}, n_2, and n_1 are the average index of refraction of the polar solute, the index of refraction corresponding to polarization along the axis of the permanent dipole, and the index of refraction of the solvent respectively. Methods of calculating n_{21}, n_2, and n_1 are discussed by Wilson. This equation should be compared with Onsager's Eq. (3.109).

Much more radical than the last two developments is Kirkwood's (*J. Chem. Phys.*, **7**, 911, 1939) improvement of Onsager's theory inasmuch as it removes the most serious objection to Onsager's treatment, namely, that it idealizes the molecule as a real cavity in a uniform dielectric which is supposed to have its macroscopic dielectric constant. Kirkwood's treatment is molecular and statistical and resembles his treatment of the translational fluctuations since averages are obtained by assuming the dielectric to be a canonical ensemble.

The dielectric is treated as a specimen of spherical form because this makes the required electrostatic problem amenable to mathematical analysis, but it is shown that the result is independent of the radius of the specimen. The result can be stated in terms of two electric moments, the moment μ pertaining to a single molecule and the moment $\bar{\mu}$ pertaining to a molecule and its neighbors.

The molecular moment μ is not necessarily equal to the moment μ_0 of a molecule in the gas phase. In Onsager's original theory the correlation is given by our formula (3.89); in Kirkwood's theory it must be worked out more accurately on the basis of a more definite molecular model.

As for the moment $\bar{\mu}$, it represents the influence of any one molecule on its environment, being the total moment of that molecule and its neighbors, in the region surrounding it, in which the local dielectric constant deviates effectively from the macroscopic dielectric constant. It is the introduction of the moment $\bar{\mu}$ (which is proved to have a definite value) which represents the improvement of Kirkwood's treatment upon Onsager's. The moment $\bar{\mu}$ reduces to μ, and Kirkwood's results to Onsager's if the region of unaffected (macroscopic) dielectric constant is assumed to extend to molecular surface.

By the aid of the two moments just introduced, the dielectric constant can be represented by the following implicit equation

$$\frac{D-1}{3} = \frac{3D}{2D+1} \cdot \frac{P_0}{V} \tag{3.147}$$

with

$$P_0 = \frac{4\pi N}{3} (\alpha + \mu \cdot \bar{\mu}/3kT) \tag{3.148}$$

or to a close approximation

$$D - 1 = 9P_0/2V \tag{3.149}$$

The formulas (3.147) and (3.148) have been generalized by Kirkwood so as to hold for polar mixtures. Eq. (3.147) and (3.148) are exact except for a minor approximation in the unimportant optical term containing α. Of course the scalar product $\mu \cdot \bar{\mu}$ has yet to be calculated and that can be done only in an approximate way.

TABLE III   The dielectric constant of water at 25° C

O $\begin{matrix}\text{H Bond}\\ \\ \text{H Angle}\end{matrix}$	μ_0	$\langle \cos j \rangle Av$	Z	$\dfrac{\mu \cdot \bar{\mu}}{\mu_0^2}$	$D(\text{calc})$	$D(\text{exp})$
90	1.88	0.50	4	4.35	82	79
100	1.88	0.41	4	3.55	67	79
109° 28′	1.80	0.33	4	2.91	55	79

To perform this calculation Kirkwood proposes "a simple approximation which is probably adequate in most cases," namely, he assumes that the local dielectric constant may be approximated by its macroscopic value outside the molecule and its first shell of neighbors. Then he obtains

$$\mu \cdot \bar{\mu} = \mu^2 (1 + Z \langle \cos j \rangle Av) \tag{3.150}$$

where Z is the average coordination number (i.e., the average number of nearest neighbors). Furthermore j is the angle between the dipole moments of a pair of neighboring molecules, and $\langle \cos j \rangle Av$ is the average over-all orientations of both molecules.

Thus the significant molecular quantities determining the dielectric constant are μ, Z, and $\langle \cos j \rangle Av$. The important quantity, clarifying the role of hindered rotation, is $\langle \cos j \rangle Av$ since it measures the correlations of the orientations of neighboring molecules.

Kirkwood has applied his formulas to the case of liquid water under the assumption of tetrahedral (quasi-rigid) coordination and the assumption of directed bonds between pairs of neighboring molecules.

The exact value of the dielectric constant of water is rather sensitive to the bond angle of the water molecule. Kirkwood has carried out his calculations for three different values, i.e., 90°, 100°, and 109° 28′ (the tetrahedral angle). With suitable values for α (1.5 cubic Å), a (the distance between neighbors = 3.27Å), and μ_0 (=1.88 Debye units), the values listed in Table III are obtained.

It will be seen that a good agreement with the observed value can be obtained with probable assumptions. The great improvement upon Onsager's theory is illustrated by the fact that the latter leads to a value of 31 for the dielectric constant of water at 25° C.

Onsager's theory has been extended in a different direction by Jaffé (*J. Chem. Phys.*, **11**, 879, 1940). It was pointed out on several occasions (p. 45 and p. 53) that in Onsager's original treatment a special value for the size of the molecular cavity a is assumed. In order to reduce the Onsager formula to that of Clausius-Mosotti for nonpolar substances, and also in order to make it agree to the second order with Van Vleck's rigorous treatment it is essential to determine a from Eq. (3.103). This means, so to speak, that the whole available volume is occupied by the molecules, and the resulting formulas cannot be applied to media of variable density. Jaffé's treatment which combines the electrostatic approach of Onsager with statistical elements extends the results to the case of media of variable density, including gases.

The procedure consists in considering such molecules at first as have their nearest neighbor at distances between s and $(s + ds)$, in applying to them Onsager's method (with $a = s$), and in finally averaging over-all values of s. This means averaging over s from a definite value s_1, the distance of nearest approach of two molecules, to $s = \infty$. The averaging can be performed by the aid of a proposition in geometrical probability by P. Hertz (*Math. Ann.*, **67,** 387, 1909) which expresses, for a random distribution of points, the probability that any one of them has its nearest neighbor between given limits.

As far as the resulting value of the dielectric constant is concerned it can be represented by the implicit formula

$$\frac{D - 1}{3} = \frac{4\pi N}{3V} \frac{3D}{2D + 1} \left(\frac{\mu_0^2}{3kT} + \phi(z_1, q)\alpha \right) \tag{3.151}$$

where ϕ is a calculable function (larger than 1) of the arguments

$$z_1 = \frac{4\pi N s_1^3}{3V}, \quad q = \frac{2(D - 1)}{2D + 1} \frac{4\pi N\alpha}{3V} \tag{3.152}$$

and μ is the moment defined by Eq. (3.89). Eq. (3.151) represents the extension of Onsager's results to dielectrics of variable density down to the densities of gases. It still depends on the distance s_1 and becomes identical with Onsager's corresponding formula if the value $z_1 = 0.435$ is chosen and if negligible terms are omitted. The formal similarity of Eq. (3.151) with Kirkwood's Eq. (3.147) and (3.148) might be pointed out. Kirkwood's treatment, however, is superior as to its atomistic foundation, whereas Eq. (3.151) establishes a more general connection between the actual electric moment μ at variable densities and the moment in vacuum μ_0.

For nonpolar substances Eq. (3.151) can be brought into the form

$$\frac{D-1}{D+2} V = P_0 \left[1 + 2(A_1 - 1)\left(\frac{P_0}{V}\right)^2 + 2(1 - A_1)\left(\frac{P_0}{V}\right)^3 + \cdots \right] \quad (3.153)$$

where A_1 is a constant which still depends in a calculable way on z_1, and thereby on s_1. The formula, like Kirkwood's Eq. (3.129), rises initially with increasing density and then passes through a maximum. That is exactly the behavior shown by the most extended measurements: those of Michels and Kleerekoper (*Physica*, **6**, 586, 1939) on CO_2 up to a pressure of 1700 atmospheres. It can be shown that Eq. (3.129) represents the measurements better than Eq. (3.153). On the other hand measurements by Michels and Hamers (*Physica*, **4**, 995, 1937) on the refractive index of CO_2 up to pressures of 2400 atmospheres are represented very well by Eq. (3.153) (with n^2 substituted for D), as was shown by Jaffé.

It is not unreasonable that the behavior of the dielectric constant is expressed better by Kirkwood's theory, and that of refractive index, better by Jaffé's. In the latter's deduction the molecules are assumed to be fixed in a random distribution (which gives rise to probability distribution in s). Kirkwood, however, takes his average over-all distributions in configuration and momentum space. Now, for the short duration of a light wave, the molecules may be considered at rest in their random distributions. If, however, the dielectric constant is measured, the thermal agitation, and thereby the translational fluctuations, become prevalent.

Furthermore Jaffé has shown that by the use of Eq. (3.151) the agreement obtained by Böttcher between the calculated values of the dipole moment and those determined in gases and dilute solutions (see Table II, p. 55) can be improved. This could be expected, since

Eq. (3.151) still contains $\delta = \alpha/s_1^3$, as an adaptable constant. In the majority of cases and excluding cases of *association* and *deformation* already suspected by Böttcher, Jaffé obtained a marked improvement, inasmuch as the values of his calculated moments change less with temperature, and are closer to the observed values of the free molecule than those of Böttcher. This can best be seen by the comparisons of Table IV.

All investigations on which we have reported so far deal exclusively with the average value of the local field, and on the theory of the dielectric constant based thereon, be it in nonpolar or polar media. There still remains the problem to establish how the actual values of the components of the electric field spread about their mean values, i.e., vary locally and in time, if thermal agitation and the mutual interactions of the molecules are taken into account.

Naturally all procedures based on either the canonical ensemble or the partition function would permit of actually calculating the average deviations (fluctuations) in question; however, the analysis has nowhere been pushed that far except in the investigation of Jaffé.

TABLE IV Comparison of dipole moments as calculated by Böttcher from data of the pure liquids with those calculated from formula (3.151)

		$\mu_0 \cdot 10^{18}$ Calculated by Böttcher		$\mu_0 \cdot 10^{18}$ Calculated from (3.151)		$\mu_0 \cdot 10^{18}$ Vapor (average)	δ
	t	0	70	0	70		
Benzonitrile						4.39	0.250
	μ_0	3.58	3.76	4.26	4.40		
	t	-100	0	-100	0		
Methyl bromide						1.77	0.319
	μ_0	1.57	1.63	1.77	1.77		
	t	-70	40	-70	40		
Methyl iodide						1.54	0.298
	μ_0	1.29	1.36	1.52	1.54		
	t	-90	30	-90	30		
Ethyl bromide						2.00	0.392
	μ_0	1.80	1.91	1.96	2.00		
	t	-90	70	-90	70		
Ethyl iodide						1.86	0.283
	μ_0	1.52	1.71	1.83	1.88		
	t	10	132	10	132		
Chlorobenzene						1.70	0.321
	μ_0	1.50	1.57	1.69	1.70		

Following an older investigation of Gans (*Ann. der. Phys.*, **64,** 481, 1921), and improving on it by the use of Hertz's (*loc. cit.*) proposition, Jaffé has established the distribution function of the field components, i.e., he has calculated the probability, that at the locus of a given molecule, the components of the field are within prescribed limits. Jaffé's calculations refer to the two cases where the average value (in the direction of the impressed field) is either of the Lorentz or Onsager type.

This is not the place to enter upon these problems but it is of interest to note how relatively large these fluctuations are. Thus for sufficiently high temperatures and for sufficiently weak impressed fields the *resultant* local force will point in all directions with equal probability and will have a mean value which is more than twice the *maximum value* which the Lorentz force can assume for a given concentration of elementary dipoles, i.e., when they are all aligned in the direction of the external field. The Lorentz force is small, compared with the possible maximum, in the case of weak external fields; hence the ratio of the resultant force to the Lorentz force can even become a large number.

CHAPTER IV

The Brönsted-Christiansen-Scatchard equation

In Chapter II it was pointed out that in order to explain certain phenomena of the kinetics of reactions in solution, the theory of Debye and Hückel concerning electrolytes in solution must be understood. Brönsted (*Z. physik. Chemie*, **102**, 169, 1922; **115**, 337, 1925), Bjerrum (*Z. physik. Chemie*, **108**, 82, 1924; **118**, 251, 1925), and Christiansen (*Z. physik. Chemie*, **113**, 35, 1924) have applied the Debye-Hückel theory to the influence of neutral salts upon the velocity of reactions in solutions.

We shall here deal with Brönsted's treatment of the neutral salt effects. These effects are of two kinds. In the first case the activities of the reactants, whether ions or polar molecules, may be altered by added electrolyte. This is the primary salt effect. In the second case the effective concentration of a reactant ion coming from a weak electrolyte may be decreased by the decreased ionization of the electrolyte due to added salt. This is the secondary salt effect. This latter effect is well illustrated by the decreased catalytic effect of acetic acid upon the inversion of cane sugar in the presence of alkali acetates. In this case the activity of the hydrogen ion reactant is increased by the added salt, but the effective concentration of ion is so reduced by the common ion effect that the inversion rate constant may be decreased by as much as 40 to 50 per cent at ordinary concentrations of acid and added salt.

The Brönsted intermediate complex

The primary salt effect can be understood on the basis of Brönsted's theory. The theory assumes that there is an intermediate complex formed which may decompose reversibly to give reactants, or which may decompose irreversibly to yield products. The reaction may be written

$$A + B \rightleftharpoons X \longrightarrow C + D$$

The first step in the reaction may be considered a thermodynamic equilibrium, and the equilibrium constant from the mass law is

$$K = \frac{a_X}{a_A a_B} = \frac{C_X f_X}{C_A f_A C_B f_B} \tag{4.1}$$

The reaction rate is proportional to the concentration of X so that

$$r = k'' C_X = k'' K C_A C_B \frac{f_A f_B}{f_X} \tag{4.2}$$

Now $k'' K$ is a constant which we may call k_0' so that

$$r = k_0' C_A C_B \frac{f_A f_B}{f_X} \tag{4.3}$$

Here $r = \dfrac{dC_C}{dt} = \dfrac{dC_D}{dt}$ and since k_0' is independent of concentration, the factor $\dfrac{f_A f_B}{f_X} = F$ is the correction to the classical rate equation due to added salt. Brönsted restricts his theory to dilute solutions, since in concentrated solution nonthermodynamic factors with which his theory is not concerned may influence the rate.

Now the observed bimolecular rate constant, k', is given by

$$k' = \frac{dC}{dt} \frac{1}{C_A C_B} \tag{4.4}$$

Therefore from Eq. (4.3) and (4.4)

$$k' = k_0' \frac{f_A f_B}{f_X} = k_0' F \tag{4.5}$$

Although k_0' is independent of concentration, it must be emphasized that it is composite, nevertheless, and must yet be referred to a standard reference state of dielectric constant and of temperature before it is independent of these factors which are so influential in rate processes.

Activity coefficients from the Debye-Hückel theory

If we consider the reactants to be ions, the equilibrium equation for the reaction

$$A^{z_A} + B^{z_B} \rightleftharpoons X^{(z_A + z_B)}$$

where z_A, z_B, and $(z_A + z_B)$ are the charges on A, B, and X respectively. Now from the Debye-Hückel theory (Eq. 2.39)

$$-\ln f_A = \frac{z_A^2 A \sqrt{\mu}}{1 + \beta a_i \sqrt{\mu}} \tag{4.6}$$

$$-\ln f_B = \frac{z_B^2 A \sqrt{\mu}}{1 + \beta a_i \sqrt{\mu}} \tag{4.7}$$

and

$$-\ln f_x = \frac{(z_A + z_B)^2 A \sqrt{\mu}}{1 + \beta a_i \sqrt{\mu}} \tag{4.8}$$

as a result

$$\ln \frac{f_A f_B}{f_x} = \frac{2 z_A z_B A \sqrt{\mu}}{1 + \beta a_i \sqrt{\mu}} \tag{4.9}$$

or

$$\frac{f_A f_B}{f_x} = e^{\frac{2 z_A z_B A \sqrt{\mu}}{1 + \beta a_i \sqrt{\mu}}} \tag{4.10}$$

and from Eq. (4.5) and (4.10) we obtain

$$k' = k_0' e^{\frac{2 z_A z_B A \sqrt{\mu}}{1 + \beta a_i \sqrt{\mu}}} \tag{4.11}$$

In logarithmic form Eq. (4.11) becomes

$$\ln k' = \ln k_0' + \frac{2 z_A z_B A \sqrt{\mu}}{1 + \beta a_i \sqrt{\mu}} \tag{4.12}$$

For very dilute solutions where μ is small Eq. (4.11) and (4.12) may be written as limiting forms, thus

$$k' = k_0' e^{2 z_A z_B A \sqrt{\mu}} \tag{4.13}$$

and

$$\ln k' = \ln k_0' + 2 z_A z_B A \sqrt{\mu} \tag{4.14}$$

Decadic logarithms may be used if for the constant A we write the constant A' where $A' = 2A/2.303$. Then Eq. (4.12) and (4.14) become

$$\log k' = \log k_0' + \frac{z_A z_B A' \sqrt{\mu}}{1 + \beta a_i \sqrt{\mu}} \tag{4.15}$$

and

$$\log k' = \log k_0' + z_A z_B A' \sqrt{\mu} \tag{4.16}$$

From Eq. (4.16) a plot of $\log k'$ vs $\sqrt{\mu}$ should, for dilute solutions of ions, yield a straight line with intercept $\log k_0'$ and slope $z_A z_B A'$.

While it is generally assumed that if one of the reactants is molecular rather than ionic, the slope of the $\log k'$ vs any function of μ should be zero since either z_A or z_B is zero, yet, as will be shown in a later chapter, k' is a function of μ in the case of ion-dipolar molecule reactions.

Application of the equation to data

The classical example of the agreement of data with the predictions of Eq. (4.16) is the figure given by LaMer (*Chem. Rev.*, **10,** 179, 1932) which, except for the data on the inversion of sucrose, is given below in Fig. 1. The data for sucrose is omitted since the data for ion-dipolar molecule reactions will be discussed under the theory dealing with those reactions.

These data show that the slopes of the log k' vs $\sqrt{\mu}$ curves for dilute solutions of ionic reactants and of other ions are about equal to the product $z_A z_B$ predicted by Eq. (4.16) since for water at 25° C the constant A' is about unity. These data are for solutions of ions of low charge. Some of the data fail to reach the theoretical slopes and in these cases, due to specific solvent effect or other cause, the Debye-Hückel expression fails to give the correct activity coefficients. The presence of ions of higher valence sometimes causes the slope of the log k' vs $\sqrt{\mu}$ empirical curve to be several times that predicted by theory.

Effect of dielectric constant of the solvent on reaction rates

Scatchard (*Chem. Rev.*, **10,** 229, 1932) develops the effect of the solvent, in so far as the dielectric constant of the solvent is concerned, upon reaction rates in solution. From Eq. (2.32)

$$\psi = \frac{z_i\epsilon}{Dr}\frac{e^{\varkappa(a_i-r)}}{1+\varkappa a_i} \tag{4.17}$$

and from Eq. (2.36) and (4.17)

$$\ln f_i = \frac{1}{kT}\int_0^{z_i\epsilon}\psi\, d(z_i\epsilon) = \frac{1}{kT}\int_0^{z_i\epsilon}\frac{z_i\epsilon}{Dr}\frac{e^{\varkappa(a_i-r)}}{1+\varkappa a_i}\, d(z_i\epsilon) \tag{4.18}$$

Integrating we obtain

$$\ln f_i = \frac{z_i^2\epsilon^2 e^{\varkappa(a_i-r)}}{2DkT(1+\varkappa a_i)r} \tag{4.19}$$

and

$$\ln\frac{f_A f_B}{f_X} = \frac{[z_A^2 + z_B^2 - (z_A + z_B)^2]\epsilon^2 e^{\varkappa(a_i-r)}}{2DkT(1+\varkappa a_i)r} = -\frac{z_A z_B \epsilon^2 e^{\varkappa(a_i-r)}}{DkT(1+\varkappa a_i)r} \tag{4.20}$$

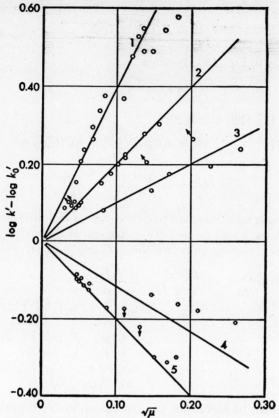

Figure 1 The influence of ionic strength on the velocity of ionic reactions.

1. $2[Co(NH_3)_5Br]^{++} + Hg^{++} + 2H_2O \longrightarrow$
$2[Co(NH_3)_5H_2O]^{+++} + Hg Br_2$ (Bimolecular). No foreign salt added.

2. Circles. $CH_2BrCOO^- + S_2O_3 = \longrightarrow CH_2S_2O_3COO^-$
$+ Br^-$ as the sodium salt. No foreign salt added. Dots. $S_2O_3^- + 2I^- \longrightarrow I_2 + 2SO_4^-$ as $Na_2S_2O_3$ and KI.

3. Saponification of nitrourethane ion by hydroxyl ion. $[NO_2 = N\text{-}COOC_2H_5]^- + OH^- \longrightarrow N_2O + CO_3^= + C_2H_5OH$.

4. $H_2O_2 + 2H^+ + 2Br^- \longrightarrow 2H_2O + Br_2$.

5. $[Co(NH_3)_5Br]^{++} + OH^-$
$\longrightarrow [Co(NH_3)_5OH]^{++} + Br^-$.

Then

$$\frac{f_A f_B}{f_X} = e^{-\frac{z_A z_B \epsilon^2}{DkT} \frac{e^{-\varkappa r}}{r} \frac{e^{\varkappa a_i}}{1+\varkappa a_i}} \tag{4.21}$$

and for $\varkappa = 0$, Eq. (4.21) becomes

$$\frac{f_A f_B}{f_X} = e^{-\frac{z_A z_B \epsilon^2}{DkTr}} \tag{4.22}$$

But from Eq. (4.2) and (4.22)

$$C_X^0 = K C_A^0 C_B^0 \frac{f_A f_B}{f_X} = K C_A^0 C_B^0 e^{-\frac{z_A z_B \epsilon^2}{DkTr}} \tag{4.23}$$

Thus

$$\ln \frac{f_A f_B}{f_X} = \ln \frac{1}{K} \frac{C_X^0}{C_A^0 C_B^0} = -\frac{z_A z_B \epsilon^2}{DkTr} \tag{4.24}$$

Now choosing some standard reference state of dielectric constant D_0, of the solvent, where the activity coefficients of the solutes, reactants and complex, become unity, we obtain from Eq. (4.24)

$$
\begin{aligned}
\ln \frac{f_A f_B}{f_X} - \ln \left(\frac{f_A f_B}{f_X}\right)_0 &= \ln \frac{f_A f_B}{f_X} \\
&= \ln \frac{C_X^0}{C_A^0 C_B^0} - \ln \left(\frac{C_X^0}{C_A^0 C_B^0}\right)_0 \\
&= -\frac{z_A z_B \epsilon^2}{DkTr} - \left(-\frac{z_A z_B \epsilon^2}{D_0 kTr}\right) \\
&= \frac{z_A z_B \epsilon^2}{kTr} \left(\frac{1}{D_0} - \frac{1}{D}\right)
\end{aligned}
\tag{4.25}
$$

A word might be said about the assumption involved in this derivation. The activity coefficients of the ionic solutes are assumed to be functions of the dielectric constant of the solvent even at infinite dilution, and it is only at the standard reference state of dielectric constant of the solvent that forces tending to lessen the activities of the ionic solutes vanish, and the activity coefficient for each of the solutes becomes unity. Equation (4.25) predicts an increase of reaction rate with increasing dielectric constant for ions of like sign and a decrease of reaction rate with increasing dielectric constant of the medium for ions of unlike sign.

Scatchard arrived at the concentration of the complex Eq. (4.23) using the method of Christiansen (*Z. physik. Chemie*, **113,** 35, 1924). This method is the direct calculation of the concentration of the complex from equations given by Debye and Hückel.

If we choose a standard reference state of dielectric constant as that of infinite dielectric constant, Eq. (4.25) becomes

$$\ln \frac{f_A f_B}{f_x} = -\frac{z_A z_B \epsilon^2}{DkTr} \qquad (4.26)$$

where the r of these equations is the radius of the complex and is written $r = r_A + r_B$. The factor r can be defined as the distance to which two ions must approach in order to react.

Thus in Eq. (4.12) and (4.14) even when the ionic strength is zero, the term k_0' is still complex and we must write

$$\ln k_0' = \ln k_{\substack{x=0 \\ D=\infty}}' - \frac{z_A z_B \epsilon^2}{DkTr} \qquad (4.27)$$

and the kinetic equation must be written

$$\ln k' = \ln k_{\substack{x=0 \\ D=\infty}}' - \frac{z_A z_B \epsilon^2}{DkTr} + \frac{z_A z_B \epsilon^2}{DkT} \frac{x}{1 + a_i x} \qquad (4.28)$$

in order to give the dependence of the reaction rate both upon the dielectric constant of the solvent and upon the ionic strength of the solution. It must be emphasized that even after the double transition $x = 0$ and $D = \infty$, the k' in the first term on the right of Eq. (4.28) is still complex and involves a temperature dependence which will be discussed later.

Equation (4.28) is generally called the Brönsted-Christiansen-Scatchard equation and is accepted as the basis for theoretical interpretation of rate data between ionic reactants.

It might be pointed out that a_i, the distance of closest approach of the ions cannot conceivably differ largely from r, the distance to which two ions must approach in order to react. Scatchard (*loc. cit.*) discusses this in some detail.

Application of the theory

Equation (4.27) predicts that a plot of $\ln k_0'$ vs $1/D$ should yield a straight line with a positive slope if z_A and z_B are of the same sign.

Amis and LaMer (*J. Am. Chem. Soc.*, **61**, 905, 1931) have graphed the data $\log k_0'$ vs $1/D$ for the reaction of the divalent negative tetra-bromophenolsulfonphthalein ion with the univalent negative hydroxide ion in ethyl alcohol-water and methyl alcohol-water solvents. The graph is reproduced in Fig. 2.

The data yield straight lines down to a dielectric constant of about 65. Furthermore, the slopes of these lines are negative. Thus the curves agree with theory.

Amis and Price (*J. Phys. Chem.*, **47**, 338, 1944) have plotted log k'_0 vs $1/D$ for the data of Svirbely and Schramm (*J. Am. Chem. Soc.*, **60**,

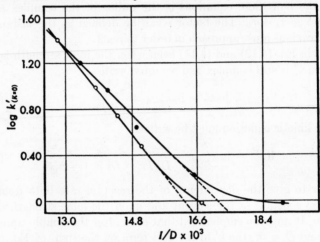

Figure 2 Log $k'_{\varkappa=0}$ at 25°C for the reaction $(B\phi B)^- +$ OH^- versus the reciprocal of the dielectric constant of the media: ●, $CH_3OH - H_2O$; ○, $C_2H_5OH - H_2O$.

330, 1938) and of Lander and Svirbely (*J. Am. Chem. Soc.*, **60**, 1613, 1938) for the reaction between the positive univalent ammonium ion and the negative univalent cyanate ion at 30° C in water-methyl alcohol and in water-glycol, respectively. These plots are reproduced in Fig. 3.

The curve for water-methyl alcohol solvent except for a slight curvature in the region of pure water is straight down to a dielectric constant of about 45. The data for the water-glycol solvent give a perfectly straight line down to a dielectric constant of about 55. The slopes of both curves are positive. Thus the shape and slope of the curves in regions of higher dielectric constants are again in agreement with theory.

The radius of the intermediate complex

A more quantitative test of the agreement of the data with theory can be obtained by calculating the values of r, the distance of approach for two ions to react, from the slopes of the log k_0' vs $1/D$ plots. From Eq. (4.27) we have for the slope S

$$S = \frac{d \ln k_0'}{d \left(\frac{1}{D} \right)} = - \frac{z_A z_B \epsilon^2}{kT} \frac{1}{r} \tag{4.29}$$

and using logarithms to the base 10 we obtain

$$r = - \frac{z_A z_B \epsilon^2}{2.303 S k T} \tag{4.30}$$

This value of r should undoubtedly be of the magnitude of molecular dimensions since it represents the radius of the intermediate complex. Thus we would expect an order of magnitude for r of 10^{-8} centimeter.

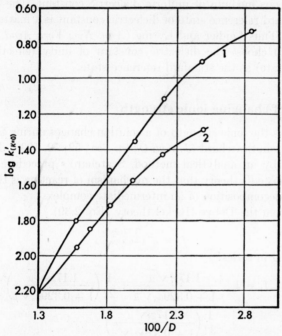

Figure 3   Plot of data of Svirbely and Schramm and of Lander and Svirbely for the ammonium ion-cyanate ion reaction.
1. Water-methyl alcohol at 30°C.
2. Water-glycol at 30°C.

Amis and LaMer (*loc. cit.*) find r to be 1.22×10^{-8} centimeter and 1.49×10^{-8} centimeter for the tetrabromophenolsulfonphthalein ion-hydroxide ion reaction in the presence of ethyl and methyl alcohols respectively and Amis and Price (*loc. cit.*) find values of r of 2.2×10^{-8} and 2.5×10^{-8} for the ammonium ion-cyanate ion reaction in water-methyl alcohol and water-glycol media respectively. Thus while there are small specific solvent effects, nevertheless, the values of r obtained are gratifying from the standpoint of theory.

Thus Eq. (4.28) gives for ionic reactants the dependence of the rate constant upon the ionic strength of the solution. The equation also gives for these reactants, the variation of rate constant with changing solvent in so far as the effect of the solvent is exerted through its dielectric constant and in so far as the solvent may be treated as a homogeneous medium of uniform dielectric constant. The choice of the standard reference state of dielectric constant is a matter of convenience. Thus Laidler and Eyring (*Ann. New York Acad. Sci.*, **39,** 303, 1940) choose the dielectric constant of unity (effectively the gaseous state) as the standard reference state.

Theory of changing ionic strength

Sometimes the ionic strength of a solution changes during the course of a reaction. Scatchard (*J. Am. Chem. Soc.*, **52,** 52, 1930) deals with this case by an analytical method. Scatchard's procedure is based upon Brönsted's theory that the mechanism of reaction is the formation and decomposition of an intermediate complex.

Now from the Debye-Hückel theory (Eq. 2.39)

$$f_i = e^{-\frac{1.17z_i^2\sqrt{\mu}}{1+0.329a_i\sqrt{\mu}}} \tag{4.31}$$

Expanding in series

$$f_i = 1 - \frac{1.17z_i^2\sqrt{\mu}}{1 + 0.329a_i\sqrt{\mu}} + \frac{1}{2!}\left(\frac{1.17z_i\sqrt{\mu}}{1 + 0.329a_i\sqrt{\mu}}\right)^2$$
$$- \frac{1}{3!}\left(\frac{1.17z_i\sqrt{\mu}}{1 + 0.329a_i\sqrt{\mu}}\right)^3 + \cdots \tag{4.32}$$

By dividing the numerator by the denominator we have

$$\frac{1.17z_i^2\sqrt{\mu}}{1 + 0.329a_i\sqrt{\mu}} = 1.17z_i^2\sqrt{\mu} - 0.385z_i^2a_i\mu + 0.1267z_i^2a_i^2\mu^{\frac{3}{2}} - \cdots \tag{4.33}$$

and from Eq. (4.32) and (4.33) and neglecting powers of μ greater than the one-half power, we obtain

$$f_i = 1 - 1.17z_i^2\sqrt{\mu} \tag{4.34}$$

Also from Eq. (4.34)

$$f_i = \frac{1}{1 + 1.17z_i^2\sqrt{\mu}} \tag{4.35}$$

Likewise from Eq. (4.10)

$$\frac{f_A f_B}{f_X} = 1 + 2.34z_A z_B\sqrt{\mu} = \frac{1}{1 - 2.34z_A z_B\sqrt{\mu}} \tag{4.36}$$

Now μ is a linear function of the extent of the reaction x and can be expressed as

$$\sqrt{\mu} = \sqrt{\mu_0}\sqrt{1 + gx} \tag{4.37}$$

where μ_0 is the original ionic strength, and $\mu_0(1 + g)$ is the ionic strength when the reaction is complete ($x = 1$).

There is not much loss of accuracy and the integration is much simplified by setting

$$\sqrt{1 + gx} = 1 + \tfrac{1}{2}gx \tag{4.38}$$

Scatchard (*loc. cit.*) uses Yost's (*J. Am. Chem. Soc.*, **48,** 374, 1926) studies on the oxidation of ammonia by persulfate ion to make a concrete test of his theory. The slow reaction in this case is

$$S_2O_8^{--} + Ag(NH_3)_2^+ \longrightarrow 2SO_4^{--} + Ag^{+++} + 2NH_3,$$

and since the silver complex is regenerated in the subsequent rapid reaction

$$3Ag^{+++} + 2NH_3 \longrightarrow 3Ag^+ + N_2 + 6H^+$$

the reaction is apparently unimolecular and $z_A z_B = -2$.

The expression for the rate can be written

$$\frac{dx}{dt} = KC_{Ag^+}(1 - x)\frac{f_A f_B}{f_X} \tag{4.39}$$

and substituting from Eq. (4.36) and (4.37)

$$\frac{f_A f_B}{f_X} = \frac{1}{1 + 4.68\sqrt{\mu}} = \frac{1}{1 + 4.68\sqrt{\mu_0}\sqrt{1 + gx}} \tag{4.40}$$

into Eq. (4.39) there results

$$\frac{dx}{dt} = \frac{k'C_{Ag^+}(1 - x)}{1 + 4.68\sqrt{\mu_0}\sqrt{1 + gx}} \tag{4.41}$$

Separating variables Eq. (4.41) gives

$$\frac{dx}{1-x}(1 + 4.68\sqrt{\mu_0}\sqrt{1+gx}) = k'C_{Ag^+}\,dt \qquad (4.42)$$

The following integrations must be made

$$\int_0^x \frac{dx}{1-x} + 4.68\sqrt{\mu_0}\int_0^x \frac{\sqrt{1+gx}}{1-x}\,dx = k'C_{Ag^+}\int_0^t dt \qquad (4.43)$$

First let us integrate the second integral on the left of Eq. (4.43). To do this let

$$z = \sqrt{1+gx} \qquad (4.44)$$

Then we have

$$\int_0^x \frac{\sqrt{1+gx}}{1-x}\,dx = -2\int_1^{\sqrt{1+gx}} \frac{z^2\,dz}{z^2-(g+1)} \qquad (4.45)$$

By dividing the numerator by the denominator the right side of Eq. (4.45) becomes

$$-2\int_1^{\sqrt{1+gx}} \frac{z^2\,dz}{z^2-(g+1)} = -2\int_1^{\sqrt{1+gx}}dz - 2\int_1^{\sqrt{1+gx}} \frac{(g+1)\,dz}{z^2-(g+1)}$$

$$= \left[-2z - 2\frac{(g+1)}{2\sqrt{g+1}}\ln\frac{z-\sqrt{g+1}}{z+\sqrt{g+1}}\right]_1^{\sqrt{1+gx}}$$

$$(4.46)$$

Hence, Eq. (4.43) when integrated completely yields

$$\ln\frac{1}{1-x} + 4.68\sqrt{\mu_0}\left[\sqrt{1+g}\ln\frac{(\sqrt{1+g}+\sqrt{1+gx})}{(\sqrt{1+g}-\sqrt{1+gx})}\frac{(\sqrt{1+g}-1)}{(\sqrt{1+g}+1)}\right.$$
$$\left. -2(\sqrt{1+gx}-1)\right] = k'C_{Ag^+}t \quad (4.47)$$

Using the more simple expression $(1 + \tfrac{1}{2}gx)$ (Eq. 4.38) for the factor $\sqrt{1+gx}$, the expression to be integrated is

$$\int_0^x \frac{dx}{1-x} + 4.68\sqrt{\mu_0}\int_0^x \frac{dx}{1-x} + \frac{4.68\sqrt{\mu_0}g}{2}\int_0^x \frac{x\,dx}{1-x} = \int_0^t k'C_{Ag^+}\,dt \quad (4.48)$$

This integrates to give

$$\ln\frac{1}{1-x}[1 + 4.68\sqrt{\mu_0}(1+g/2)] - 2.34\sqrt{\mu_0}gx = k'C_{Ag^+}t \quad (4.49)$$

Neglecting the change of environment, i.e., letting $g = 0$, gives

$$(1 + 4.68\sqrt{\mu_0})\ln\frac{1}{1-x} = k'C_{Ag^+}t \qquad (4.50)$$

Table I shows the applications of these equations to the measurements of Yost starting with $0.01388M$ $(NH_4)_2S_2O_8$ and $0.0059M$ $AgClO_4$. The ammonia concentration is given in the table. From these data, and since the ionization of the NH_4OH is negligible in the presence of its salts $\mu_0 = 0.0473$ and after reaction was complete $(x = 1)$ $\mu = 0.0887$. Therefore from Eq. (4.37)

$$0.0887 = 0.0473(1 + g) \tag{4.51}$$

or $g = 0.875$.

The first column of the table gives the time, the second the fraction of persulfate converted, and the last three columns give the constants calculated by Eq. (4.50), (4.47), and (4.49).

TABLE I Oxidation of ammonia by the persulfate ion

$$NH_3 = 0.0687M$$

Time	x	k' 4.50	k' 4.47	k' 4.49
5.5	0.18	12.4	12.6	12.6
15.5	.41	11.7	12.3	12.3
26	.59	11.8	12.7	12.7
40	.73	11.2	12.2	12.3
57	.84	11.0	12.2	12.3
91	.84	10.2	11.5	11.7 (12.2)
125	.97	0.95	11.0	11.3 (12.1)

$$NH_3 = 0.1123M$$

Time	x	k' 4.50	k' 4.47	k' 4.49
5	0.22	16.7	17.1	17.1
17	.54	15.4	16.4	16.4
26	.71	15.6	16.9	17.0
39.5	.83	15.1	16.7	16.8
57.5	.91	14.5	16.2	16.5
91	.97	13.2	15.2	15.4 (16.6)
125	.99	11.6	13.5	13.6 (15.9)

Comparison of the last two columns shows that the error introduced by the approximation of Eq. (4.38) is negligible.

By Eq. (4.50) where the change in ionic strength during the course of the reaction is entirely neglected, the constants decrease about 20 per cent. By either Eq. (4.47) or Eq. (4.49) there is no trend up to about 90 per cent conversion. The figures in the parentheses were included by Scatchard to show that the decrease of the rate constant beyond 90 per cent conversion could be prevented by decreasing the observed values of persulfate ion concentration by one unit in the last place given, which should be within the experimental error.

Warner and coworkers (Svirbely and Warner, *J. Am. Chem. Soc.*, **57,** 1833, 1935); Warner and Warrick (*J. Am. Chem. Soc.*, **57,** 1491, 1935), and Svirbely and coworkers (Svirbely and Schramm, *J. Am. Chem. Soc.*, **60,** 330, 1938); Lander and Svirbely (*J. Am. Chem. Soc.*, **60,** 1613, 1938) have studied the decomposition of ammonium cyanate to give urea. The reaction is

$$NH_4^+ + OCN^- \rightleftharpoons CO(NH_2)_2$$

By the Brönsted-Christiansen theory of the salt effect, the rate equation, neglecting the back reaction which is unimportant up to 70 per cent conversion, is

$$- \frac{dC}{dt} = k_0' C_{NH_4^+} C_{OCN^-} \frac{f_{NH_4^+} f_{OCN^-}}{f_X} \tag{4.52}$$

Now the activity coefficients are a function of μ, which is changing during the reaction, and Eq. (4.52) cannot be integrated as it stands.

By using Scatchard's treatment of a reaction rate in a changing environment Eq. (4.52) can be integrated. For this reaction $z_A z_B = -1$, and from Eq. (4.36)

$$\frac{f_{NH} f_{OC_4^+ N^-}}{f_X} = \frac{1}{1 + 2A\sqrt{\mu}} \tag{4.53}$$

where A is the Debye-Hückel constant.

Let x be the fraction of NH_4OCN converted into urea. The concentration of NH_4OCN and hence μ may be expressed in terms of the initial ionic strength, μ_0, and x as given by Eq. (4.37). For this reaction $\mu = 0$ when $x = 1$ and, therefore, by Eq. (4.37) $g = -1$ and

$$\sqrt{\mu} = \sqrt{\mu_0}\sqrt{1 - x} \tag{4.54}$$

The following conditions also maintain $x = \dfrac{C^0 - C}{C^0}$; $dC = -C^0 dx$,

$C_{NH_4^+} = C_{OCN^-} = C^0 - C^0 x$, and $\mu_0 = C^0$. Therefore substituting Eq. (4.53) and (4.54) into Eq. (4.52), we have

$$C^0 \frac{dx}{dt} = \frac{k^{0'} C^{02}(1 - x)^2}{1 + 2A\sqrt{\mu_0}\sqrt{1 - x}} \tag{4.55}$$

and the equation to be integrated is

$$k^{0\prime} C^0 \int_0^t dt = \int_0^x \frac{dx}{(1-x)^2} + 2A \sqrt{C^0} \int_0^x \frac{dx}{(1-x)^{\frac{3}{2}}} \qquad (4.56)$$

Integrating and inserting limits, we obtain

$$C^0 k^{0\prime} t = \frac{1}{1-x} - 1 + \frac{4A \sqrt{C^0}}{1-x} - 4A \sqrt{C^0} \qquad (4.57)$$

Inserting $x = \dfrac{C^0 - C}{C^0}$ and rearranging gives

$$k^{0\prime} t = \left[\frac{1 + 4A \sqrt{C}}{C} \right] - \left[\frac{1 + 4A \sqrt{C^0}}{C^0} \right] \qquad (4.58)$$

Limiting velocity constants were calculated from Eq. (4.58). Svirbely and Warner's data for these constants $k_S^{0\prime}$, in methyl alcohol-water solvents are compared with the limiting constants, $k_G^{0\prime}$, calculated from bimolecular constants determined by the method of slopes (Warner and Stitt, *J. Am. Chem. Soc.*, **55**, 4807, 1933) and using Eq. (4.15) which for this reaction can be written

$$\log k_0' = \log k_1' + \frac{3.63 \times 10^6 \sqrt{\mu}}{(TD)^{\frac{3}{2}} + 100.6 DT \sqrt{\mu}} \qquad (4.59)$$

See Table II.

TABLE II Limiting velocity constants in water and in media of fixed dielectric constant

$$H_2O$$

VARIABLE D

Temp. °C	$k_S^{0\prime}$	$k_G^{0\prime}$
30	0.00625	0.00647
40	.0217	.0227
50	.0680	.0710
60	.205	.212
70	.584	.609

$$CH_3OH-H_2O$$
$$D_0 = 63.5$$

Temp.° C	Wt. % CH₃OH	$k_S^{0\prime}$	$k_G^{0\prime}$	Wt. % CH₃OH	$k_S^{0\prime}$	$k_G^{0\prime}$
30	28.3	0.0159	0.0166	46.6	0.0304	0.0330
40	21.4	.0413	.0432	39.6	.0785	.0833
50	14.8	.106	.110	33.4	.192	.207
60	8.1	.263	.270	27.5	.468	.502
70	0.0	.584	.609			

Equation (4.59) yields somewhat higher values for k'_0 than Eq. (4.58). There is no real reason for believing that Eq. (4.58) should yield better results in this case than Eq. (4.59). Better agreement was obtained between calculated results for k'_1 from Eq. (4.58) and (4.59) when the ionic strength was 0.194, employing the relationship from the application of Eq. (4.53) to the Brönsted theory:

$$k'_1 = \frac{k'_0}{1 + 2A\sqrt{\mu}} \tag{4.60}$$

The reader is referred to the original manuscript of Svirbely and Warner to check this agreement.

Bjerrum's derivation

Although the treatment in this chapter has dealt only with Brönsted's derivation of reaction velocity based on the hypothesis that the velocity depends only on the difference in potentials between initial and critical states of the reactants, yet it should be pointed out that both Bjerrum and Christiansen have made satisfactory derivations of reaction velocity based on somewhat different assumptions.

Bjerrum (*Z. physik. Chem.*, **108**, 82, 1924; **118**, 251, 1925) assumes that a thermally induced spontaneous monomolecular decomposition of a collision complex determines the reaction rate. This *Stosscomplex* is not a chemical compound but is merely of a physical nature. Thus

$$A + B \rightleftharpoons X_s \longrightarrow C + D \tag{4.61}$$

The rate of the reaction at any instant is proportional to the concentration of the collision complex C_{X_s} at that instant. This gives

$$-\frac{dC_A}{dt} = -\frac{dC_B}{dt} = k^1_{X_s} C_{X_s} \tag{4.62}$$

The collision equilibrium in terms of activities is from the mass law

$$\frac{a_{X_s}}{a_A a_B} = \frac{C_{X_s} f_{X_s}}{C_A f_A C_B f_B} = K_a \tag{4.63}$$

Solving for C_{X_s} out of Eq. (4.63) and substituting this into Eq. (4.62) yields a formula identical with the Brönsted formula so long as no distinction is made between the critical complex X of Brönsted and the Stosscomplex X_s of Bjerrum.

According to Brönsted it is the rate of formation of the complex which determines the reaction velocity. Brönsted makes this rate of formation of the complex depend on activities. Furthermore, the temperature coefficient of the reaction depends entirely upon the rate of complex formation. From Bjerrum's viewpoint, reaction velocities are proportional to concentrations. The ionic strength influences only the primary equilibrium according to Bjerrum, and also the reaction of the X_s complex to yield products is strongly dependent upon temperature.

LaMer (*Chem. Rev.*, **10,** 179, 1932) criticizes the concentration hypothesis of Bjerrum from the standpoint of reversible monomolecular reactions such as

$$A \rightleftharpoons Y \tag{4.64}$$

Assuming the validity of Bjerrum's hypothesis, the mass law in terms of concentrations must hold, and hence

$$\frac{C_A}{C_Y} = \text{Constant} \tag{4.65}$$

irrespective of change in the properties of the medium. But displacement does occur upon addition of salts except in the insignificant case when the two activity coefficients are affected equally. LaMer also points out that the theory of Bjerrum is hardly analogous to radioactivity, since such transformations are due to instability of the nucleus for which there is a finite probability of decomposition, quite independent of external conditions.

Christiansen's theory

Christiansen (*Z. physik. Chem.*, **113,** 35, 1924) avoids the troublesome factors of concentrations of a critical complex or of a collision complex by basing his theory upon the number of collisions of reacting molecules. In his treatment the reaction velocity is set equal to

$$V = C_A C_B Z_{AB} \sqrt{T} e^{-\frac{Q_{AB}}{RT}} \Omega \frac{\rho}{\rho + \sum NC} \tag{4.66}$$

Here $C_A C_B Z_{AB} \sqrt{T}$ is the number of collisions per second per liter, Q_{AB} is the energy of activation, Ω is the steric factor, ρ is the probability that the complex will react to yield products, and ΣNC is the probability that it will be deactivated again to reactants by molecules of concentration C each with an individual probability N. It must be emphasized that C is not the bulk concentration, but the concentration of the various molecules in the vicinity of the reacting molecules.

For very small concentrations the factor $\dfrac{\rho}{\rho + \Sigma NC}$ approaches unity and for high concentrations it approaches the value $\dfrac{\rho}{\Sigma NC}$. For limiting cases of low concentrations Eq. (4.66) is therefore simplified.

The concentrations C_A' and C_B in the vicinity of colliding reactant ions used in Eq. (4.66) are not the bulk concentrations C_A^1 and C_B^1 of the reactants, but are calculated in the case of ionic reactants, from these bulk concentrations by means of the Debye theory,

$$C_A = C_A^1 e^{-\frac{\epsilon z_A \phi_B}{kT}} \tag{4.67}$$

where z_A is the valence of ion A and ϕ_B is the electrostatic potential at the collision distance a from ion B and is given by the equation

$$\phi_B = \frac{\epsilon z_B}{D} \frac{e^{-\varkappa a}}{a} \tag{4.68}$$

In this equation $\varkappa$ is the Debye kappa and D is the dielectric constant of the medium.

According to Christiansen Eq. (4.67) requires a concentration of ions around an ion of opposite sign, but ions of opposite sign do not collide with any greater average kinetic energy because of electrostatic attraction between them.

By setting Ω and $\dfrac{\rho}{\rho + \Sigma NC}$ each equal to unity, Christiansen finally obtains

$$\ln k' = \ln k_0'' - \frac{z_A z_B \epsilon^2}{DkTa} + 2.31 z_A z_B \sqrt{\mu} \tag{4.69}$$

where $\ln k_0''$ is the sum of several terms which for a given set of conditions are constants. At infinite dilution

$$\ln k_{\varkappa=0}' = \ln k_0'' - \frac{z_A z_B \epsilon^2}{DkTa} \tag{4.70}$$

If the dielectric constant D becomes infinite or if any other condition prevails which would eliminate the effect of the electric charges, k_0'' would then be the observed rate constant at infinite dilution. LaMer (*loc. cit.*) points out that though k_0'' is thus the value of k' extrapolated to infinite dilution and to a condition freed from all effects due to net electric charges, yet k_0'' will still be influenced by effects arising from electric moments.

Thus in Christiansen's theory it is the distribution of concentrations arising from interionic attractions which predominately influence the velocity of ionic reactions. Further the last term in Eq. (4.69) is concentration dependent and corresponds to the Brönsted activity coefficient term, i.e., to $-\ln \dfrac{f_A f_B}{f_x}$.

Scatchard (*Chem. Rev.*, **10**, 229, 1932) concludes that it is unimportant whether the rate is calculated from the concentration of reacting complexes or from the number of collisions with the necessary orientation and energy multiplied by a factor which allows for the duration of a collision. If the molecules obtain the necessary energy and become sufficiently deformed and correctly orientated before collision, reaction will ensue when the molecules collide. If the molecules collide before any of the other steps have taken place, there will be preliminary complex formation.

CHAPTER V

The temperature coefficient of reaction rates; energy of activation

A chemical reaction rate roughly doubles or trebles for each ten-degree rise in temperature. Arrhenius proposed the formula

$$k' = Ze - \frac{\Delta E}{RT} \qquad k' = Z e^{-\frac{\Delta E}{RT}} \qquad (5.1)$$

to account for this temperature effect upon reaction rates. The constant Z has come to be known as the Arrhenius frequency factor and ΔE is commonly termed the energy of activation for the reaction process. Recently Eyring (*J. Chem. Phys.*, **3**, 107, 1935) and co-workers (*The Theory of Rate Processes*, New York, McGraw-Hill Book Co., 1941) have developed and applied an equation for the absolute rate process which lends significance to the Z and ΔE terms in the Arrhenius equation. LaMer (*J. Chem. Phys.*, **1**, 289, 1933) has also interpreted the Z term from the standpoint of theory. These points will be taken up in more detail later. Here we will only point out that the ΔE of the Arrhenius equation is shown to be really the heat of activation ΔH, and the Z is proved to be a product of a universal frequency $\frac{RT}{Nh}$ and $e^{\frac{\Delta S}{R}}$ where ΔS is the entropy of activation. Since in solutions there is ordinarily very small change of volume due to the chemical reaction taking place, ΔE and ΔH are practically identical, and so we will speak of the energy of activation ΔE. The energy of activation may be thought of as the energy per mole required to raise the reactants from the energy level at which they exist to the level of energy at which the intermediate complex exists. Once the reactants attain this energy and form the complex, then the complex may fall down from the mountain top of energy either to the energy valley of reactants or that of products. Hence our rate expression will

90

need a statistical weight factor which will give the probability that an activated complex will give the products of the reaction. In many cases this probability is practically unity. In Fig. 1 a graphical representation of the energy of activation is given. In this figure ΔE_R is the energy necessary to bring a mole of reactant to the activated state and is therefore the energy of activation of the forward reaction. ΔE_P is in like manner the energy of activation of the reverse reaction so that both the forward and reverse process may be represented by the equation.

$$\text{Reactants} \underset{\Delta E_P}{\overset{\Delta E_R}{\rightleftharpoons}} \text{Products}$$

The calorimetric heat of reaction is given by

$$\Delta H = \Delta E_R - \Delta E_P \tag{5.2}$$

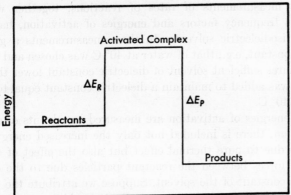

Figure 1 Diagrammatic representation of the energy of activation for reactants going to products and vice versa.

The energy of activation is ordinarily calculated by transforming Eq. (5.1) into the logarithmic form thus

$$\log k' = \log Z - \frac{\Delta E}{2.303RT} \tag{5.3}$$

and substituting two values of k' at two temperatures into the transformed equation, or by plotting $\log k'$ as $1/T$ and setting the slope of the straight line thus obtained equal to $-\dfrac{\Delta E}{2.303R}$. Z can be calculated from the intercept of the line on the $\log k'$ axis at $1/T = 0$. Since the specific reaction rates are measurable only for reactions which run their course between the time limits of not less than a few seconds and not more than a few months, ΔE ordinarily lies between 10,000 and 75,000 calories per mole. The lower activation energies are obtained for reactions measurable at lower temperatures and the higher activation energies are found in reactions measurable at higher temperatures. (See Daniels, *Chemical Kinetics*, Ithaca, N. Y., Cornell University Press, 1938, p. 23.)

"Coulombic energy of activation"

In most instances the temperature coefficients of reaction rates have been measured in a solvent of constant composition. Generally pure water has been used, though other pure solvents or water-constant percentage of some other solvents have been employed. Recently measurements of rates of reactions, together with the Arrhenius frequency factors and energies of activation, have been made in isodielectric solvents. In these measurements a given dielectric constant, e.g., that of water at 40° C was chosen and at lower temperatures sufficient solvent of dielectric constant lower than that of water was added to maintain a dielectric constant equal to that of water at 40° C.

When energies of activation are measured in solvents of constant composition, there is included not only the increased energy of the reactants due to pure thermal effect but also the effect of different electrical forces between the reactant particles due to the changed dielectric constant of the solvent. Suppose we attribute the effect of the solvent upon reactants (ions or dipoles) mainly to an influence upon the coulombic forces between the charged particles in the case of ions, between the charged particles and the electrically unsymmetrical particles in the case of ions and molecules, and between the electrically unsymmetrical particles in the case of molecules. For simplicity let us consider ionic reactants and let us suppose it is possible to hold constant all factors except the dielectric constant of the solvent. Then for oppositely charged reactants the lower the dielectric constant of the solvent the greater the attraction of the particles for each other and the more readily they would react. This follows from Coulomb's law. For reactants of like sign, repulsion would increase with decreasing dielectric constant of the solvent, and hence, the rates would be slower the lower the dielectric constant of the media. For increased dielectric constants of the solvent the opposite would hold true. This change in force between charged particles immersed in a polar liquid medium may be thought of as a solvation effect whereby the polar molecules of the solvent orientate themselves around reactants, effectively neutralizing part of their charge. There is less orientation and less cancellation of electrostatic forces the less polar the solvent or the less concentration of highly polar solvent there is present.

Assuming the coulombic energy between reactants is that part of the energy which is altered when the temperature coefficient is measured in isodielectric media of different dielectric constants, the effect can be calculated from the expression for the coulombic energy between the two particles (Amis, *J. Am. Chem. Soc.*, **63**, 1606, 1941). Six classes of electrostatic forces between particles are given by E. A. Moelwyn-Hughes and Albert Sherman (*J. Chem. Soc.*, **101**, 1936). To bring an ion from infinity to within a distance r of another ion energy given by the equation

$$E_c = \frac{z_1 z_2 \epsilon^2}{Dr} \tag{5.4}$$

is required.

Therefore, to bring the two ions together at two different constant dielectric constants of the same solvent pair requires an activation energy difference of

$$\Delta E_c = \frac{-z_1 z_2 \epsilon^2}{D_1 D_2 r} \Delta D \tag{5.5}$$

from Eq. (5.4), and the over-all activation energies in the two solvents will differ by ΔE_c. In these equations E_c is the coulombic energy between the two ions, z_1 and z_2 are the valences of the two ions, ϵ is the electronic charge, D the dielectric constant of the media, and r the distance of approach of the ions. For univalent ions 1Å apart in a vacuum, $E = 329.7$ kilogram calories per mole, and therefore for other values of valence, dielectric constant and r

$$\Delta E_c = -329.7 \frac{z_1 z_2}{D_1 D_2 r} \Delta D \tag{5.6}$$

According to this equation for ionic reactants of like charge sign there will be an increase in the energy of activation arising from coulombic effects when the dielectric constant is lowered and vice versa. For reactants of unlike sign the energy of activation will decrease due to coulombic forces when the dielectric constant of the solvent is diminished and vice versa.

Of the five other coulombic energy types, only the ion-dipole type

will be given here. The interpretation of the equations will be clear
from what has been said concerning the ion-ion reactants. For the
ion-dipole reactants

$$E_c = -z\epsilon\mu \cos \theta / Dr^2 \tag{5.7}$$

where $z\epsilon$ is the charge on the ion, μ is the dipole moment of the molecule, and θ is the angle formed by the line joining the centers of
charge in the dipole and the line drawn from the ion to one of these
centers of charge. (See Fig. 2.) Then

$$\Delta E_c = \frac{z\epsilon\mu \cos \theta}{D_1 D_2 r^2} \Delta D \tag{5.8}$$

and for head-on alignment we obtain

$$\Delta E_c = \frac{z\epsilon\mu}{D_1 D_2 r^2} \Delta D \tag{5.9}$$

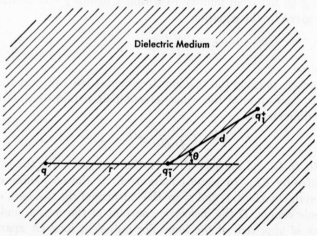

Figure 2 Illustrating the orientation of a dipole $q_1^- q_1^+$ with
respect to an ion of charge q.

In Table I is given a comparison of energy of activation between
ion-ion reactants considered as a change of coulombic energy from
Eq. (5.5) and the actual experimental energy change between specified constant dielectric constants of the mixed solvents.

For the reaction between the negative bivalent brom phenol blue
ion and the negative univalent hydroxide ion, the calculated change
of coulombic energy agrees with the observed change when the
parameter r is taken as 2Å in both ethyl alcohol-water and methyl

alcohol-water isodielectric solvents. For the reaction between the positive univalent ammonium ion and the negative univalent cyanate ion, calculated and observed values of coulombic energy of activation agree well down to a dielectric constant of between 45 and 40 when r is taken as 2Å and 5Å respectively for methyl alcohol-water and glycol-water solvents. The parameter r thus seems to be more a function of the solvent than of the charge type or chemical nature of the reactants. For lower dielectric constant ranges the calculated values of the energies are progressively greater than the observed changes. This is in harmony with the fact that the logarithms of the specific rate constants begin, at low dielectric constants, to depart from being inversely proportional to the dielectric constant of the solvent, and this departure becomes more marked as the dielectric constant is continually decreased (LaMer, *J. Franklin Institute*, **225**, 709, 1938).

TABLE I Calculated changes of coulombic energies of activation as a function of dielectric constant of the solvent compared with observed changes of energy of activation

The observed changes are the averages for the following temperature ranges: Amis and LaMer, 5–45° C; Svirbely and Warner, 30–70° C; Svirbely and Schramm, 30–70° C; Lander and Svirbely, 30–60° C.

$\sqrt{\mu}$	r	Dielectric range (ΔD = diff.)	$\Delta E_c =$ change of coulombic energy	ΔE_c obsd.	
\multicolumn{6}{l}{AMIS AND LAMER, $B\phi B^= + OH^-$, MeOH-H$_2$O}
0.300	2	71.42 – 64.86	470	390	
\multicolumn{6}{l}{AMIS AND LAMER, $B\phi B^= + OH^-$, EtOH – H$_2$O}
.300	2	71.42 – 64.86	470	560	
\multicolumn{6}{l}{SVIRBELY AND WARNER, $NH_4^+ + CNO^-$, MeOH – H$_2$O}
.0	2	63.5 – 55.0	−400	−340	
.194	2	63.5 – 55.0	−400	−530	
\multicolumn{6}{l}{SVIRBELY AND SCHRAMM, $NH_4^+ + CNO^-$, MeOH – H$_2$O}
.0	2	63.5 – 55	−400	−340	
.0	2	63.5 – 50	−700	−730	Calcd. by their
.0	2	63.5 – 45	−1070	−1000	Eq. (5)
.0	2	63.5 – 40	−1520	−1250	
.0	2	63.5 – 35	−2110	−1470	

TABLE I—*Continued*

$\sqrt{\mu}$	r	Dielectric range (ΔD = diff.)	ΔE_c = change of coulombic energy	ΔE_c obsd.	
.194	2	63.5 – 55	−400	−290	
.194	2	63.5 – 50	−700	−610	Av. from their
.194	2	63.5 – 45	−1070	−860	Eq. (5) and (9)
.194	2	63.5 – 40	−1520	−1070	
.194	2	63.5 – 35	−2110	−1250	

LANDER AND SVIRBELY, $NH_4^+ + CNO^-$, Glycol – H_2O

.0	5	63.5 – 60	−60	−80	
.0	5	63.5 – 55	−160	−90	Calcd. by their
.0	5	63.5 – 50	−280	−160	Eq. (3)
.0	5	63.5 – 45	−430	−160	
.0	5	63.5 – 40	−610	−140	
.194	5	63.5 – 60	−60	−80	
.194	5	63.5 – 55	−160	−70	
.194	5	63.5 – 50	−280	−160	Av. from their
.194	5	63.5 – 45	−430	−150	Eq. (3) and (6)
.194	5	63.5 – 40	−610	−210	

Table II gives the data of Amis and Holmes (*J. Am. Chem. Soc.*, **63**, 2231, 1941) for the comparison of calculated and observed values of coulombic energies of the dipolar sucrose molecule reacting with the positive hydrogen ion in isodielectric dioxane-water media. The calculations were made using Eq. (5.9) where r was again taken as 2Å and μ as 3.4 Debye units (Landt, *Naturwissenschaften*, **22**, 809, 1934).

TABLE II Comparison of the change of energy of activation in isodielectric dioxane-water media from 21° to 41° C with change in electrostatic energy calculated from Eq. (5)

Dielectric range	(ΔE_c), calcd. from Eq. (5.9)	(ΔE_c), obsd. from Table II
60 – 50	−200 cal.	−135 cal.
60 – 45	−330 cal.	−270 cal.

Contribution of the ionic atmosphere to energy of activation

LaMer and Kamner (*J. Am. Chem. Soc.*, **57**, 2662, 1935) derived an expression for ΔE_{In}, the contribution of the ionic atmosphere to the energy of activation valid for small values of the ionic strength. The derivation is as follows

$$\Delta E_{In} = \frac{\partial \left(\dfrac{\Delta F_{In}}{T} \right)}{\partial \left(\dfrac{1}{T} \right)} \tag{5.10}$$

But ΔF_{In} per mole is given by the equation. (From Eq. 4.28 applied to very dilute solutions. See Chapter IV, p. 77.)

$$\Delta F_{In} = - \frac{N z_A z_B \epsilon^2}{2D} \varkappa \tag{5.11}$$

and therefore

$$\Delta E_{In} = - \frac{3 N z_A z_B \epsilon^2}{4D} \varkappa \left[1 + \frac{\partial \ln D}{\partial \ln T} + \frac{1}{3} \frac{\partial \ln V}{\partial \ln T} \right] \tag{5.12}$$

See also Moelwyn-Hughes (*Proc. Roy. Soc.* (London), **155,** 308, 1936; **A157,** 667, 1936) for an almost identical equation derived more explicitly by means of the collision theory. Knowing the dielectric constant D, and the specific volume V, of a solvent, together with the temperature coefficients of these properties, the terms in the brackets of Eq. (5.12) may be determined. For water Wyman (*Phys. Rev.*, **35,** 623, 1930) gives the following equation for D in terms of absolute temperature.

$$D = 78.54[1 - 0.00460(T - 298.13) + 0.0000088(T - 298.13)^2] \tag{5.13}$$

and therefore

$$\frac{\partial \ln D}{\partial \ln T} = T \left[\frac{-0.00460 + 0.0000176(T - 298.13)}{1 - 0.00460(T - 298.13) + 0.0000088(T - 298.13)^2} \right] \tag{5.14}$$

From data on the density of water (*Handbook of Chemistry and Physics, 29th Edition*, Cleveland, Ohio, Chemical Rubber Publishing Co., 1945, p. 1652) we can obtain the following equation for the specific volume of water as a function of the absolute temperature

$$V = 1.45517 - 3.3056 \times 10^{-3} T + 0.6 \times 10^{-5} T^2 \tag{5.15}$$

and thus

$$\frac{\partial \ln V}{\partial \ln T} = \frac{T}{V} [-3.306 \times 10^{-3} + 1.20 \times 10^{-5} T] \tag{5.16}$$

Substituting the values of D and $\dfrac{\partial \ln D}{\partial \ln T}$ from Eq. (5.13) and (5.14) and the values of V and $\dfrac{\partial \ln V}{\partial \ln T}$ from Eq. (5.15) and (5.16) into Eq. (5.12)

we can write this equation in the form

$$\frac{\Delta E_{In}}{2.3RT} = z_A z_B A_1 \sqrt{\mu} \tag{5.17}$$

where A_1 depends on temperature and dielectric constant and is 0.45, 0.52, and 0.60 at 15°, 25°, and 35° C, respectively, for water. In Fig. 3 we give a plot of the data of Amis and LaMer (*J. Am. Chem.*

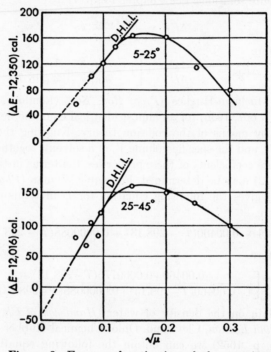

Figure 3 Energy of activation of the reaction $(B\phi B)^= + OH^-$ as a function of ionic strength.

Soc., **61,** 905, 1939) for the fading of negative bivalent brom phenol blue ion by the negative univalent hydroxide ion. The total energy of activation minus a constant quantity is plotted against the square root of the ionic strength of the solutions. The slopes of the curves in regions of low ionic strengths correspond to the limiting slopes predicted by the Debye-Hückel limiting law, Eq. (5.17).

Energies of activation in isocomposition and isodielectric solvents

Sometimes energies of activation are measured in constant composition solvent, the dielectric constant of which varies with temperature, and sometimes these energies are measured in isodielectric solvents. Svirbely and Warner (*J. Am. Chem. Soc.*, **57**, 1883, 1935) first measured energy of activation in isodielectric solvents. Their equation for calculating their *true energies of activation* in infinitely dilute solutions was obtained by setting

$$\ln k'_{x=0} = f(D, T) \tag{5.18}$$

Then differentiating with respect to T and multiplying the resulting equation through by $2.303RT^2$ they obtained

$$\Delta E^0_{f.c.} = \Delta E^0_D + 2.303RT^2 \left(\frac{\partial \log k'_{x=0}}{\partial D} \right)_T \frac{dD}{dT} \tag{5.19}$$

Here $\Delta E^0_{f.c.}$ is the energy of activation for the reaction at infinite dilution of reactants and at constant composition of solvent and ΔE^0_D is the energy of activation of the reaction at infinite dilution of reactants and constant dielectric constant of the solvent. The agreement of the calculated and observed differences between $\Delta E^0_{f.c.}$ and ΔE^0_D for the ammonium ion-cyanate ion reaction at infinite dilution in methyl alcohol-water solvent was excellent.

If we consider the Brönsted-Christiansen-Scatchard equation (Eq. 4.28)

$$\log k' = \log k'_{\substack{x=0 \\ D=\infty}} - \frac{z_A z_B \epsilon^2 N}{DRTr} + \frac{z_A z_B \epsilon^2 N}{DRT} \varkappa \tag{5.20}$$

we can by taking the difference between the expressions obtained when this equation is differentiated with respect to T, with T and D variable, and the one when it is differentiated with respect to T, with D constant, and multiplying by RT^2 obtain

$$\Delta E'_{f.c.} - \Delta E'_D = \frac{z_A z_B \epsilon^2 NT}{D^2 J} \left(\frac{1}{r} - \frac{3\epsilon}{10} \sqrt{\frac{2\pi N \mu}{10 DkT}} \right) \frac{dD}{dT} \tag{5.21}$$

This equation was obtained by Amis and Holmes (*J. Am. Chem. Soc.*, **63**, 2231, 1941) and checked by observation for both the brom phenol blue ion-hydroxide ion and the ammonium ion-cyanate ion reactions in various mixed solvents. Amis and Potts (*J. Am. Chem.*

Soc., **63,** 2833, 1941) further modified this equation to contain the coulombic energy of activation and thus obtained

$$\Delta E_{f.c.} - \Delta E_D = \frac{z_A z_B \epsilon^2 N}{D_c J} \left[\left(\frac{1}{r} - \frac{3\epsilon}{10} \sqrt{\frac{2\pi N \mu}{10 D_c kT}} \right) \frac{T}{D_c} \frac{dD}{dT} - \frac{\Delta D}{D_D r} \right] \quad (5.22)$$

In this equation $\Delta D = D_c - D_D$, where D_c and D_D are the dielectric constants of the isocomposition and of the isodielectric runs, respectively. When centimeter-gram-second electrostatic units are used for the other quantities and the mechanical equivalent of heat J is in ergs per calorie, then $\Delta E_{f.c.} - \Delta E_D$ is in calories. This equation can be used for calculating the difference in energies of activation for a constant composition run of given dielectric constant and for an isodielectric run of any dielectric constant.

In Table III are the calculated and observed data for $\Delta E_{f.c.} - \Delta E_D$ given by Amis and Potts (*J. Am. Chem. Soc.*, **63,** 2883, 1941). The calculations were made using Eq. (5.22) and the data were for the iodide ion-persulfate ion reaction. In column 1 the dielectric constants of the constant composition solvents corresponding to the mid-point of the temperature range being studied are recorded. Column 2 contains the dielectric constants of the isodielectric solvents. The solvents used were water and mixtures of ethyl alcohol and water. The agreement between calculated and observed values is within the experimental error of the data.

Nonelectrostatic effects

In a kinetic equation of the type of Eq. (4.28) a term of the nature of ϕ/kT must be included to account for the nonelectrostatic effects, which can be treated as repulsions beginning suddenly at the distance of closest approach, modified to take into account van der Waals attractions which may be of considerable importance. Laidler and Eyring (*Ann. New York Acad. Sci.*, **39,** 303, 1940) pointed out the necessity of such a term, and Amis and Jaffé (*J. Chem. Phys.*, **10,** 646, 1942) developed the term. Their reasoning and procedure were as follows:

The mutual potential energy between two reacting particles cannot be restricted to their electrostatic potential energy if the observed temperature dependence of the rate constant is to be properly accounted for. A potential must be added which will account for the

TABLE III Comparison of observed and calculated differences in energies of activation for the iodide ion–persulfate ion reaction in isodielectric and isocomposition water-ethyl alcohol media

D of iso-composition run	D of iso-dielectric run	o/o EtOH in isocomposition runs	Obsd. $\Delta E_{f.c.} - \Delta E_D$	Calcd. $\Delta E_{f.c.} - \Delta E_D$
		TEMP. RANGE $20-30°$ C., MID. TEMP., $°A = 298.1$		
78.54	73.12	0.0	−5710	−5850
78.54	69.00	0.0	−6180	−6440
74.15	73.12	7.7	−5240	−5690
74.15	69.00	7.7	−5710	−6240
69.70	73.12	15.4	−5590	−5470
69.70	69.00	15.4	−6060	−6070
		TEMP. RANGE $30-40°$ C., MID. TEMP., $°A = 308.1$		
74.87	73.12	0.0	−6390	−5820
74.87	69.00	0.0	−6440	−6420
74.87	60.00	0.0	−8420	−8010
74.87	55.00	0.0	−8690	−9120
70.70	73.12	7.7	−6410	−5670
70.70	69.00	7.7	−6460	−6270
70.70	60.00	7.7	−8440	−7860
70.70	55.00	7.7	−8710	−8970
66.40	73.12	15.4	−5430	−5450
66.40	69.00	15.4	−5480	−6050
66.40	60.00	15.4	−7460	−7640
66.40	55.00	15.4	−7730	−8750

repulsion between particles charged or uncharged at close distances of approach.

These authors assumed that a Brönsted complex is formed between particles A and B when the two are undergoing the process of reacting to form a product or products. Further they assumed that spherical symmetry exists around each particle and that the mutual potential of the two particles at a distance r is given by the expression

$$\psi(r) = \phi_1(r) + \phi_2(r) \qquad (5.23)$$

In Eq. (5.23) $\phi_2(r)$ is the contribution of the electrostatic forces in the case that A and B are charged. Thus if A and B are ions of valency z_A and z_B, respectively, then, under the usual assumptions we have

$$\phi_2(r) = \frac{z_A z_B \epsilon^2 e^{\varkappa(a_i - r)}}{Dr(1 + \varkappa a_i)} \qquad (5.24)$$

Where x is defined by Eq. (2.8) and a_i is the distance of closest approach.

As to $\phi_1(r)$ Amis and Jaffé assumed (1) that ϕ_1 is independent of the dielectric constant D, and (2) that ϕ_1 is positive for those distances r at which the formation of the intermediate complex X occurs. ϕ_1 was called the nonelectrostatic potential. If ϕ_1 is electric in origin, it must be assumed independent of the dielectric constant. This could be entirely possible since for such short distances between particles the dielectric constant of the solvent would have no significance.

If the concentrations of A and B are C_A and C_B, respectively, and using the potential from Eq. (5.23), then the probability of finding a molecule B at a distance between r_0 and $r_0 + dr_0$ from a molecule A will become proportional to

$$C_A C_B e^{-\frac{\psi(r_0)}{kT}} r_0^2 \, dr_0 \tag{5.25}$$

and if the formation of X ensues for values of r within these limits, then the reaction rate will be given by (Christiansen, *Z. physik. Chem.* **113**, 35, 1924; Scatchard, *J. Am. Chem. Soc.*, **52**, 52, 1930)

$$k' = kT^{\frac{1}{2}} \frac{C_A C_B}{C_X} e^{-\frac{\psi(r_0)}{kT}} \tag{5.26}$$

where k' and K are constants.

Let k_0' be the rate constant for some standard reference temperature T_0, and let the unimportant term $T^{\frac{1}{2}}$ be neglected in the usual way; then our final formula becomes

$$\ln k' = \ln k_0' + \frac{\psi(r_0)}{kT} - \frac{\phi_1(r_0)}{kT} - \frac{z_A z_B \epsilon^2 e^{x(a-r_0)}}{DkTr_0(1 + xa)} \tag{5.27}$$

It is not necessary for our present purpose to extrapolate k_0' to standard reference states of concentration and of dielectric constant.

For the dependence on $1/T$ Eq. (5.27) gives

$$a_T = \frac{d \ln k'}{d \left(\dfrac{1}{T}\right)} = -\frac{1}{k} \left[\phi_1(r_0) + \frac{z_A z_B \epsilon^2 e^{x(a-r_0)}}{Dr_0(1 + xa)} \right] \tag{5.28}$$

Thus a_T will be negative whatever the charges z_A and z_B are, if the nonelectrostatic potential at $r = r_0$ is sufficiently large compared with the electrostatic potential.

For the dependence on $1/D$ we obtain from Eq. (5.27)

$$a_D = \frac{d \ln k'}{d \left(\dfrac{1}{D}\right)} = -\frac{z_A z_B \epsilon^2 e^{x(a-r_0)}}{kTr_0(1 + xa)} \tag{5.29}$$

Thus from Eq. (5.28) and (5.29) and from known values of a_T and a_D we can derive both the electrostatic potential $z_A z_B \epsilon^2 / D r_0$ and the nonelectrostatic potential $\phi_1(r_0)$ for the critical distance.

Also from Eq. (5.28) and (5.29) we can obtain the following two inequalities which connect measurable quantities only:

(1) For A and B of like charge sign:

$$a_T/a_D > T/D \qquad (5.30)$$

(2) For A and B of unlike sign:

$$a_T/a_D < T/D \qquad (5.31)$$

Applications using inequality (5.30) were tested by Amis and Jaffé (loc. cit.) using the data on the persulfate-iodide reaction in ethyl alcohol-water solvents (Amis and Potts, J. Am. Chem. Soc., 63, 2883, 1941) and the brom phenol blue-hydroxide reaction in both ethyl alcohol-water and methyl alcohol-water media (Amis and LaMer, J. Am. Chem. Soc., 61, 901, 1939). From Table IV it is clear that a_T/a_D is three to four times as large as T/D. Inequality (5.31) was applied to data on the ammonium cyanate reaction in methyl alcohol-water (Svirbely and Schramm, J. Am. Chem. Soc., 60, 330, 1938) and also to date on the same reaction in glycol-water media (Lander and Svirbely, J. Am. Chem. Soc., 60, 1613, 1938). From Table IV it can be seen that $a_T/a_D < T/D$ to the extent of inversion of sign of a_T/a_D.

TABLE IV. **Tests on inequalities**

Reaction	Medium	T	D	a_T	a_D	T/D	a_T/a_D
A. IONS OF LIKE SIGN							
$S_2O_8^{--} + I^-$	EtOH – H_2O	313.1	73.12	−10140	−624	4.27	16.24
$B\phi B^{--} + OH^-$	MeOH – H_2O	298.1	71.42	−11000	−737	4.18	15.24
$B\phi B^{--} + OH^-$	EtOH – H_2O	298.1	71.42	−11120	−921	4.18	12.08
B. IONS OF UNLIKE SIGN							
$NH_4^+ + CNO^-$	MeOH – H_2O	323.1	63.5	−9370	260	5.09	−36.0
$NH_4^+ + CNO^-$	Glycol – H_2O	323.1	63.5	10140	184	5.09	−55.2

Table V presents recorded values of $\phi_1(r_0)$ and $\phi_2(r_0)$ as well as their ratios. These quantities are given for reactions between various sign and valence types of reactants in different media. As is expected the ratio of the nonelectrostatic potential to the electrostatic potential is much greater (about three times as great) for reactions between

TABLE V. A comparison of the nonelectrostatic potentials at a distance $r = r_0$ with electrostatic potential between ions

Reaction	Medium	T	D	$\phi_2(r_0)$ $\times$ 10^{+13}	$\phi_1(r_0)$ $\times$ 10^{+12}	$\dfrac{\phi_1(r_0)}{\phi_2(r_0)}$
$NH_4^+ + CNO^-$	MeOH – H_2O	323.1	63.4	1.83	1.29	7.0
$HN_4^+ + CNO^-$	Glycol – H_2O	323.1	63.4	1.28	1.39	10.9
$S_2O_8^{--} + I^-$	EtOH – H_2O	313.1	73.12	3.66	1.39	3.8
$B\phi B^{--} + OH^-$	EtOH – H_2O	298.1	73.42	5.27	1.52	2.9
$B\phi B^{--} + OH^-$	MeOH – H_2O	298.1	73.42	4.22	1.51	3.6

univalent ions than for reactions between bivalent and univalent ions. It can be noted that the solvent plays a rather important part in determining the ratios of these potentials.

From Eq. (5.28) and (5.29), $\phi_1(r_0)$ and $\phi_2(r_0)$ can be calculated when reactions obey electrostatics in their dielectric constant dependence. If a_D in Eq. (5.29) is not known $\phi_1(r_0)$ can be calculated from Eq. (5.28) provided r_0 is known from some other source or provided as a first approximation the second term on the right of Eq. (5.28) is neglected. This latter method of calculation should yield $\phi_1(r_0)$ values substantially alike for reactions between ions and ions in solution, ions and molecules in solution, molecules and molecules in solution, and reactants in the gaseous state. That $\phi_1(r_0)$ should be of the same order of magnitude for all the types of reactions arises from the fact that this nonelectrostatic potential comes from repulsive forces between the reactants at very close distances where electrostatic forces depending upon charge and dielectric constant are perhaps no longer appreciable.

The results of the two methods described above for calculating $\phi_1(r_0)$ are recorded in Table VI. In column 6 of Table VI $\phi_1(r_0)$ is calculated from Eq. (5.28) alone neglecting the second term on the right, while in column 7 the values of $\phi_1(r_0)$ come from using both Eq. (5.28) and Eq. (5.29). It can be observed that the variation in $\phi_1(r_0)$ calculated by the two methods is not great and is that predicted by electrostatics, i.e., $\phi_1(r_0)$ calculated from a_T and a_D is less than that calculated from a_T, neglecting the electrostatic term, for ions of like sign and vice versa for ions of unlike sign. It can also be seen for all the reactions irrespective of charge type, and irrespective of whether in solution or in the gaseous state, that the values of $\phi_1(r_0)$ do not vary by an order of magnitude and are in many cases very close together in value. Even the regeneration of alkaline faded brom phenol blue by hydrochloric acid (Amis and Price, *J. Phys. Chem.*, **47,** 338, 1944) which did not obey electrostatics in its dielectric constant

TABLE VI. A comparison of the nonelectrostatic potential between reactants calculated from the rate dependence on temperature alone and calculated from the rate dependence on both temperature and dielectric constant

Reaction	Range of Temp.	d.c.	Value used in calculating column 7 of Temp.	d.c.	$\phi_1(r_0)$ from rate dependence on $T \times 10^{+12}$	$\phi_1(r_0)$ from rate dependence on T and $D \times 10^{+12}$	Media
			°C				
$S_2O_8^{--} + I^{-a}$	20–40	55.0–76.7	40	73.12	1.39	1.04	EtOH – H_2O
$B\phi B^{--} + OH^{-b}$	5–45	64.5–78.5	25	71.42	1.52	0.93	EtOH – H_2O
$B\phi B^{--} + OH^{-b}$	5–45	64.5–78.5	25	71.42	1.51	1.13	MeOH – H_2O
$NH_4^+ + CNO^{-c}$	30–60	40.0–63.5	50	63.5	1.39	1.70	Glycol – H_2O
$NH_4^+ + CNO^{-d}$	30–70	35.0–69.9	50	63.5	1.29	1.32	MeOH – H_2O
$B\phi BOH^- + H_3O^{+e}$	25–45				2.12		EtOH – H_2O
Sucrose + H_3O^{+f}	21–41				1.83		EtOH – H_2O
Sucrose + H_3O^{+f}	21–41				1.67		Dioxane – H_2O
$*AsO_3^{---} + FeO_4^{--g}$	89–120				0.74		H_2O
$*Fe^{+++} + Sn^{++h}$	0–25				1.50		H_2O
$N_2O_5^{i}$	25–65				1.73		Gaseous
$2N_2O^{j}$	565–852				4.13		Gaseous
$C_2H_5OCOCl^{k}$	150–195				1.99		Gaseous
$2HI^{l}$	283–508				3.09		Gaseous
$H_2 + I_2^{l}$	283–508				3.06		Gaseous
$H + H_2(P)^{m}$	10–100				0.49		Gaseous

[a] E. S. Amis and J. E. Potts, Jr., *J. Am. Chem. Soc.*, **63,** 2883 (1941).

[b] E. S. Amis and V. K. LaMer, *J. Am. Chem. Soc.*, **61,** 901 (1939).

[c] J. Lander and W. J. Svirbely, *J. Am. Chem. Soc.*, **60,** 1613 (1938).

[d] W. J. Svirbely and A. Schramm, *J. Am. Chem. Soc.*, **60,** 330 (1938).

[e] E. S. Amis and J. B. Price, *J. Phys. Chem.*, **47,** 338 (1944).

[f] E. S. Amis and F. C. Holmes, *J. Am. Chem. Soc.*, **63,** 2231 (1941).

[g] P. T. Stroup and V. W. Meloche, *J. Am. Chem. Soc.*, **53,** 3331 (1931).

[h] W. F. Timofeew, G. E. Muchin, and W. G. Gurewitsch, *Z. physik. Chem.*, **115,** 161 (1925).

[i] F. Daniels and E. H. Johnston, *J. Am. Chem. Soc.*, **43,** 43 (1921); see F. H. MacDougall, *Physical Chemistry*, New York, The Macmillan Co., 1936, p. 404.

[j] C. N. Hinshelwood and R. E. Burk, *Proc. Roy. Soc. A*, **106,** 284 (1924).

[k] A. R. Choppin, H. A. Frediani, and G. F. Kirby, Jr., *J. Am. Chem. Soc.*, **61,** 3176 (1939).

[l] M. Bodenstein, *Z. physik. Chem.*, **29,** 295 (1899); see H. S. Taylor and H. A. Taylor, *Elementary Physical Chemistry*, New York, D. van Nostrand Co., 1937, p. 242.

[m] K. H. Geib and P. Harteck, *Z. physik. Chem., Bodenstein-Festband,* 849–62 (1931); see H. S, Taylor and H. A. Taylor, *Elementary Physical Chemistry*, New York, D. van Nostrand Co., 1937, p. 235.

* k was not extrapolated to $k_{\kappa = 0}$ in these cases.

dependence of the rate, gave a $\phi_1(r_0)$ value which compared favorably with that for the fading reaction the kinetics of which met the requirements of electrostatics.

Amis and Jaffé (*loc. cit.*) point out that these nonelectrostatic potentials compare roughly with intermolecular energies as calculated from the second virial coefficient.

Hammett and co-workers (Price and Hammett, *J. Am. Chem. Soc.*, **63**, 2387, 1941; Gettler and Hammett, *ibid.*, **65**, 1824, 1943) have pointed out that there is no significant change of energy of activation with change of structure of reactants and that the effect of this change of structure upon reaction rates is reflected in change of the entropy of activation. This topic will be dealt with more extensively in the next chapter which deals with the temperature coefficient of reaction rates in relation to the Arrhenius frequency factor.

The components of energy of activation

LaMer (*J. Franklin Inst.*, **225**, 709, 1938) shows that from Eq. (4.28) we may write

$$\Delta F = \Delta F_0 + \Delta F_D + \Delta F_{In} \tag{5.32}$$

and that, therefore,

$$\Delta E = \Delta E_0 + \Delta E_D + \Delta E_{In} \tag{5.33}$$

where the subscripts 0, D, and In refer to the contributions to the free energy of activation (Eq. 5.32) and to the energy of activation (Eq. 5.33), respectively: of the reactants with no net charge effects of the reactants, i.e., for uncharged molecules, or for ions at infinite dielectric constant of the medium; of the reactants as ions in the absence of an ionic atmosphere but in a medium of finite dielectric constant; and of the reactants as ions surrounded by other ions and immersed in a medium of finite dielectric constant. The method of calculating ΔE_{In} has been given (Eq. 5.12). Now

$$\Delta E_D = \frac{\partial\left(\dfrac{\Delta F_D}{T}\right)}{\partial\left(\dfrac{1}{T}\right)} \tag{5.34}$$

and from Eq. (4.28)

$$\Delta F_D = \frac{z_A z_B N \epsilon^2}{D} \frac{1}{r_A + r_B} \tag{5.35}$$

therefore

$$\Delta E_D = \Delta F_D \left(1 + \frac{\partial \ln D}{\partial \ln T}\right) \tag{5.36}$$

When $\varkappa = 0$, ΔE_{In} vanishes and for isodielectric solvents

$$\Delta E_D = \Delta F_D = -RT \ln k'_D \tag{5.37}$$

from Eq. (5.36). Therefore for isodielectric solvents and when $\varkappa = 0$

$$\Delta E_0 = \Delta E + RT \ln k'_D \tag{5.38}$$

We have by using data on the brom phenol blue-hydroxide ion reaction in isocomposition and isodielectric media calculated ΔE_0 at 25° C for the reaction to be 14,650 calories compared with an energy of activation of 21,100 calories in isodielectric solvents and 12,220 in constant composition media and when the two latter energies of activation were measured at other than zero ionic strength. The energy of activation of 21,100 calories in isodielectric media was the sum of ΔE_0, ΔE_D, and ΔE_{In}. The ΔE_D was calculated by taking the averages of the slopes in methyl alcohol-water and in ethyl alcohol-water of $\log k'_{x=0}$ vs. $1/D$. This average of the slopes was -357. Hence, $\log k'_D$ (at $1/D = 0.013$) was -4.64, and ΔE_D was by Eq. (5.37), $4.64 \times 1365 = 6330$ calories. ΔE_{In} was about 120 calories and hence ΔE_0 was obtained by subtracting the sum of ΔE_D and ΔE_{In} from 21,100 calories.

CHAPTER VI

The temperature coefficient of reaction rates; the Arrhenius frequency factor

The composition of the frequency factor

The differential form of the Arrhenius equation

$$\frac{d \ln k}{dT} = \frac{\Delta E}{RT^2} \tag{6.1}$$

is integrated by LaMer (*J. Chem. Phys.*, **1**, 289, 1933) who, instead of assuming ΔE independent of T, recognizes the temperature dependence in his method of integration of Eq. (6.1). If u is set equal to ΔE and dv is equated to $\dfrac{dT}{T^2}$ then integration of Eq. (6.1) yields

$$\ln k' = -\frac{\Delta E}{RT} + \frac{1}{R} \int \frac{d \Delta E}{T} = -\frac{\Delta E}{RT} + \frac{1}{R} \int \frac{\partial \Delta E}{\partial T} \frac{dT}{T} = -\frac{\Delta E}{RT}$$
$$+ \frac{1}{R} \int \Delta C \, d \ln T \tag{6.2}$$

Here ΔC is the heat capacity of activation and the integral $\int \Delta C \, d \ln T$ is analogous to the thermodynamic entropy function ΔS, i.e., $\Delta S = \int \dfrac{\partial \Delta E}{\partial T} \, d \ln T$. This entropy function is termed by LaMer the *entropy of activation*. He also points out that ΔS contains certain kinetic factors arising from the temperature dependence of the energy of activation obtained by differentiating Tolman's bimolecular rate equation which is based upon statistical mechanics.

The entropy of activation is the difference between the entropy of the intermediate complex and the sum of the entropies of the reactants. This entropy difference can be conceived of as measuring the difference in the total complexity of the intermediate state as compared with the reactant state. This complexity is, among other things,

108

a function of the degrees of freedom or rigidity of the species concerned. Thus if the formation of the complex decreases the total degrees of freedom within the molecules, there will be a decrease of entropy and vice versa, provided this factor alone were contributing to the entropy change. However, there are other contributing factors. The especially important thing to be considered is the total complexity of complex and reactant states. Thus the movement of reactants can be considered completely haphazard, while the motion of the complex can, from Eyring's theory (see Chapter VII), be considered as only either forward or backward along the reaction path which leads over the least energy barrier from the energy state of reactants to the energy state of products. This effect is external to the molecules concerned. There are probably many other things influencing the entropy of activation. The entropy of activation determined is the sum of all the entropy changes when the reactants form the intermediate complex, taking into account factors which are both internal and external to the molecules involved. Now

$$\Delta C = C_X - (C_A + C_B) \tag{6.3}$$

for the bimolecular reaction $A + B \rightleftharpoons X \longrightarrow P$, and cannot be assumed equal to zero *a priori*. Also to neglect the entropy of activation by assuming ΔE independent of T is no more justifiable than would be the omission of terms involved in a thermodynamic equilibrium.

In the Eq. (1.67)

$$\ln k' = C + \tfrac{1}{2} \ln T - \frac{\Delta F}{RT} \tag{6.4}$$

it has been shown that

$$C = \ln z_0 - \tfrac{1}{2} \ln T \tag{6.5}$$

where z_0 is, for dilute gases, the gas kinetic constant for the number of collisions per unit of time and is given by Eq. (1.65). Therefore, substituting Eq. (6.5) in Eq. (6.4), we obtain

$$\ln k' = \ln z_0 + \frac{\Delta S}{R} - \frac{\Delta E}{RT} \tag{6.6}$$

since $\Delta F = \Delta E - T \Delta S$.

Comparing Eq. (6.6) with the Arrhenius equation

$$\ln k' = \ln Z - \frac{\Delta E}{RT} \tag{6.7}$$

we see that the Arrhenius frequency factor is a measure of the frequency of collision for bimolecular reactions (or of the frequency of atomic vibrations in unimolecular reactions) and of the entropy of activation.

The contribution of the ionic atmosphere to the entropy of activation

Assuming that the critical complex is in equilibrium with the reactants, and that the rate of reaction depends only upon the frequency ν with which the molecules leave the critical state, we can write for the rate of reaction r the equation

$$r = \nu C_X = \nu K C_A C_B \tag{6.8}$$

or for unit concentrations of reactants

$$k' = \nu K. \tag{6.9}$$

LaMer (*J. Franklin Inst.*, **225**, 709, 1938) points out that since K for the activation process $A + B \rightleftharpoons X$ is related to the increase in standard free energy by the equation

$$\Delta F = -RT \ln K \tag{6.10}$$

then the reaction velocity constant becomes

$$k' = \nu e^{-\Delta F / RT} \tag{6.11}$$

or

$$k' = \nu e^{\frac{\Delta s}{R}} e^{\frac{\Delta H}{RT}} \tag{6.12}$$

But in solutions since the difference between ΔH and ΔE, i.e.; $P \, \Delta V$ is minor, the equation

$$k' = \nu e^{\frac{\Delta s}{R}} e^{\frac{\Delta E}{RT}} \tag{6.13}$$

holds.

We have from Eq. (6.6) and (6.13) that ν is apparently equal to z_0, the collision number. LaMer (*J. Chem. Phys.*, **1**, 289, 1927; *J. Franklin Inst.*, **225**, 709, 1938) makes the two equal. Eyring (*J. Chem. Phys.*, **3**, 107, 1935; *Chem. Rev.*, **17**, 65, 1935), however, makes $\nu = RT/Nh$, where R/N is the Boltzmann gas constant, h is Planck's constant, and T is the absolute temperature. Hence, $\nu = RT/Nh$ is a universal frequency proportional to the absolute temperature. Eyring makes his entropy of activation ΔS contain all degrees of freedom (translational and internal). LaMer's treatment of entropy of activation ΔS

makes the collision number z_0 contain the two translational degrees of freedom entering into the collision process. Then

$$\ln k' = \ln \frac{RT}{NH} + \frac{\Delta S}{R} - \frac{\Delta E}{RT} \tag{6.14}$$

Multiplying Eq. (4.28) through by RT we obtain

$$RT \ln k' = RT \ln k_{\substack{x=0 \\ D=\infty}} - \frac{z_A z_B N \epsilon^2}{D} \frac{1}{r_A + r_B} + \frac{z_A z_B N \epsilon^2}{D} \frac{\varkappa}{1 + a\varkappa} \tag{6.15}$$

and subtracting $RT \ln \nu$ from each side yields

$$\Delta F = \Delta F_0 + \Delta F_D + \Delta F_{In} \tag{6.16}$$

and neglecting the unimportant term PV, LaMer gets from the thermodynamic relationship $\Delta F = \Delta H - T \Delta S$ that

$$\Delta E = \Delta E_0 + \Delta E_D + \Delta E_{In} \tag{6.17}$$

and

$$\Delta S = \Delta S_0 + \Delta S_D + \Delta S_{In} \tag{6.18}$$

Now

$$-\Delta S = \frac{\partial \Delta F}{\partial T} \tag{6.19}$$

and from Eq. (5.11) for very dilute solutions

$$\Delta F = - \frac{N z^2 \epsilon^2}{2D} \varkappa \tag{6.20}$$

and since $\varkappa$ is proportional to $(DTV)^{-\frac{1}{2}}$ then

$$\Delta S_{In} = \frac{\Delta F_{In}}{T} \frac{3}{2} \left[\frac{\partial \ln D}{\partial \ln T} + \frac{1}{2} \frac{\partial \ln V}{\partial \ln T} + \frac{1}{2} \right] \tag{6.21}$$

Again supplying the values of $\dfrac{\partial \ln D}{\partial \ln T}$ and $\dfrac{\partial \ln V}{\partial \ln T}$ for water as given by Eq. (5.14) and (5.16), we obtain

$$\frac{\Delta S}{2.3R} = z_A z_B A_2 \sqrt{\mu} \tag{6.22}$$

where A_2 depends on dielectric constant and temperature and equals 1.44, 1.53, and 1.64 at 15°, 25°, and 35° C respectively for water.

In Fig. 1, we give a plot of the data of Amis and LaMer (*J. Am. Chem. Soc.*, **6**, 905, 1939) for the brom phenol blue-hydroxide ion reaction which is a reaction between a negative bivalent ion and a negative univalent ion. The plot is that of the Arrhenius frequency factor versus the ionic strength. However from Eq. (6.6) and (6.14) this factor equals to a frequency dependent only on temperature plus an entropy of activation term which is dependent upon both temperature and concentration. Thus for a given temperature

$$\log Z = \log \frac{RT}{NH} \text{ (a constant) } + \frac{\Delta S}{2.3R} \qquad (6.23)$$

and hence a plot of the frequency factor versus $\sqrt{\mu}$ at constant temperature should give from Eq. (6.22) a straight line with a slope $z_A z_B A_2$. Figure 1 shows that the agreement of the data with theory is all that could be expected up to $\sqrt{\mu} = 0.12$.

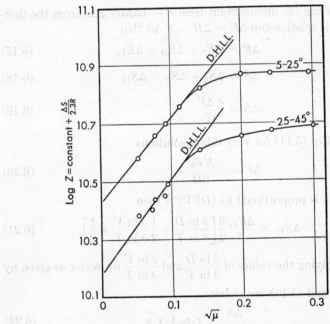

Figure 1 Entropy of activation for the reaction $(B\phi B)^- + OH^-$ as a function of the ionic strength.

When $a\varkappa$ cannot be neglected, but neglecting terms in $\partial V/\partial T$, then for the interaction term

$$\Delta S_{In} = \frac{3}{2} \frac{\Delta F_{In}}{T} \left[\left(\frac{1}{3} + \frac{\partial \ln D}{\partial \ln T} \right) - \frac{1}{3} \frac{a\varkappa}{1 + a\varkappa} \left(1 + \frac{\partial \ln D}{\partial \ln T} \right) \right] \qquad (6.24)$$

Contribution of the dielectric constant of the media to ΔS.

From LaMer (*J. Franklin Inst.*, **225**, 709, 1938) we also have the value of ΔS_D arrived at as follows. From Eq. (6.15)

$$\Delta F_D = \frac{z_A z_B N \epsilon^2}{D} \frac{1}{r_A + r_B} \tag{6.25}$$

and using the relationship from (6.19)

$$\Delta S_D = \Delta F_D \left[\frac{1}{D} \frac{\partial D}{\partial T} \right] \tag{6.26}$$

and multiplying both the numerator and denominator of the term on the right of Eq. (6.26) by T gives

$$\Delta S_D = \frac{\Delta F_D}{T} \left[\frac{T}{D} \frac{\partial D}{\partial T} \right] = \frac{\Delta F_D}{T} \left[\frac{\partial \ln D}{\partial \ln T} \right] \tag{6.27}$$

Thus when the temperature coefficients of reaction rates are measured at constant dielectric constant by use of isodielectric solvents, the contribution ΔS_D vanishes since $\partial D/\partial T = 0$. The contribution ΔS_{In} can be eliminated by substituting in the Arrhenius equation the values of $\log k'$ extrapolated to $\varkappa = 0$. The frequency factor obtained in this manner will be freed from all electrostatic contributions to the entropy of activation arising from the net charges of the ions. Except for perhaps some minor dipolar effects, the value of the frequency factor thus calculated should represent that for a reaction between uncharged molecules possessing the same chemical characteristics as those of the ions. This procedure readily permits the comparison of data obtained for an ionic reaction with that predicted by collision theory for a reaction between uncharged molecules.

Method of checking collisions and thermodynamic rate theories

In the notation of the English school for the collision theory

$$k' = P z_0 e^{-\Delta E/RT} \tag{6.28}$$

where P is called the *probability factor*, and from Eq. (6.14) and (6.28)

$$P z_0 = \frac{RT}{Nh} e^{\Delta S/R} \tag{6.29}$$

Now the value for z_0, the gas kinetic collision frequency can be written

$$z_0 = \frac{N}{1000} \sigma_{12}^2 \left[8\pi RT \left(\frac{1}{M_1} + \frac{1}{M_2} \right) \right]^{\frac{1}{2}} \tag{6.30}$$

when k' is in liters per mole per second. In this equation σ_{12} is the distance of approach between centers of reactants for an effective collision, N is Avogadro's number, and M_1 and M_2 are the molecular weights of the reactants. From Eq. (6.29) and (6.30) we obtain

$$\log \sigma_{12} = \frac{1}{2}\left[\frac{\Delta S}{2.3R}\right] + \frac{1}{2}\log\left[\frac{M_1 M_2}{M_1 + M_2}\right]^{\frac{1}{2}} - 6.9425 \qquad (6.31)$$

and combining this with Eq. (6.23) gives

$$\log \sigma_{12} = \frac{1}{2}\left(\log Z - \log \frac{RT}{Nh}\right) + \frac{1}{2}\log\left[\frac{M_1 M_2}{M_1 + M_2}\right]^{\frac{1}{2}} - 6.9425 \quad (6.32)$$

Amis and LaMer (*J. Am. Chem. Soc.*, **61,** 905, 1939) use the data on the brom phenol blue-hydroxide ion reaction in which $M_1 = 17$ and $M_2 = 668$, and for which $\log Z$ has average values of 16.71 and 16.49 for ethyl and methyl alcohol additions to the solvent, respectively, when time was measured in days, to check the agreement of collision and thermodynamic rate theories on the basis of Eq. (6.32). Substituting the above values of M_1, M_2, $\log Z$, and also $\log RT/Nh = 17.731$ (days^{-1}) into Eq. (6.32) gives σ_{12} as 7.10 and 5.51Å, respectively, as the gas-kinetic collision diameters in ethyl alcohol-water and methyl alcohol-water solvents. These values are certainly reasonable and show that for this reaction the collision and thermodynamic rate theories are in complete agreement.

The Arrhenius frequency factor in isocomposition and in isodielectric media

By multiplying both sides of Eq. (4.28) by T, differentiating the resulting equation with respect to T, considering T and D variables, then differentiating the equation with respect to T, holding D constant and subtracting the latter differential equation from the former, one obtains an expression for the Arrhenius frequency factor $\ln Z$, when comparing kinetic measurements in constant composition and constant dielectric constant media. Using decadic logarithms, Amis and Cook (*J. Am. Chem. Soc.*, **63,** 2621, 1941) derived the equation in the form

$$\log Z_{f.c.} - \log Z_D = \frac{z_A z_B N \epsilon^2}{2.3 D^2 R}\left[\frac{1}{r} - \frac{3\epsilon}{10}\sqrt{\frac{2\pi N^2 \mu}{10 DRT}}\right]\frac{dD}{dT} \qquad (6.33)$$

In this equation the terms have their usual significance. In this derivation Amis and Cook, based on the reasoning of Amis and Holmes

(*J. Am. Chem. Soc.*, **63**, 2231, 1941), assumed $T \ln k'$ independent of D at $D = \infty$. Since dD/dT is negative for ordinary solvents, Eq. (6.33) predicts that for ions of like sign the Arrhenius frequency factor observed in constant composition media is less than the same quantity measured in isodielectric solvents, and vice versa for ions of unlike sign. The equation tells nothing about reactions between ions and molecules since the equation for the rates of reaction between such reactants is entirely different from the Brönsted-Christiansen-Scatchard equation for the rates of reaction between ionic reactants (see Chapter VIII).

In Table I are given the data of Amis and Cook (*loc. cit.*) for the difference of $\log Z_{f.c.} - \log Z_D$ calculated from Eq. (6.33), and the same quantity from the data of various investigations found in the literature. The dielectric constant used in these calculations was the dielectric constant of the constant composition run for the midpoint of the temperature range. No electrostatic corrections were necessary to bring the constant dielectric constant runs to the same dielectric constant as the constant composition run, since the value of $\ln Z$ is sensibly constant for all values of D when measurements are made at constant dielectric constant. This arises from the fact that the dielectric constant dependent part of the Arrhenius frequency factor, namely, the entropy of activation, does not change with dielectric constant in constant dielectric constant media as is predicted by Eq. (6.27).

The value of $\log Z_D$ was obtained by averaging all the $\log Z$ terms given at constant dielectric constant. The $\log Z_{f.c.}$ was the average for the temperature range at a given composition. The magnitude and sign of the observed and calculated values are in good agreement in all cases, even though the values of r used for calculating $\log Z_{f.c.} - \log Z_D$ were not always those which could have been chosen for best agreement between experimental and calculated results, but were the values of r used in calculating $\Delta E_{f.c.} - \Delta E_D$ (Chapter V) by Amis and Holmes (*J. Am. Chem. Soc.*, **63**, 2231, 1941). The value of r for the brom phenol blue fading reaction is 1.20, 1.30, and 1.75 for ethyl alcohol-water, methyl alcohol-water, and glycerol-water, respectively. Likewise a difference of r values is noted for the ammonium ion-cyanate ion reaction in methyl alcohol-water and glycol-water solvents, being 2.00Å for the former and 2.50Å for the latter. Thus the solvent exerts upon reaction rates important influences

116

TABLE I A comparison of log $Z_{f.c.}$ − log Z_D calculated from equation (6.33) and the observed values found in the literature

Observer	Reaction	Solvent	$\sqrt{\mu}$	r in Eq. (6.33) Å	Intermed. dielec. (for const. comp.)	Dielec. range (iso-dielectric)	$-\log Z_{f.c.}$.log Z_D calcd.	$-\log Z_{f.c.}$.log Z_D obs.
Amis and Cook	$B\phi B^- + OH^-$	Glycerol-water	0.300	1.75	74.9	72.2-60.0	-3.86	-4.17
			.300	1.75	63.9	72.2-60.0	-4.57	-4.45
			.300	1.75	57.0	72.2-60.0	-5.14	-4.97
Amis and Holmes	Sucrose + H_3O^+	Dioxane-H_2O	.316	...	...	60.0-45.0	0.00	0.60
		EtOH-H_2O	.316	...	...	68.2-45.0	0.00	-0.34
Amis and LaMer	$B\phi B^- + OH^-$	MeOH-H_2O	.300	1.30	78.54	71.42-64.86	-5.40	-5.75
			.300	1.30	71.42	71.42-64.86	-6.00	-6.34
			.300	1.30	64.55	71.42-64.86	-6.41	-5.90
			.1415	1.30	78.54	71.42-64.86	-6.08	-5.79
		EtOH-H_2O	.300	1.20	78.54	71.42-64.86	-5.95	-5.96
			.300	1.20	71.42	71.42-64.86	-6.75	-7.19
			.300	1.20	64.55	71.42-64.86	-7.10	-7.23
			.1415	1.20	78.54	71.42-64.86	-6.49	-5.99
Svirbely and Warner	$NH_4 + CNO^-$	MeOH-H_2O	.194	2.00	69.8	63.5	1.96	2.44
			.194	2.00	69.8	55.0	1.96	2.65
			.000	2.00	69.8	63.5-55.0	2.43	2.98
Svirbely and Schramm			.194	2.00	63.5	63.5-35.0	2.25	2.16
			.194	2.00	69.8	63.5-35.0	1.96	2.59
			.000	2.00	63.5	63.5-35.0	2.84	2.57
			.000	2.00	69.8	63.5-35.0	2.43	3.02
Lander and Svirbely		Glycol-H_2O	.194	2.50	69.76	63.5-40.0	1.47	1.57
			.000	2.50	69.76	63.5-40.0	1.95	2.34

other than those arising from the dielectric constant. To cover our ignorance we call these influences specific solvent effects.

Some instances of reactions between ions and dipolar molecules are included in Table I. Equation (6.33) does not apply to such data since it can give only zero for the difference of $\log Z_{f.c.} - \log Z_D$ when either z_A or z_B or both are zero. The data do emphasize that when one of the reactants is dipolar rather than ionic, there are yet ion-dipole forces which cause a difference in $\ln Z$ measured in constant composition media and in isodielectric media.

Effect of structure on rates and the entropy of activation

A characteristic phenomenon observed in reactions of ketones and aldehydes with typical carbonyl reagents such as hydroxylamine, hydrazine, and semicarbazide, is the dependence of reaction rate upon the structure of the carbonyl compound. The following discussion of this phenomenon is taken from the work of Hammett and co-workers (*J. Am. Chem. Soc.*, **63**, 2387, 1941; *J. Am. Chem. Soc.*, **65**, 1824, 1943; *Physical Organic Chemistry*, New York, McGraw-Hill Book Co., Inc., 940).

From the standpoint of potential energies alone, i.e., in terms of internal electron displacements or of external electrical fields due to a substituting group, the effect of change in structure upon rate of reaction can be explained only when there is a nullifying of other effects due to the internal kinetic energies of the reactants. If such cancellation takes place, then

$$\Delta S_1 - \Delta S_2 = \frac{\partial}{\partial T} (RT \ln k_1'/k_2') \qquad (6.34)$$

must necessarily vanish. In Eq. (6.34) the subscripts 1 and 2 refer to two different reactants, k' is the specific reaction rate constant, and ΔS is termed by Hammett and co-workers the entropy of activation and is equal to $R \ln Z$ in the notation used up to this time in the present work.

Price and Hammett (*loc. cit.*) studied the reactions of several carbonyl compounds with semicarbazide in phosphate buffer of pH 7.0. They give the stoichiometric equation for the reaction as

$$\begin{matrix} R_1 \\ \diagdown \\ \diagup \\ R_2 \end{matrix} C{=}O + H_2N{-}NH{-}CO{-}NH_2 \rightleftharpoons \begin{matrix} R_1 \\ \diagdown \\ \diagup \\ R_2 \end{matrix} CN{-}NH{-}CO{-}NH_2 + H_2O$$

but point out that Conant and Bartlett (*J. Am. Chem. Soc.*, **54,** 2881, 1932) proved the reaction to be subject to general acid catalysis. Price and Hammett indicate that this transition state is composed of carbonyl compound, semicarbazide, and the catalyzing acid (in this case $H_2PO_4^-$).

Since the problem being considered is the effect of structure upon reaction rates, the values of the free energy ΔF, entropy ΔS, and heat ΔH (or energy ΔE), of activation relative to that of a standard reactant are the quantities required. Acetone was chosen as the standard reactant and factors pertaining to it are designated by a zero subscript in the following equations given by Price and Hammett for the relative quantities listed above.

$$\Delta F - \Delta F_0 = -RT \ln k'/k_0' \tag{6.35}$$

$$\Delta S - \Delta S_0 = \frac{\partial}{\partial T} (RT \ln k'/k_0') \tag{6.36}$$

$$\Delta E - \Delta E_0 = RT^2 \frac{\partial}{\partial T} (\ln k'/k_0') \tag{6.37}$$

These relative free energies, entropies, and energies of activation can be visualized as appertaining to the thermodynamic functions of the process

$$A + Acetone^* \rightleftharpoons A^* + Acetone$$

with the starred symbols representing the transition states for semicarbazone formation of the substance referred to and A standing for any carbonyl compound.

In actual computations finite increments were substituted for the differentials in Eq. (6.36) and (6.37).

Where the determination of the equilibrium constant was possible, the rate constants for the semicarbazone formation were determined by the equation of Conant and Bartlett

$$k't = \frac{1}{2x_e + C + K} \ln \left(\frac{x + x_e + C + K}{x - x_e} \right) + C' \tag{6.38}$$

which applies to a second-order forward and first-order reverse reaction. In Eq. (6.38), k' is the second-order constant for the forward reaction; t is the time in seconds; x is the semicarbazide concentration at time t; x_e is the equilibrium concentration of semicarbazide; C is the difference between the initial concentrations of carbonyl compound and semicarbazide; K is the equilibrium constant for hydrolysis, i.e.,

$K = k'_{reverse}/k'_{forward}$; and C' is a constant involving initial and final concentrations. k' was determined by a least squares plot of the first term on the right of Eq. (6.38) against t. This method was used for acetone, diethyl ketone, cyclopentanone, and cyclohexanone semicarbazone formation. For pinacolone, furfural, and acetophenone the constants were calculated on the basis of an irreversible second-order forward reaction. In the case of pinacolone a least-squares plot showed a considerable falling off of the rate constant during the time the reaction was studied. In this case the initial slope of the curve was obtained by a graphical method of numerical differentiation.

Table II contains the data of Price and Hammett (*loc. cit.*) for the rate constant for semicarbazone formation from acetone, diethyl ketone, pinacolone, cyclopentanone, cyclohexanone, furfural, and acetophenone at two temperatures and in a buffer of pH 7.0.

TABLE II Rate constants k' in liters per mole sec. for semicarbazone formation in buffer of pH 7.0 (buffer: 0.0571 M Na$_2$HPO$_4$, 0.0286 M NaH$_2$PO$_4$)

Acetone		0.04°	25.11°
		0.0612	0.0863
		.0630	.0873
		.0638	.0847
		.0661	
	Av.	.0635	Av. .0861
Diethyl ketone		0.03°	25.00°
		0.00687	0.00827
		.00659	.00860
		.00716	.00878
	Av.	.00688	Av. .00855
Pinacolone		0.04°	25.00°
		0.000741	0.000999
		.000753	.000992
		.000817	.001027
	Av.	.000771	Av. .001006
Cyclopentanone		0.04°	25.10°
		0.00822	0.0152
		.00817	.0153
		.00814	.0147
		.00850	.0160
	Av.	.00826	Av. .0153

TABLE II—*Continued*

Cyclohexanone		0.03°		25.11°
		0.423		.495
		.430		.563
		.458		.485
	Av.	.437	Av.	.512
Furfural		0.03°		25.00°
		0.00647		0.0120
		.00645		.0122
		.00674		.0127
	Av.	.00656	Av.	.0123
Acetophenone		0.04°		25.01°
		0.000204		0.000417
		.000204		.000410
		.000203		.000414
	Av.	.000204	Av.	.000413

Table III contains the data for the equilibrium constants K_H and hydrolysis constants k'_h listed by these authors for acetone, diethyl ketone, cyclopentanone, and cyclohexanone. Rate constants k'_h for hydrolysis of semicarbazones were calculated from equilibrium constants and rate constants for formation.

TABLE III   **Equilibrium constants, K_H, and rate constants, k_h', for hydrolysis of some semicarbazones. Same medium as in Table II**

	Temp. °C	$K_H \times 10^3$	$k'_h \times 10^4$, sec.$^{-1}$
Acetone	25.11	3.23	2.78
	0.04	0.804	0.511
Diethyl ketone	25.00	26.4	2.26
	0.03	8.86	0.609
Cyclopentanone	25.10	1.48	0.226
	0.04	0.461	0.0381
Cyclohexanone	25.11	2.06	10.6
	0.03	0.510	2.23

Table IV contains the relative entropies, heats (energies), and free energies of activation for the semicarbazone formation. In Table V are given analogous functions for the reverse reaction.

In the series of carbonyl compounds listed the entropies of activation for semicarbazone formation vary over a range of 13 calories per

TABLE IV Relative entropies, heats, and free energies of activation for semicarbazone formation at 12.5° C. ΔH_0 = 2000 calories

	$\Delta S - \Delta S_0$, cal./° C	$\Delta H - \Delta H_0$, cal.	$\Delta F - \Delta F_0$, cal.
Acetone	0.00	0	0
Diethyl ketone	−6.50	−600	1300
Pinacolone	−9.70	−200	2500
Cyclopentanone	3.30	2000	1100
Cyclohexanone	0.40	−900	−1100
Furfural	3.20	2100	1200
Acetophenone	−1.90	2600	3200

TABLE V Relative entropies, heats, and free energies of activation for semicarbazone hydrolysis at 12.5° C. ΔH_0 = 11,000 calories

	$\Delta S - \Delta S_0$, cal./° C	$\Delta H - \Delta H_0$, cal.	$\Delta F - \Delta F_0$, cal.
Acetone	0.00	0	0
Diethyl ketone	−8.70	−2500	0
Cyclopentanone	−3.20	600	1500
Cyclohexanone	−0.40	−900	−800

degree centigrade, which is equivalent to three orders of magnitude in the rate of reaction. These variations are many times larger than the probable error in measurement of these activation entropies. In fact the authors estimate the error of measurement of the entropy differences to be about 0.70 calorie per degree centigrade. The typical and familiar phenomenon of the decrease in reactivity of a carbonyl compound with substitution of the methyl radical for hydrogen on the α-carbon atom, as in the series acetone, diethyl ketone, pinacolone, may be attributed entirely to an entropy effect. The variation of the heat (or energy) of activation is relatively unimportant. Price and Hammett remark that the effect of changing structure upon reactivity of aldehydes and ketones is so consistent in its nature, that it is probable that the entropy of activation is the controlling factor in this phenomenon for semicarbazone reaction in other buffer mixtures or in other solvents, or, indeed, in other typical carbonyl reactions.

These authors point out that the entropies of activation for the whole series of reactions parallel to a marked extent the rigidity of the carbonyl compounds. Thus cyclopentanone with its planar ring structure and slightly strained bond angles, and furfural with its rigid ring and partial double bond character of the link between the carbonyl group and the ring, are the most rigid of these substances and also show the highest entropies of activation. Pinacolone, on the other hand, has a large number of internal degrees of freedom and exhibits the lowest entropy of activation. Acetophenone is the only one of these compounds which does not fit reasonably well into this sequence. This compound would presumably be relatively rigid because of the partial double character of the link between the carbonyl and the phenyl group; however, its entropy of activation is low enough to suggest a less rigid structure.

It is suggested that the entropy change and change of reactivity with structure in the semicarbazone reaction is explained by assuming the transition state to be of relatively rigid structure, so that a carbonyl compound possessing many degrees of freedom loses most of these on activation, whilst a more rigid carbonyl compound cannot do so. These less rigid carbonyl compounds, therefore, show a less positive entropy of activation due to the freezing out of internal motion upon the formation of the activated state.

Price and Hammett point out that a charged body (the carbonyl group) immersed in a high dielectric solvent repels a body of low dielectric constant (methyl groups), and if this repulsion is strong enough to cause the carbon chains in diethyl ketone and pinacolone to lie as far as possible in the transition state from the carbonyl group which is probably strongly polar, these carbon chains lose their freedom of rotation, and this could account for the low entropy of activation.

The nearly identical values of the heats (energies) of activation for furfural and acetophenone suggests that the difference of reactivity of aldehydes as compared with ketones can be attributed to an entropy effect. As can be seen from Table II the rate of reaction of furfural is some thirty times as great as that of acetophenone although the potential energy barrier opposing the formation of the transition state is nearly the same height for the two reactants.

In the hydroxyl ion catalyzed aldol condensation of benzaldehyde with methyl ethyl ketone and acetone in dioxane-water mixtures Gettler and Hammett (*J. Am. Chem. Soc.*, **65**, 1824, 1943) find that energy and entropy of activation values lend additional support to the theory of Price and Hammett with regard to the effect of structure on the reactivity of carbonyl compounds.

This somewhat lengthy discussion of the effect of structure on reactivity of carbonyl compounds was given to emphasize that the height of the energy barrier over which reactants must pass in order to become products is not alone the determining factor in the rates of chemical reactions. As has been suggested to the author, there is the factor of *flux*, that is, the rate at which those molecules with sufficient energy can flow up to and across the mountain pass or energy barrier. It is conceivable that reactant molecules with numerous flailing appendages, even with the same energy requirements, would have a longer average time of approach to and of crossing over the barrier than a rigid molecule, just as viscous or even turbulent flow would require a longer time to deliver a given amount of fluid than laminar flow under the same conditions of energy input. The tieing down of these flailing appendages, as the theory of rigid intermediate state implies, would lead to a more ordered intermediate than reactant state and hence a lowered entropy in going from reactant to intermediate complex.

Heats and entropies of activation

Laidler and Eyring (*Ann. New York Acad. Sci.*, **39,** 303, 1940) give an empirical relationship between heats and entropies of activation. With regard to heats and entropies of solution it has been pointed out by Evans and Polanyi (*Trans. Faraday Soc.*, **32,** 1333, 1936) that the following equation often holds:

$$T \, \Delta S = \alpha \, \Delta H + \beta \qquad (6.39)$$

where α is always positive and less than unity. Bell (*Trans. Faraday Soc.*, **33,** 496, 1937) gives a theoretical discussion of this relationship. Laidler and Eyring reason that since Eq. (6.39) is applicable to the reactants, the intermediates, and the activated complex in a reaction, an analogous linearity between the heats and entropies of activation is to be expected, and this was pointed out by Evans and Polanyi. Fairclough and Hinshelwood (*J. Chem. Soc.*, **1937,** 538) believe that the entropy (or log PZ) is related to the reciprocal of the square root of the energy of activation.

In Fig. 2 is given the plot of the heat of activation versus the entropy of activation multiplied by the absolute temperature, given by Laidler and Eyring for the alkaline hydrolysis of ethyl benzoate. Equation (6.39) holds accurately for this case. There are deviations from linearity when there is solvation of reactants or of the activated complex, and it is probable that such deviations, and the deviations

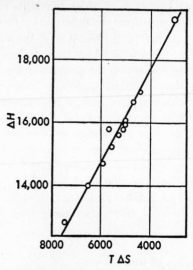

Figure 2 Plot of the heat of reaction against the entropy of reaction for the alkaline hydrolysis of ethyl benzoate in alcohol-water mixtures.

of the specific rates from their expected relationship with the dielectric constant, parallel each other. Changing solvent apparently always causes a change in the entropy of activation.

CHAPTER VII

Semiempirical calculation of activation energies; the theory of absolute reaction rates

In the simple Arrhenius equation there are two quantities which if known would permit the calculation of absolute reaction rates. If for a given reaction the frequency factor Z and the energy of activation ΔE were known, it would be possible to calculate the specific reaction rate constant at a given temperature. Now it has been made possible in some cases to calculate ΔE theoretically using quantum mechanics, and semiempirically in other cases, from energy contour maps constructed by use of certain spectroscopic data and of the Morse curve. It has been shown by Eyring that Z can be calculated statistically, so that for reactions involving reactants for which certain data are known or can be taken, the rate may be determined absolutely. Since the use of the Morse curve is a standard procedure for constructing potential energy surfaces from which energies of activation may be determined, a discussion of this equation and of its application is first in order.

The Morse formula (*Phys. Rev.*, **34**, 57, 1929)

The purpose is to obtain the total potential energy of a diatomic molecule with reference to the energy of the atoms which compose it. This total energy is wanted for different atomic distances and can be obtained from spectroscopic and other data. The method most often used is the application of the empirical formula proposed by Morse, which relates the binding energy E between two atoms to the distance r between them referred to the energy of the completely separated atoms as zero. The function as given by Morse is

$$E = D'(e^{-2a(r-r_0)} - 2e^{-a(r-r_0)}) \tag{7.1}$$

In this equation a is a constant, r_0 is the equilibrium distance between

125

the atoms in the molecule, and D' is the heat of dissociation of the molecule plus the zero point energy and is given by the equation

$$D' = D + \frac{hW_0}{2} \tag{7.2}$$

where h is Planck's constant, W_0 is the equilibrium frequency, and D is the heat of dissociation of the molecule.

The constant a is found from the expression

$$a = 0.1227 W_0 \sqrt{\frac{M'}{D}} \tag{7.3}$$

Where M' is the reduced mass which is related to the mass of the two atoms M_1 and M_2 by the equation

$$M' = \frac{M_1 M_2}{M_1 + M_2} \tag{7.4}$$

Now D', W_0, and r_0 may be obtained from spectroscopic data and hence the energy of a diatomic molecule for any separation of the two atoms may be calculated.

When the energy calculated from Eq. (7.1) is plotted as ordinates against interatomic distance as abscissas a curve of the form given in Fig. 1 is obtained. The minimum in the curve gives the distance between the atoms for a stable diatomic molecule. To the left of the minimum the atoms repel each other and to the right of the minimum the atoms attract each other. D' is shown in the curve to be the dissociation energy with reference to the lowest point of the curve instead of the level where the vibrational quantum number $v = 0$, as is usually the case. The energy represented by the distance $v = 0$ to $v = v_c$ is the ordinary energy of dissociation D. v_c is the vibrational quantum number when the nuclei can become infinitely separated, i.e., when the molecule is dissociated.

Application of the Morse formula in calculation of energies of activation

Eyring and Polanyi (*Z. physik. Chem.*, **B12**, 279, 1931) indicated that potential energy surfaces could be plotted, and from them activation energies could be calculated. The potential energy surfaces could be obtained from the total potential energies of diatomic molecules, with reference to the energies of their constituent atoms. As has been said, the simplest way to obtain the total energy of a diatomic molecule for different distances between the atoms is to use the Morse formula, substituting into it the values of the constants obtained from spectroscopic data. This total energy of the diatomic molecule with reference to its constituent atoms is composed of two forms of

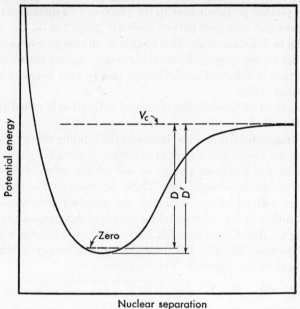

Figure 1 Potential energy curve for a two atom system.

energy, namely, coulombic and exchange (resonance) energies. The equations for three and four electrons are then made up of terms consisting of coulombic and exchange energies between electron pairs. From the total energy the two types of energy may be calculated in fair approximation by assuming that each is a constant fraction of the whole. The total energy J thus calculated is the potential energy of the atoms referred to the atoms at infinite distance from each other as zero energy. But what we want is the energy of the atoms referred to their stable reactant states. Thus for hydrogen chloride reacting with ethylene we would be interested in the energy referred to the stable H—Cl and C=C compounds as zero. Thus it would be necessary to subtract J from the total energy D required to break the H—Cl and the C=C bonds.

In making the plot of the potential energy surface it is required that the variation of potential energy with interatomic distance for the various electron pairs involved in the reactants be reduced to a three dimensional model, namely energy as a function of two independently variable distances. The energy as a function of the distances is plotted perpendicular to the plane of two distances taken as coordinates and constant energy lines are projected on the plane in which the two distances lie. This results in an energy contour map or a potential *energy surface*. From this energy contour map the energy of activation is obtained as the lowest energy pass between reactant and product states.

This method of determining energy of activation is called the *semiempirical method*.

In writing potential energy equations the binding energy, or energy necessary to break the bonds in question is usually given. This is negative of the potential energy of the system referred to the zero state of complete dissociation. These expressions for the binding energy are derived by application of the so-called *perturbation theory* to the solution of the corresponding quantum mechanical problem.

Eyring (*J. Am. Chem. Soc.*, **53**, 2537, 1931) used London's equation (*Z. Elektrochem.*, **35**, 552, 1929) for the binding energy holding three monovalent atoms together. The equation is

$$J = A + B + C - \sqrt{\tfrac{1}{2}[(\alpha - \beta)^2 + (\alpha - \gamma)^2 + (\beta - \gamma)]^2}   (7.5)$$

where $(A + B + C)$ is the coulombic or electrostatic energy binding the three atoms, and the square root term is the energy of exchange binding. Consider the three atoms W, X, and Y forming the triangle in Fig. 2.

The energy J of Eq. (7.5) is the energy necessary to make distances r_1, r_2, and r_3 very large simultaneously. The binding energy $J_1 = A + \alpha$ between the atoms W and X when atom Y is far away depends only on the distance r_1. This energy can be calculated using Eq. (7.1) provided D, W_0, and r_0 are known from spectroscopic data for the atoms W and X in the combined state. The coulombic part A of the binding energy J_1 can then be calculated using the approximate wave functions of Zener (*Phys. Rev.*, **36**, 51, 1930) and Slater (*ibid.*, **36,** 57, 1930), or easier still, as was explained before, it can be assumed that the coulombic is a definite fraction of the total binding energy. Thus Eyring and Polanyi (*Z. physik. Chem.*, **B12**, 279, 1931) show that in the case of H_2, for all values of r important in determining the energy of activation, the theoretical coulombic binding energy is 10 per cent of the total theoretical binding energy and about 8 per cent of the empirically found binding energy. Eyring (*J. Am. Chem. Soc.*, **53**, 2537, 1931) assumes the coulombic binding energy is 10 per cent of the total binding energy for the reaction:

$$H_2 \text{ para} + H \longrightarrow H_2 \text{ ortho} + H$$

In later work Eyring assumed the coulombic to be 14 per cent of the total energy. In any case from J_1 and A, α may be calculated. Proceed-

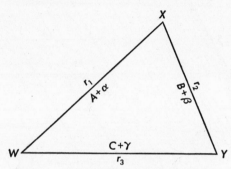

Figure 2 Diagram for calculating the potential energy of a three-atom system.

ing in like manner $B + \beta$, and B and β, and also $C + \gamma$, and C and γ may be obtained for various values of r_2 and r_3. Substitution of the values of A, B, C, α, β, and γ in Eq. (7.5) makes it possible to calculate J. It can be shown that the potential energy of the system is lowest (has largest negative value) when X is on a straight line passing through Y and W. Therefore this corresponds to the configuration yielding the lowest energy barrier for activation, and is the manner of approach of the atom to the molecule for reaction to take place between the two. Distance r_3 will be the sum of r_1 and r_2 and hence will not be an independent variable. Therefore, the energy of the system is a function of two distances which can vary independently. The representation of the potential energy, or of the energy of activation, as a function of interatomic distance will be a three-dimensional model and this diagrammatic representation of the potential energy is called a *potential-energy surface*. The contour maps obtained by projecting lines of equal energy onto the plane of the distances r_1 and r_2 are actually used and are likewise called potential-energy surfaces.

To summarize, Eyring's use of the Morse potential-energy curve for each pair of atoms is based on the following assumptions according to Van Vleck and Sherman (*Phys. Rev.*, **7**, 165, 1935): (1) All directional

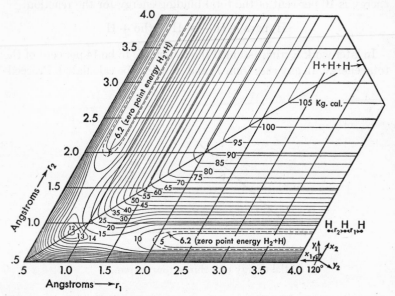

Figure 3 Potential energy surface for the system of three hydrogen atoms. The coulombic energy is taken as 14 per cent.

valence effects were neglected. (2) Since the equation gives the sum of the coulombic and exchange energies of an electron-pair bond as a function of distance between nuclei, Eyring assumed a ratio of these two energies of $\frac{14}{86}$ in order to calculate the energies separately. This ratio makes his theory yield the observed activation energy, determined from para-ortho conversion, for the simplest chemical reaction given in the above equation. (3) The same ratio holds for all non-metallic electron-pair bonds.

Thus it is clear why the method is called semiempirical. Van Vleck and Sherman point out, however, that agreement with theory is obtained with this ratio only if the zero-point energy of the activated state is neglected.

The potential-energy surface for three collinear hydrogen atoms taken from Eyring, Gershinowitz and Sun (*J. Chem. Phys.*, **3,** 786, 1935) is given in Fig. 3.

The contour lines are equipotentials with a spacing of 5 kilogram calories. It was assumed that the coulombic energy was 14 per cent of the total, and the following constants for the Morse curve for hydrogen were used: $D = 102.4$ kilogram calories; $W_0 = 4375 \text{ cm}^{-1}$; $a = 1.94 A^{-1}$; $r_0 = 0.74 A$. This surface has many features in common with other surfaces which represent the interaction of three atoms, any two of which can form a diatomic molecule. The angle that the axes make with each other is a function of the relative masses, but for three like atoms the angle is always 60°. In any case the angle is so chosen that the free frictionless motion under the influence of gravity of a mass point on the surface will be representative of the similar motion of the reacting system. In the region of high potentials, there is a dividing line along which $r_1 = r_2$. This line divides the surface into two regions. The two valleys representing $H + H_2$ and $H_2 + H$, respectively, are clearly discernible. It can be observed also that the height of the gap at the top of the barrier through which the system must pass before reaction can occur is at about 14 kilogram calories per mole. Glasstone, Laidler and Eyring (*The Theory of Rate Processes*, New York and London, McGraw-Hill Book Co., Inc., 1941) point out that there is a shallow basin about 2.5 kilogram calories deep at the top of the basin. The bottom of this basin corresponds to an energy of 12 or less kilogram calories. These authors also mention that in the activated state r_1 is about 1.25Å, and r_2 is very close to 0.78Å.

Eyring, Gershinowitz and Sun (*loc. cit.*) give a plot of energy contours for three hydrogen atoms forming an isosceles triangle. This configuration is for one hydrogen atom moving in a direction perpendicular to and toward (or away from) the center of the line joining the other two. This third atom carries off the excess energy of the two reacting atoms moving along the line. (See Fig. 4.)

FOUR-ATOM SYSTEMS

Equation (7.5) for three-atom systems will hold for four-atom systems also. However, the bonds are $J_1 = A + \alpha$, $J_2 = B + \beta$, and $J_3 = C + \gamma$ in the case of the three-atom system, while for four atoms (see Altar and Eyring, *J. Chem. Phys.*, **4,** 661, 1936)

$$J_1 = A_1 + A_2 + \alpha_1 + \alpha_2 = A + \alpha$$
$$J_2 = B_1 + B_2 + \beta_1 + \beta_2 = B + \beta$$
$$J_3 = C_1 + C_2 + \gamma_1 + \gamma_2 = C + \gamma \tag{7.6}$$
$$A = A_1 + A_2, \text{ etc.}$$
$$\alpha = \alpha_1 + \alpha_2, \text{ etc.}$$

that is, the quantities α, β, γ which in the case of three atoms refer to the exchange energy of one electron pair only, now represent the sum of the exchange energies for two pairs. Altar and Eyring assume

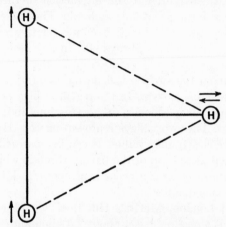

Figure 4 Three-atom system with the third atom approaching or receding along the line perpendicular at the center to the line joining the other two atoms.

that the actual amounts of coulombic and exchange energy for each pair are constant fractions of the total interaction energy as given by the Morse curve for that pair. Thus

$$A_1 = \lambda J_1', \qquad \alpha_1 = (1 - \lambda)J_1',$$
$$B_1 = \lambda J_2', \qquad \beta_1 = (1 - \lambda)J_2', \tag{7.7}$$
$$C_1 = \lambda J_3', \qquad \gamma_1 = (1 - \lambda)J_3'.$$

Altar and Eyring conclude that as for three monovalent atoms the activated complexes should be linear, so for four monovalent atoms the activated complexes are planar. Since there are now six parameters the energy cannot be visualized in configuration space; therefore these authors describe the potential function J of a three- or four-particle system in bond space instead of the usual configuration space, i.e., they represent the system by using the three bond energies J_1, J_2, J_3 as orthogonal coordinates. For four atoms this is possible since the three pairs of bonds J_1' and J_1'', J_2' and J_2'', J_3' and J_3'' enter into Eq. (7.5) only as their sums. In general, to express the interaction energy of an even-numbered particle system, containing $2n$ particles, requires no more linearly independent combinations of bonds than does the one containing $(2n - 1)$ atoms.

One disadvantage of using the bond-space representation is that the configurational changes of the system in a reaction can no longer

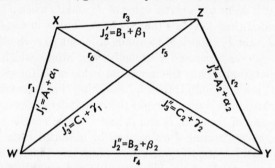

Figure 5 Diagram for calculating the potential energy of a four-atom system.

be represented by the motion of a mass point subjected to the known potential J, which obeys the laws of ordinary mechanics. This method of visualization is feasible for no more than three atoms.

Of the six parameters necessary to specify the configuration of four particles in space, only two, J_1 and J_2, may need be considered truly independent and as determining a surface which contains the best reaction path, i.e., which contains the sequence of configurations by which the reaction takes place in a manner most economical of potential energy.

A reaction is again described by starting with a configuration where J_1 is a maximum and $J_2 = J_3 = 0$, and going to a configuration where J_2 is a maximum and $J_1 = J_3 = 0$. The point of highest potential energy along the reaction path represents the activated configuration.

For different values of r_1, J_1' is calculated for the reactant molecule WX (Fig. 5) from its D, r_0, and W_0 values taken from spectroscopic data, and using the equation for the Morse curve. Values of J_1'' as a function of r_2 are calculated in like manner for the reactant molecule YZ (Fig. 5). Then values of J_1 as a function of the distances separating the atoms W and X in molecule WX, and the atoms Y and Z in molecule YZ are taken as the sums of J_1' and J_1''. In like manner values of J_2' and J_2'' as functions of r_3 and r_4, respectively, are obtained for product molecules WY and XZ (Fig. 5). The J_2 values for various r_3 and r_4 values are taken as the sums of J_2' and J_2''.

Different values of J_1 and J_2 are taken, and the value of J_3, equal to $J_3' + J_3''$, that together with them gives the lowest potential energy J of the system is found. Let us be a little more explicit. The lowest value of J will occur for a given value of J_1 and J_2 when J_3 is a minimum, provided that J_3 is less than J_1 or J_2. This will usually be the case since J_1 and J_2 appertain to atoms adjacent to each other, while J_3 refers to atoms separated diagonally, i.e., atoms which have the greatest separations. Thus the minimum value of J_3 for given values of J_1 and J_2 must be found; then by assuming that a certain fraction of these potentials is coulombic and the remainder exchange binding, the magnitudes of A and α, B and β, and C and γ can be found and, from these, corresponding J values can be obtained from Eq. (7.5). These J quantities are the potentials which are plotted against J_1 and J_2, and the equal potential lines so obtained constitute the potential-energy surface in bond space.

Altar and Eyring give a device constructed of six rulers by means of which a minimum value of J_3 for given values of J_1 and J_2 can be found. The device is used in investigating a four-atom system, H_2 and ICl which has no symmetry at all. The six interatomic distances between the four atoms H, H, I, Cl, together with their respective bond energies are marked on scales, and the scales are attached to each other so as to form a model of the plane configurations of these four atoms. Various combinations of J_1' and J_1'' which add up to the same J_1, and various values of J_2' and J_2'' which add up to the same J_2 are taken, and the diagonals are read for each constant-valued combination of J_1' and J_1'' and J_2' and J_2'' until the minimum absolute sum of the energies, J_3' and J_3'', represented by the diagonals is found. This is the minimum J_3 for a given J_1 and J_2. In this manner a sufficient number of combinations (J_1, J_2, J_3) is determined and J's calculated therefrom using Eq. (7.5) to map out the potential diagram. Thus the potential surface is a two-dimensional diagram in spite of the fact that the number of parameters in the dynamical problem is six. Figure 6 shows a sketch of the device used by Altar and Eyring for finding the lowest sum, J_3, for the diagonal bonds for a given J_1 and J_2. The plot for the reaction

$$H_2 + ICl \longrightarrow HI + HCl$$

given by Altar and Eyring is given in Fig. 7. This figure shows the projections on the $J_1 J_2$ plane of the intersections of the equipotentials with the boundary surface for the above reaction.

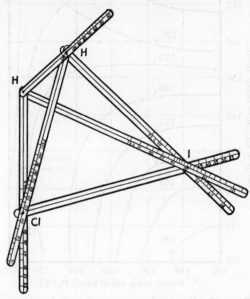

Figure 6 Sliding rulers for determining the configuration of a four-atom system possessing minimum energy.

These authors point out that the points J_1, J_2, and J_3 may be used for different fractions of additive binding. They located the activated point and determined the activation energy for 14, 17, and 20 per cent of additive binding.

In Fig. 7 the reaction path is represented by the line with arrow points. The point of highest energy which the path crosses corresponds to the activation energy and the point also gives the position of the activated state. This latter position is marked with an x in Fig. 7.

Daniels (*Chemical Kinetics*, Ithaca, N. Y., Cornell University Press, 1938), by making certain assumptions, represents in configuration space the potential-energy surface for the bromination of ethylene, which is a four-atom reaction. The bromine atoms and the carbon atoms all lie in a plane, and also the four atoms have a plane of

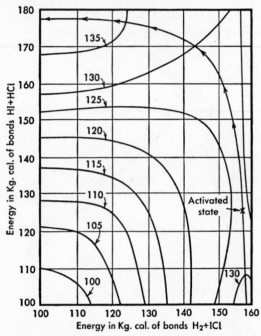

Figure 7 Potential energy surface in bond space for the chemical process

$$H_2 + ICl \longrightarrow HI + HCl$$

symmetry shown at AB in Fig. 8. The carbon-carbon distance r_{C-C} is taken constant and equal to the average of the distances between the carbons in the unbrominated and brominated ethylenes. The two carbon-bromine distances are equal due to symmetry. The two distances which are taken as variables are the bromine-bromine distance r_{Br-Br} (one-half of this distance, r_2, is really used) and the perpendicular distance r_1 between the line joining the two carbon atoms and that joining the two bromine atoms. Due to the symmetry, all distances between the various atoms may be calculated as functions of r_1 and r_2, and from the Morse curve the potential energies may be calculated for the various atom pairs as a function of r_1 and r_2, using the corresponding atomic distances and the constants for these atomic pairs from spectroscopic data. These various energies of atom pairs are then separated by Daniels into their coulombic and exchange components by assuming the former is 14 per cent and the latter 86 per cent of the total. Using Eq. (7.5) the potential energy J of the four-atom system is determined and is plotted as functions of r_1 and r_2 taken as

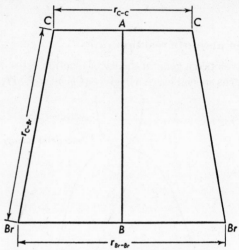

Figure 8 Diagram for calculating the potential energy of a symmetric four-atom system.

axes, and a potential-energy surface in configuration space is obtained for the four atoms. Now J is the potential energy of the four-atom system referred to the four atoms at infinite distance from each other taken as zero. But the energy of activation is measured from the stable C=C and Br—Br molecules taken as zero. Therefore, the energies really used by Daniels for plotting against r_1 and r_2 were obtained by subtracting the values of J from the total energy (the sum of D's) required to break both the C=C and the Br—Br bonds. The minimum value of ΔE for this reaction was found to be 23,200 calories, and occurred at $r_1 = 1.14\text{Å}$ and $r_2 = 2.40\text{Å}$. This energy is the energy of activation for the bromination of ethylene.

In reality, not only must the energy of activation be calculable theoretically or semiempirically in order to obtain absolute reaction rates, but also two other quantities must be obtainable by like means. One of these is not included in the simple Arrhenius equation, and were this equation sufficient this term could be neglected. This factor is the transmission coefficient which has been treated by Hirschfelder and Wigner. The other term, mentioned at the beginning of this chapter, is the frequency factor which Eyring has shown can be determined using statistical mechanics. Thus absolute reaction rates may be calculated and it is to a consideration of these that we now turn.

The theory of absolute reaction rates

Eyring has developed a general theory of reaction rates which includes earlier theories as special cases. He gives (*Chem. Rev.*, **17,** 65, 1935) the

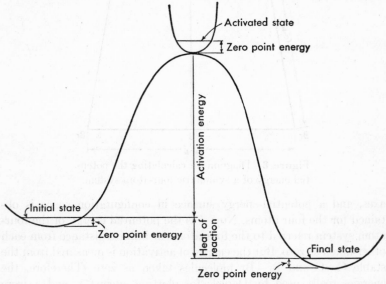

Figure 9 Energy profile of the path of a reacting system on a many dimensional surface.

energy profile of the path of the reacting system on a many-dimensional surface as represented in Fig. 9.

Eyring assumed that in the general theory for the rate of reaction in any phase, the slow process is the passage over a potential-energy barrier. The activated complex has properties almost identical with those of an ordinary molecule, except that instead of only the three regular degrees of translational freedom it has the equivalent of a fourth. In the coordinate of decomposition, the normal vibrational frequency of the molecule has an imaginary value. In the direction of decomposition the molecule is unstable for atomic displacements, and in this direction it breaks up. Figure 9 shows the path of a particle representing our reacting system along the many-dimensional potential-energy surface. The rate of the reaction is given by the equilibrium number C'_* of activated complexes per unit of volume lying in length δ at the top of the potential barrier, multiplied by the product of the frequency at which the complexes cross the barrier and the probability $\varkappa$ of their not returning.

Thus the rate of reaction for the process

$$A + B \rightleftharpoons (AB)_* \longrightarrow \text{Products}$$

is given by the expression

$$\text{Rate of reaction} = \varkappa C'_* \frac{\bar{v}}{\delta} \tag{7.8}$$

and the specific reaction rate constant k' is calculated from the formula

$$k' = \varkappa \frac{C'_*}{C_A C_B} \frac{\bar{v}}{\delta} \tag{7.9}$$

In these equations $\bar{v}$ is the mean velocity of crossing the barrier and $\bar{v}/\delta$ is the mean frequency at which activated complexes cross the barrier. C_A and C_B are the concentrations of reactants A and B. The other quantities have been defined.

Since C_A and C_B can always be determined from analytical data, or from controlled addition of reactants, and since the length of the barrier can be made to cancel out, it becomes possible to calculate a specific velocity constant for a given reaction if $\varkappa$, C'_x, and $\bar{v}$ can be obtained.

The transmission coefficient

The transmission coefficient $\varkappa$ is the ratio of the number of systems crossing the barrier to the number of systems reacting, and for many of the simpler reactions has the value of about unity. Hirschfelder and Wigner (*J. Chem. Phys.*, **7**, 616, 1939) derive formally an expression for the transmission coefficient based upon the assumption that there is a definite probability of a system which has crossed the transition state being reflected back to the transition state. Let this probability be denoted by ρ_i and ρ_f for crossings from left to right and right to left, respectively. The authors also assume that these probabilities are equal for systems originating from the two sides of the transition state and are independent of the number of times the system has crossed this state.

When thermal equilibrium has been established, half of the systems in the transition state are moving from left to right and the other half from right to left. At complete thermal equilibrium, A systems enter, per unit time, the transition state directly from the initial state, and B systems come from the final state. Figure 10 represents schematically the flux of the different types of systems through the transition region.

By addition the number of systems crossing the transition state from left to right in unit time is

$$N_{l \to r} = A(1 + \rho_i\rho_f + \rho_i^2\rho_f^2 + \cdots) + B\rho_i(1 + \rho_i\rho_f + \rho_i^2\rho_f^2 + \cdots)$$
$$= (A + B\rho_i)(1 - \rho_i\rho_f)^{-1} \tag{7.10}$$

and the number of those crossing it from right to left is

$$N_{r \to l} = A\rho_f(1 + \rho_i\rho_f + \rho_i^2\rho_f^2 + \cdots) + B(1 + \rho_i\rho_f + \rho_i^2\rho_f^2 + \cdots)$$
$$= (A\rho_f + B)(1 - \rho_i\rho_f)^{-1} \tag{7.11}$$

At equilibrium $N_{l \to r} = N_{r \to l}$, and hence

$$B = \frac{A(1 - \rho_f)}{(1 - \rho_i)} \tag{7.12}$$

Inserting this value of B in Eq. (7.10) yields

$$N_{l \to r} = \frac{A}{(1 - \rho_i)} \tag{7.13}$$

Now the number of systems which have originated in the initial state and which go to the final state without suffering reflection is

$$N_{i \to f} = A(1 - \rho_f)(1 + \rho_i\rho_f + \rho_i^2\rho_f^2 + \cdots)$$
$$= A(1 - \rho_f)/(1 - \rho_i\rho_f) \tag{7.14}$$

But by definition

$$\varkappa = \frac{N_{i \to f}}{N_{l \to r}} = \frac{(1 - \rho_i)(1 - \rho_f)}{(1 - \rho_i\rho_f)} \tag{7.15}$$

It is true that the transmission coefficient for any one value of the energy cannot be expected to satisfy Eq. (7.15) in the case of a one-dimensional barrier. The average transmission coefficient for many systems with slightly different energies does fulfill the expectations of Eq. (7.15). From Eq. (7.15) it is evident that for x to approach unity both ρ_i and ρ_f must be small, i.e., very little probability exists that a system will be reflected back to the transition state from the

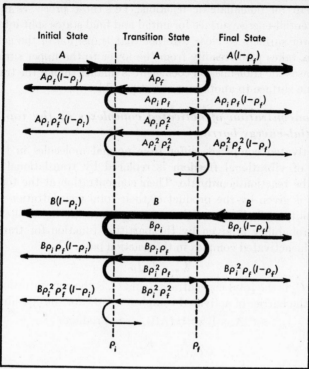

Figure 10 Diagram for calculating the transmission coefficient.

state which it enters upon crossing the transition state. The interchange of translational and vibrational energy affects the transmission coefficients in systems having several degrees of freedom. For rapid vibrational motion as compared with translational motion along the reaction path, the transmission coefficient will probably be of the order of unity. Eyring (*Chem. Rev.*, **17,** 65, 1935) states that for many reactions, especially simple ones, negligible error is made by assuming x to be unity.

The discussion of the frequency factor given above applies to adiabatic reactions, i.e., processes which take place on one potential energy surface. Glasstone, Laidler and Eyring (*The Theory of Rate Processes*, New York and London, McGraw-Hill Book Company, Inc., 1941) (with permission of the publishers) discuss also the transmission coefficient for nonadiabatic reactions, i.e., those processes in which the potential-energy surface for initial and final states split into upper and lower surfaces so close together that transition of the activated complex takes place readily from the lower to the upper surface. In these cases the transmission coefficient is smaller than if the transition from one surface to another were not possible.

The concentration of activated complexes at the top of the potential-energy barrier

The activated complexes differ from normal molecules in that one degree of vibrational freedom is replaced by translational motion along the reaction coordinate. Their concentration at the top of the barrier is given by the product of their total concentration and the probability of finding an activated complex at the top of the barrier. This probability is given by the partition function for translation, f_{tr}, of the activated complex in the reaction path. Thus

$$C'_* = C_* f_{tr} \tag{7.16}$$

Where C_* is the total concentration and C'_* is the concentration at the top of the barrier of activated complexes. Now for the equilibrium

$$A + B \rightleftharpoons (AB)_* \longrightarrow \text{Products}$$

$$\frac{C_*}{C_A C_B} = K_* \tag{7.17}$$

Where K_* is the equilibrium constant for the activation, and

$$C_* = K_* C_A C_B \tag{7.18}$$

Hence

$$C'_* = K_* C_A C_B f_{tr} \tag{7.19}$$

Therefore C'_* can be found if K_* and f_{tr} can be calculated. Now the equilibrium of the activated complex is treated as a true thermodynamic equilibrium, and therefore the free energy of activation is given by

$$\Delta F = -RT \ln K_* \tag{7.20}$$

or

$$K_* = e^{-\frac{\Delta F}{RT}} = e^{\frac{\Delta S}{R}} e^{-\frac{\Delta H}{RT}} \tag{7.21}$$

For reactions in solution $P \Delta V$ is usually very small, and $\Delta H = \Delta E$, hence for solutions

$$K_* = e^{\frac{\Delta S}{R}} e^{-\frac{\Delta E}{RT}} \tag{7.22}$$

Now turning to f_{tr}, if g is the degeneracy (statistical weight or *a priori* probability) of a quantum state, then the probability of an atom having energy ϵ in that quantum state is proportional to $ge^{-\epsilon/kT}$. The total probability of the occurrence of a particular atomic or molecular species, that is, the relative number of that species in a given volume is proportional to the sum of the $ge^{-\epsilon/kT}$ terms. That sum is called the *partition function* for the species concerned and for translation is given by

$$f_{tr} = \sum g_{tr} e^{-\frac{\epsilon_{tr}}{kT}} \tag{7.23}$$

where the *tr* subscript refers to motion of translation. Each type of energy likewise has its appropriate term. Here, however, we are interested in evaluating the partition function of translation f_{tr} of the activated complex in the direction of reaction.

Now the translational energy levels are so closely spaced that the energy may be regarded as continuous, and integration may be substituted for the summation indicated in Eq. (7.23). Also g_{tr} may be exchanged for dn, the number of levels in the energy range $d\epsilon_{tr}$. The integration to be performed is therefore

$$f_{tr} = \int_0^\infty e^{-\frac{\epsilon_{tr}}{kT}} \tag{7.24}$$

Let us keep in mind that we are striving to obtain an absolute value of the specific reaction rate constant k' and to do so we must derive methods of calculating $\varkappa$, C'_*, and $\bar{v}$. We have already discussed $\varkappa$ and are now engaged in evaluating C'_*. This quantity was shown to be given by Eq. (7.19). K_* of this equation has been evaluated in a simple manner and has been shown to be expressed for reactions in solution by Eq. (7.22). Now we are occupied with the determination of f_{tr} from Eq. (7.19). Once this quantity is known, C'_* will be calculable since C_A and C_B can always be determined. However, before f_{tr} can be obtained by integration of Eq. (7.24), the number of energy levels in the energy range $d\epsilon_{tr}$ must be evaluated. This can be done by solving the problem of quantization of the translational energy of a particle in a box. For a single particle in the box represented in Fig. 11, the potential energy v is zero. Now if the particle has a mass m and obeys the wave equation, the equation

$$-\frac{h^2}{8\pi^2 m}\left(\frac{\partial^2\psi}{\partial x^2} + \frac{\partial^2\psi}{\partial y^2} + \frac{\partial^2\psi}{\partial z^2}\right) = (E - v)\psi = E\psi \qquad (7.25)$$

holds. In this equation ψ is a function of x, y, and z, and h is Planck's constant. To separate variables, ψ is written

$$\psi = X(x)Y(y)Z(z) = XYZ \qquad (7.26)$$

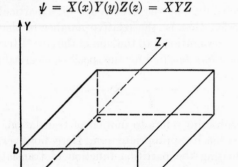

Figure 11 Rectangular box containing the gaseous particle.

where X is a function of x only, Y is a function of y only, and Z is a function of z only. From Eq. (7.25)

$$\frac{-h^2}{8\pi^2 m}\frac{1}{\psi}\left(\frac{\partial^2\psi}{\partial x^2} + \frac{\partial^2\psi}{\partial y^2} + \frac{\partial^2\psi}{\partial z^2}\right) = E \qquad (7.27)$$

and from Eq. (7.26)

$$\frac{\partial^2\psi}{\partial x^2} = YZ\frac{\partial^2 X}{\partial x^2};\ \frac{\partial^2\psi}{\partial y^2} = XZ\frac{\partial^2 Y}{\partial y^2};\ \frac{\partial^2\psi}{\partial z^2} = XY\frac{\partial^2 Z}{\partial z^2} \qquad (7.28)$$

Substituting ψ from Eq. (7.26) and the second partials of ψ from Eq. (7.28) into Eq. (7.25) gives

$$E = \frac{-h^2}{8\pi^2 m}\left(\frac{1}{X}\frac{\partial^2 X}{\partial x^2} + \frac{1}{Y}\frac{\partial^2 Y}{\partial y^2} + \frac{1}{Z}\frac{\partial^2 Z}{\partial z^2}\right) \qquad (7.29)$$

Now since X is a function of x alone, Y is a function of y alone, and Z is a function of z alone, terms involving either coordinate will be independent of the other two coordinates. Therefore

$$E = E_x + E_y + E_z \qquad (7.30)$$

where

$$E_x = \frac{-h^2}{8\pi^2 m}\left(\frac{1}{X}\frac{\partial^2 X}{\partial x^2}\right) \tag{7.31}$$

and similarly for E_y and E_z. The general solution for X is

$$X = C \sin (Ax + B) \tag{7.32}$$

where A, B, and C are constants, and to evaluate these it must be realized that the probability of finding the particle in the walls of the box is zero. This amounts to making the potential (barrier) in the walls infinitely high. Thus $X = 0$ for $x = 0$ and for $x = a$. These conditions are met only if

$$A = \frac{n_x \pi}{a}, \text{ and } B = 0 \tag{7.33}$$

where n_x is an integer. Eq. (7.32) therefore becomes

$$X = C \sin \frac{n_x \pi}{a} x \tag{7.34}$$

From Eq. (7.34)

$$\frac{\partial^2 X}{\partial x^2} = -\frac{n_x^2 \pi^2}{a^2} C \sin \frac{n_x \pi}{a} x \tag{7.35}$$

and dividing Eq. (7.35) by Eq. (7.34)

$$\frac{1}{X}\frac{\partial^2 X}{\partial x^2} = -\frac{n_x^2 \pi^2}{a^2} \tag{7.36}$$

and from Eq. (7.31) and (7.36)

$$E_x = \frac{n_x^2 h^2}{8a^2 m} \tag{7.37}$$

and letting $E_x = \epsilon_{tr}$ for the complex and dividing by kT gives

$$\frac{\epsilon_{tr}}{kT} = \frac{n^2 h^2}{8a^2 mkT} = n^2 L \tag{7.38}$$

where

$$L = \frac{h^2}{8a^2 mkT} = \text{a constant} \tag{7.39}$$

Thus from Eq. (7.24) and (7.39)

$$f_{tr} = \int_0^\infty e^{-n^2 L} dn \tag{7.40}$$

Eq. (7.40) represents a normal distribution function over a number of energy levels. Therefore

$$e^{-x^2} e^{-y^2} = e^{-(x^2+y^2)} = e^{-r^2} \tag{7.41}$$

where x and y are cartesian coordinates and r is the radius of the circle. (See Fig. 12.) The integral to be evaluated is then

$$\int_{x=-\infty}^{x=\infty} \int_{y=-\infty}^{y=\infty} e^{-(x^2+y^2)} dx\, dy = \left[\int_{-\infty}^{\infty} e^{-x^2}\, dx\right]^2 \tag{7.42}$$

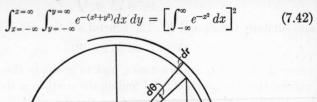

Figure 12 Diagrammatic representation of x, y, r, θ, dr and $d\theta$.

since $x = y$. This can be also written as

$$\left[\int_{-\infty}^{\infty} e^{-x^2}\, dx\right]^2 = \left[2\int_{0}^{\infty} e^{-x^2}\, dx\right]^2 \tag{7.43}$$

Substituting polar coordinates $dx = dr$, $dy = rd\theta$, $x^2 + y^2 = r^2$,

$$\left[2\int_{0}^{\infty} e^{-x^2}\, dx\right]^2 = \int_{\theta=0}^{\theta=2\pi} \int_{r=0}^{r=\infty} e^{-r^2} r\, dr\, d\theta \tag{7.44}$$

Setting $v = r^2$ and $dv = 2r\, dr$, we have

$$\left[2\int_{0}^{\infty} e^{-x^2}\, dx\right]^2 = \tfrac{1}{2}\int_{0}^{2\pi} d\theta = \pi \tag{7.45}$$

Therefore

$$f_{tr} = \int_{0}^{\infty} e^{-n^2 L}\, dn = \int_{0}^{\infty} e^{-x^2 L}\, dx = \tfrac{1}{2}\sqrt{\frac{\pi}{L}} \tag{7.46}$$

Substituting the value for L from Eq. (7.39) into Eq. (7.46) gives

$$f_{tr} = \frac{(2\pi mkT)^{\frac{1}{2}}a}{h} \tag{7.47}$$

and inserting the value of K_* from Eq. (7.22) and the value of f_{tr} from Eq. (7.47) into Eq. (7.19) gives

$$C'_* = C_A C_B \frac{(2\pi mkT)^{\frac{1}{2}}a}{h}\, e^{\frac{\Delta S}{R}} e^{-\frac{\Delta E}{RT}} \tag{7.48}$$

It now remains for us to determine the mean velocity $\bar{v}$ with which the particles cross the potential energy barrier, and then we will have all the quantities given in Eq. (7.9) which are necessary to determine the specific velocity constant k'.

The mean velocity of crossing the barrier

This mean velocity is measured in one direction, namely, that of decomposition. Now the number of particles moving along the x-coordinate with a kinetic energy $\dfrac{m\dot{x}^2}{2}$ is proportional to the factor $e^{-\frac{m\dot{x}^2}{2kT}}$. The number moving along the y-coordinate with a kinetic energy $\dfrac{m\dot{y}^2}{2}$ is proportional to $e^{-\frac{m\dot{y}^2}{2kT}}$, and those moving along the z-coordinate with a kinetic energy $\dfrac{m\dot{z}^2}{2}$ is proportional to $e^{-\frac{m\dot{z}^2}{2kT}}$. In these factors $\dot{x} = v_x$, the velocity in the x-direction, etc. The number of particles having simultaneously components of motion with kinetic energies $\dfrac{m\dot{x}^2}{2}, \dfrac{m\dot{y}^2}{2}$, and $\dfrac{m\dot{z}^2}{2}$ along the x-, y-, and z-coordinates, respectively, is proportional to $\left(e^{-\frac{m\dot{x}^2}{2kT}}\right)\left(e^{-\frac{m\dot{y}^2}{2kT}}\right)\left(e^{-\frac{m\dot{z}^2}{2kT}}\right)$. The proportionality becomes an equality upon introducing a proportionality constant A, and if $\dot{x}, \dot{y}, \dot{z}$ are taken over a range the total number of particles can be expressed by the integration

$$\int dn = A \iiint e^{-\frac{m}{2}\left(\frac{\dot{x}^2 + \dot{y}^2 + \dot{z}^2}{kT}\right)} d\dot{x}\, d\dot{y}\, d\dot{z} \tag{7.49}$$

To evaluate A consider the total number of particles as given by the integration

$$n = A \left[\int_0^\infty e^{-\alpha \dot{x}^2} d\dot{x}\right]^3 \tag{7.50}$$

This will be true since the velocity components $\dot{x}, \dot{y}$, and $\dot{z}$ are equal in probability. In Eq. (7.50), α is a constant and is equal to $m/2kT$. The integration of Eq. (7.50) is carried out similarly to that of Eq. (7.43) and yields

$$n = A \left(\frac{2\pi kT}{m}\right)^{\frac{3}{2}} \tag{7.51}$$

Whence

$$A = n \left(\frac{m}{2\pi kT}\right)^{\frac{3}{2}} \tag{7.52}$$

Now the mean velocity is obtained by taking the sum of the products of the number of molecules having a given velocity v, by the velocity, and dividing by the total number of molecules. Expressed as an integral the mean velocity is

$$\bar{v} = \frac{A\int_0^\infty \int_{-\infty}^\infty \int_{-\infty}^\infty v e^{-\frac{m}{2}\left(\frac{\dot{x}^2 + \dot{y}^2 + \dot{z}^2}{kT}\right)} \, d\dot{x}\, d\dot{y}\, d\dot{z}}{n} \qquad (7.53)$$

$$\bar{v} = \left(\frac{m}{2\pi kT}\right)^{\frac{3}{2}}\left(\frac{2\pi kT}{m}\right)\int_0^\infty \dot{x}\, e^{-\frac{m\dot{x}^2}{2kT}} \, d\dot{x} \qquad (7.54)$$

In the x-direction, $\dot{x}$ is taken between the limits zero and infinity instead of between the limits minus infinity and plus infinity, because in the coordinate of decomposition the molecules can move only in one direction if they are to form products and remain as such. Substituting for $\frac{m\dot{x}^2}{2kT}$, $\sqrt{\frac{m}{2kT}}\,\dot{x}$, and $\sqrt{\frac{m}{2kT}}\,d\dot{x}$, q^2, q, and dq, respectively, in Eq. (7.54) gives

$$\bar{v} = \left(\frac{2kT}{\pi m}\right)^{\frac{1}{2}}\int_0^\infty q e^{-q^2}\, dq = \frac{1}{2}\left(\frac{2kT}{\pi m}\right)^{\frac{1}{2}} = \left(\frac{kT}{2\pi m}\right)^{\frac{1}{2}} \qquad (7.55)$$

It now becomes possible to set up an equation for the specific reaction rate constant in terms of quantities obtainable from semiempirical, or theoretical considerations.

The equation for the specific reaction rate constant

Let the transmission coefficient still be represented by $\varkappa$, though a means of evaluating it based on probability consideration has been discussed. This is probably the best way to insert the transmission coefficient since it is generally estimated empirically anyway. Take the value of the distance a in Eq. (7.48) to be the same as the value of distance δ in Eq. (7.9). Then inserting the value of C'_* from Eq. (7.48) and of $\bar{v}$ from Eq. (7.55) into Eq. (7.9) gives for the specific reaction rate constant the expression

$$k' = \varkappa \frac{C_A C_B \frac{(2\pi m kT)^{\frac{1}{2}}}{h}\delta e^{\frac{\Delta S}{R}} e^{-\frac{\Delta E}{RT}}}{C_A C_B}\frac{1}{\delta}\left(\frac{kT}{2\pi m}\right)^{\frac{1}{2}}$$

$$= \varkappa \frac{kT}{h} e^{\frac{\Delta S}{R}} e^{-\frac{\Delta E}{RT}} \qquad (7.56)$$

which is Eyring's equation in simple form. It is seen that under the assumption $a = \delta$ made above, this distance drops out of the final result.

In many cases the equilibrium constant K_* is not written as simply as in Eq. (7.21) but is written to include the partition functions of the complex and the reactant molecules instead of the entropy term, which involves the ratio of probabilities of complex and reactant states. Glasstone, Laidler and Eyring (*The Theory of Rate Processes*, New York, McGraw-Hill Book Co., Inc., 1941) (with permission of the publishers) write for K_* where the concentration units are in molecules per unit volume the expression

$$K_* = \frac{F_*}{F_A F_B} e^{-\frac{\Delta E_0}{RT}} \tag{7.57}$$

where ΔE_0 is the energy of activation of the reaction at $0°$ K, ΔE_0 is also the ordinary energy of activation of the reaction, assuming this energy to be independent of the temperature. Thus Eq. (7.56) becomes

$$k' = \varkappa \frac{kT}{h} \frac{F_*}{F_A F_B \cdots} e^{-\frac{\Delta E_0}{RT}} \tag{7.58}$$

where F_*, F_A, F_B, $\cdots$, are the partition functions of the species indicated by the subscripts, e.g., F_* is the partition function of the activated complex. These partition functions F_*, F_A, and F_B become very complex when translational, rotational, and vibrational degrees of freedom are included. However they are calculable from fundamental constants and specific properties of the molecules concerned. Thus, since ΔE_0 is obtainable semiempirically, an absolute rate may be calculated.

Let us imagine the case of two atoms A and B of masses m_A and m_B and collision diameters σ_A and σ_B colliding to give the activated molecule $(AB)_*$. The atoms would each have three degrees of translational freedom, while the molecule will have three degrees of translational and two degrees of rotational freedom. An ordinary diatomic molecule would have in addition one degree of vibrational freedom, but since a molecule can have only $3n$ energy variables (where n is the number of atoms in a molecule), and since the complex is assumed to have an additional degree of translational freedom along the reaction path, the degree of vibrational freedom is assumed to be absent from the complex and replaced by the translational degree of freedom just mentioned. Now if the three translational and the three rotational degrees (of A and B) are assumed to be equivalent, the partition function of the three particles can be shown to be

$$F_A = \frac{(2\pi m_A kT)^{\frac{3}{2}}}{h^3} \tag{7.59}$$

$$F_B = \frac{(2\pi m_B kT)^{\frac{3}{2}}}{h^3} \tag{7.60}$$

and

$$F_* = \frac{(2\pi(m_A + m_B)kT)^{\frac{3}{2}}}{h^3} \frac{8\pi^2 IkT}{h^2} \tag{7.61}$$

where the moment of inertia I of the complex is given by the expression

$$I = \sigma_{AB}^2 \frac{m_A m_B}{m_A + m_B} \tag{7.62}$$

In this equation σ_{AB} is the distance between the centers of atoms A and B in the activated complex $(AB)_*$.

Inserting these values of F_A, F_B, and F_* into Eq. (7.58) yields

$$k' = \kappa \sigma_{AB}^2 \left(\frac{8\pi RT(M_A + M_B)}{M_A M_B} \right)^{\frac{1}{2}} e^{-\frac{\Delta E_0}{RT}} \tag{7.63}$$

where R is the gas constant per mole and the M terms are molecular weights and are equal to the products mN, N being the Avogadro number. This equation is identical with that given by the collision hypothesis. However, inclusion of rotational and vibrational contribution to the partition functions will not lead to the same final results as for this reaction where two atoms are reacting to give diatomic molecules. Hence there is not in more general cases the same correspondence between the absolute and collision rate theories as is given by the reaction between two atoms to give a diatomic molecular complex. (See Glasstone, *Textbook of Physical Chemistry*, New York D. Van Nostrand Company, 1940, p. 1080 (from which this brief mention is taken with the consent of the publishers) for a fuller discussion of the comparison of the two theories.) Since

$$\Delta F = -RT \ln K_* \tag{7.64}$$

and since for reactions in solution

$$\Delta S = \frac{\Delta H - \Delta F}{T} = \frac{\Delta E - \Delta F}{T} \tag{7.65}$$

therefore, if ΔE and K_* can be obtained from semiempirical and/or theoretical considerations, then Eq. (7.64) and (7.65) allow the calculation of ΔS, and with quantities then known, Eq. (7.56) allows the calculation of an absolute reaction rate.

In the case of reactions taking place in solution, Eq. (7.58) may be modified to include terms which allow for the influence of the medium

These terms will occur in the partition functions of the activated complex and of the reactant species and will therefore be included in K_*. Thus

$$k' = \varkappa \frac{kT}{h} K_*^0 \frac{f_A f_B}{f_*} \tag{7.66}$$

where f_A, f_B, and f_* are activity coefficients of the species indicated by the subscripts and take into account the effects of the solvents, and where K_*^0 is written in terms of activities instead of concentrations. For systems involving ideal gases the activity coefficients f_A, f_B, and f_* which account for the effects of the solvent are unity, and Eq. (7.66) is identical with Eq. (7.58).

Comparing Eq. (7.56) with the Arrhenius equation (Eq. 1.60), Z of the latter equation must be given by the relationship

$$Z = \varkappa \frac{kT}{h} e^{\frac{\Delta S}{R}} \tag{7.67}$$

Now for unimolecular reactions Z is in many cases of the order of magnitude of 10^{13}. In these reactions $\varkappa$ is often unity and ΔS is zero. Therefore Z becomes identifiable with $\frac{kT}{h}$. For 25° C, $\frac{kT}{h}$ is equal to $6.23 \times 10,^{12}$ which is in satisfactory agreement with the expected value of Z.

The activity coefficients, for those unimolecular reactions where the reactant molecules and also the activated complex form ideal solution in the solvent, will cancel out thus

$$k_r' = K_*^0 \frac{f_A}{f_*} \frac{kT}{h} = K_*^0 \frac{kT}{h} \tag{7.68}$$

and the reaction will proceed at the same rate as it would were the species concerned in the gaseous state. Thus Eyring and Daniels (*J. Am. Chem. Soc.*, **52**, 1472, 1930) find f_A/f_* for the decomposition of N_2O_5 in saturated solutions of the solvents nitromethane, carbon tetrachloride, and liquid N_2O_4 to be 1.71, 2.32, and 2.01, respectively. These values are obtained by taking the ratios of the specific rate constants in the respective solvents to the rate constant in the gas phase. These data are taken from Table V of the paper by Eyring and Daniels. Wynne-Jones and Eyring (*J. Chem. Phys.*, **3**, 493, 1935) point out that these values for the f_A/f_* ratio indicate that the activated complex has the same vapor pressure as that of a practically normal molecule. Since we know the actual rate of reaction, and the heat of activation has been determined, the theoretical equation allows the calculation of the entropy of activation. In the gas phase the experimental results can be represented by the equation

$$k' = 5.08 \times 10^{13} e^{-\frac{24,700}{RT}} \tag{7.69}$$

If x is taken as unity, which it probably will be for this reaction since it is unimolecular, then

$$\frac{kT}{h} e^{\frac{\Delta S}{R}} = 5.08 \times 10^{13} \tag{7.70}$$

from which ΔS is found to be 4.27, which is about a normal value for unimolecular reactions.

The theory of absolute reaction rates has been applied to many types of reactions with promising results.

CHAPTER VIII

Reactions between ions and dipolar molecules and between dipolar molecules and dipolar molecules

Necessity of kinetic equations for ion-dipole and for dipole-dipole reactions

In Chapter IV was given the derivation of an equation (Eq. 4.28) which for ionic reactants gave the dependence of the reaction rate upon the dielectric constant of the solvent and also upon the charge types and concentrations of the reactants and other ionic solutes. In Chapter V the equation was enlarged to contain a term which gave the temperature dependence of the reaction rate. This temperature dependence term is general for all types of reactants and will be included in kinetic equations for rates between reactants irrespective of whether they are charged ions, dipolar molecules, nonpolar molecules, or any combination of these. Equations similar to that for ions and which express the concentration and dielectric effect upon ion-dipole and upon dipole-dipole reactions are available (Amis and Jaffé, *J. Chem. Phys.*, **10**, 598, 1942; Laidler and Eyring, *Ann. New York Acad. Sci.*, **39**, 299, 1940). In this chapter a derivation of these equations together with their experimental verification will be given.

The potential for the exterior of the dipole

To derive the equation of Amis and Jaffé we must first obtain the potential ψ_0 in the neighborhood of any one dipolar molecule. For the atmosphere around a dipolar molecule we shall disregard the interaction between dipoles; then the differential equation for the potential ψ_0 will be the same as for the potential around an ion. The difference between the two problems is only with regard to the boundary conditions at the surface of the molecule.

For s different species of ions, n_i the number of the species i per cubic centimeter, and z_i the valence of species i, then as in the case for the potential around an ion, we have

$$\nabla^2 \psi_0 = \varkappa^2 \psi_0 \tag{8.1}$$

when ψ_0 is small and when $\varkappa$ is defined by Eq. (2.8).

If we treat the dipole as a point singularity, we obtain a particular solution of Eq. (8.1) by polarizing the solution of Debye and Hückel for the case of an ion (Eq. 2.26); this is

$$\psi_0 = \frac{C_1 e^{-\varkappa r}}{r} \tag{8.2}$$

Let the position of the dipole coincide with the origin and its direction with the positive z-axis. Let, also, the idealized dipole be represented by a sphere of radius a. Then for $r \geq a$, a solution having the same dependence as a dipole potential is obtained by differentiating Eq. (8.2) partially with respect to z. Thus

$$\frac{\partial \psi}{\partial z} = \frac{\partial \psi}{\partial r} \frac{\partial r}{\partial z} \tag{8.3}$$

but

$$r^2 = x^2 + y^2 + z^2 \tag{8.4}$$

and

$$\frac{\partial r}{\partial z} = \frac{z}{r} = \cos \theta \tag{8.5}$$

also

$$\frac{\partial \psi}{\partial z} = \frac{- C_1 e^{-\varkappa r}}{r^2} (1 + \varkappa r) \frac{dr}{dz} \tag{8.6}$$

Therefore

$$\psi_0 = \frac{C_1 e^{-\varkappa r}}{r^2} (1 + \varkappa r) \cos \theta, \, r \geq a \tag{8.7}$$

Kirkwood (*J. Chem. Phys.*, **2,** 351, 1934) has solved the problem for the potential of a particle with the most general distribution of charge. The solution (Eq. 8.7) of the very special case considered above has also been given by Bateman, Church, Hughes, Ingold, and Taher (*J. Chem. Soc.*, **1940,** 979).

Potential for the interior of the dipole

Holding D constant for the interior of a dipole molecule and following the Debye-Hückel procedure we might obtain the potential, ψ_i, for the interior of the molecule from the equation

$$\nabla^2 \psi_i = 0, \, r \leq a \tag{8.8}$$

ψ in this domain must be continuous except for a singularity at the origin corresponding to a dipole of a given strength. This procedure gives a reasonable formula for the ionic atmosphere; however the dipoles must be chosen of the order 10×10^{-18}, i.e., about five times too large, to make the formula reproduce experimental kinetic data. Evidently the procedure does not properly account for some influential electrostatic forces, probably those having to do with the interaction of the dipole and the dielectric solvent.

Onsager (*J. Am. Chem. Soc.*, **58**, 1486, 1936) has shown that any one immersed dipole acts upon distant charges with an *external moment* different from its moment in vacuo. The medium modifies both the action of the permanent and induced dipole moments. The necessary step then is to combine the Debye-Hückel theory of ionic atmospheres with the Onsager model of a dipole immersed in a dielectric liquid.

As did Onsager, we shall assume a spherically shaped molecule characterized by its permanent moment μ_0 (in vacuo) and its polarizability α, where α is related to an internal refractive index n by the equation

$$\alpha = \frac{n^2 - 1}{n^2 + 2}\, a^3 \tag{8.9}$$

Now we must solve the problem of joining a solution of Eq. (8.8) having a dipole singularity at $r = 0$ to our solution Eq. (8.7) in the proper way at $r = a$. To do this we must determine the external characteristic moment μ_*^* such as it becomes under the action of the polarization created by itself.

Suppose first a rigid dipole of moment m is introduced into a cavity of radius a. For the exterior the solution for the potential given by Eq. (8.7) is to hold. For the interior the solution for the potential is

$$\psi_i = \left(\frac{m}{r^2} + Br \right) \cos\theta, \; r \leq a \tag{8.10}$$

where B is a constant.

The potential of the ionic atmosphere around the dipolar molecules

Constants A and B are determined for the usual boundary conditions of the electrostatic field, that is, by setting $\psi_i = \psi_0$ and $\dfrac{\partial \psi_i}{\partial r} = \dfrac{\partial \psi_0}{\partial r}$.

This gives

$$\frac{C_1 e^{-\varkappa a}}{a^2} (1 + \varkappa a) = \frac{m}{a^2} + Ba \tag{8.11}$$

and

$$\frac{DC_1 e^{-\varkappa a}}{a^3} (2 + 2\varkappa a + \varkappa^2 a^2) = \frac{2m}{a^3} - B \tag{8.12}$$

and hence

$$C_1 = \frac{3m e^{\varkappa a}}{D(2 + 2\varkappa a + \varkappa^2 a^2) + (1 + \varkappa a)} \tag{8.13}$$

and

$$B = -\frac{m}{a^3} \frac{[D(2 + 2\varkappa a + \varkappa^2 a^2) - 2(1 + \varkappa a)]}{[D(2 + 2\varkappa a + \varkappa^2 a^2) + (1 + \varkappa a)]} \tag{8.14}$$

We must now determine m as a function of μ_0 and n^2. Onsager gives the condition for internal equilibrium in the relationship

$$m = \mu_0 + \alpha F_z \tag{8.15}$$

where F_z is the force acting on the dipole owing to the polarization created by itself. In words Eq. (8.15) says that the total electric moment m of a molecule in an electric field F is the sum of the permanent moment μ_0, and the induced moment αF_z.

The local field, F_z, is

$$F_z = -\frac{\partial}{\partial z} \left[\psi_i - \frac{m \cos \theta}{r^2} \right] \tag{8.16}$$

This gives

$$F_z = -B \tag{8.17}$$

and from Eq. (8.9), (8.15), and (8.17)

$$m = \mu_0 - \frac{n^2 - 1}{n^2 + 2} a^3 B \tag{8.18}$$

and substituting the value of B from Eq. (8.14) into Eq. (8.18), transposing, and solving for m gives

$$m = \mu_0 \frac{[n^2 + 2][D(2 + 2\varkappa a + \varkappa^2 a^2) + (1 + \varkappa a)]}{3[D(2 + 2\varkappa a + \varkappa^2 a^2) + n^2(1 + \varkappa a)]} \tag{8.19}$$

This value of m written into Eq. (8.13) makes it possible to write the expression for the potential of the ionic atmosphere around a dipolar molecule of moment μ_0 as follows,

$$\psi_0 = \frac{\mu^* e^{-\varkappa r} (1 + \varkappa r)}{Dr^2} \cos \theta \tag{8.20}$$

where μ^* the *external moment* of the molecule in the dielectric solvent is given by

$$\mu^* = \frac{\mu_0(n^2+2)De^{\varkappa a}}{D(2 + 2\varkappa a + \varkappa^2 a^2) + n^2(1 + \varkappa a)} \tag{8.21}$$

When $\varkappa = 0$, i.e., in the absence of an ionic atmosphere this solution and the corresponding one for ψ_i reduce, as they should, to Onsager's solution.

For $n^2 = 1$, Eq. (8.20) and (8.21) represent the simplified case where the molecule has a permanent dipole but no polarizability.

The kinetic equation

The kinetic equation for the rate of formation of an intermediate complex X from a dipolar molecule A of moment μ_0 and an ion B of charge ϵz_B will now be calculated from the potential given in Eq. (8.20). We will follow the procedure of Christiansen and Scatchard, remembering, however, that the potential depends on θ as well as on r.

Let C_X, C_A, and C_B be the concentrations of X, A, and B, respectively, and let us introduce r, θ, and ϕ as polar coordinates about the center of dipole A. The probability of finding an ion B in a specified element of volume defined by the limits r and $r + dr$, θ and $\theta + d\theta$, and ϕ and $\phi + d\phi$ will by Boltzmann's theorem be proportional to

$$C_A C_B e^{-\frac{\psi_0 \epsilon z_B}{kT}} r^2 \sin\theta\, dr\, d\theta\, d\phi \tag{8.22}$$

To obtain the rate of formation of X, and hence the velocity of the reaction, we must establish some criterion for the formation of X. This can be done in either of two ways. (a) We can assume sensitive zones on the exterior of the molecule and further assume that whenever one of these areas is touched by the ion B, formation of X ensues. (b) We can assume that there is from each direction a critical distance of approach of ion B to molecule A in order for X to be produced. Let us follow the first alternative which means that r, θ, and ϕ must assume specified values between comparatively narrow limits r_0 and $r_0 + \Delta r_0$, θ_0 and $\theta_0 + \Delta\theta_0$, ϕ_0 and $\phi_0 + \Delta\phi_0$.

For the case of rotational symmetry about the z-axis, ϕ need not be specified, and Eq. (8.22) can be integrated with respect to ϕ, giving 2π. If the proportionality constant be taken as k', then

$$C_X = 2k' C_A C_B r_0^2 \sin\theta\, \Delta r_0\, \Delta\theta_0 e^{-\frac{\psi_0 \epsilon z_B}{kT}} \tag{8.23}$$

and setting

$$K = 2k' r_0^2 \sin\theta_0\, \Delta r_0\, \Delta\theta_0 \tag{8.24}$$

Equation (8.23) becomes

$$\ln \frac{C_X}{C_A C_B} = \ln K - \frac{\epsilon z_B \psi_0(r_0, \theta_0)}{kT} \tag{8.25}$$

But the value of ψ_0 is given by Eq. (8.20) and this for $\varkappa = 0$, is

$$\psi_0 = \frac{\mu_0^*}{D r_0^2} \cos \theta \tag{8.26}$$

Where μ_0^* is Onsager's value and for $\varkappa = 0$ is from Eq. (8.21)

$$\mu_0^* = \frac{\mu_0(n^2 + 2)D}{2D + n^2} \tag{8.27}$$

From Eq. (8.25) and (8.26)

$$\ln \frac{C_X^0}{C_A^0 C_B^0} = \ln K - \frac{\epsilon z_B \mu_0^* \cos \theta}{DkT r_0^2} \tag{8.28}$$

We thus have

$$\ln \frac{f_A f_B}{f_X} = \ln \frac{C_X}{C_A C_B} - \ln \frac{C_X^0}{C_A^0 C_B^0} = \frac{\epsilon z_B \cos \theta}{DkT r_0^2} [\mu_0^* - \mu^* e^{-\varkappa a}(1 + \varkappa a)]$$

$$= \frac{\epsilon z_B \cos \theta}{DkT r_0^2} \left[\frac{(n^2 + 2)D}{2D + n^2} - \frac{(1 + \varkappa a)(n^2 + 2)D}{D(2 + 2\varkappa a + \varkappa^2 a^2) + n^2(1 + \varkappa a)} \right] \tag{8.29}$$

Transforming Eq. (8.29) by substituting μ_0 in terms of μ_0^* we obtain

$$\ln \frac{f_A f_B}{f_X} = \frac{\epsilon z_B \mu_0^* \cos \theta}{DkT r_0^2} \left[\frac{D \varkappa^2 a^2}{2D \left(1 + \varkappa a + \dfrac{\varkappa^2 a^2}{2} \right) + n^2(1 + \varkappa a)} \right] \tag{8.30}$$

Now

$$k' = k_0' \frac{f_A f_B}{f_X} \tag{8.31}$$

and

$$\ln k' = \ln k_0' + \ln \frac{f_A f_B}{f_X} \tag{8.32}$$

therefore from Eq. (8.30) and (8.32)

$$\ln k' = \ln k_0' + \frac{\epsilon z_B \mu_0^* \cos \theta}{DkT r_0^2} \left[\frac{D \varkappa^2 a^2}{2D \left(1 + \varkappa a + \dfrac{\varkappa^2 a^2}{2} \right) + n^2(1 + \varkappa a)} \right] \tag{8.33}$$

This can be written as

$$\frac{\ln k' - \ln k_0'}{\epsilon z_B \mu_0^* \cos \theta / 2DkT r_0^2} = W = \frac{\varkappa^2 a^2}{1 + \varkappa a + \dfrac{\varkappa^2 a^2}{2} + \dfrac{n^2}{2D}(1 + \varkappa a)} \tag{8.34}$$

Choosing the second alternative, Eq. (8.22) must be integrated to give the resultant probability of formation of X. In the most general case, the critical distance will be a function of θ and ϕ, and this functional relation constitutes the *shape of the molecular dipole*. For ψ_0 to be valid as the potential throughout, r must be greater than a. After Eq. (8.22) is integrated, the further procedure follows the same lines as above.

If r is assumed constant, i.e., between r_0 and $r_0 + \Delta r_0$, and if θ is unrestricted, the ion must approach, *in all directions,* the same critical distance r_0. For a dipole this would not be expected to be the case, and this assumption leads to the wrong sign for the dependence of k' on concentration and dielectric constant. It is better to assume that the critical surface is a prolonged spheroid with the dipole in one of the foci directed along the long axis. The results of such calculations, restricted to weak potentials (as in the derivation of Debye's Eq. 8.1), are similar to those for Eq. (8.33) and coincide with Eq. (8.33) for $\varkappa$ small. The only difference is that $\cos \theta$ is replaced by ϵ', the eccentricity of the spheroid. This indicates that the results may be chosen with the required sign depending on whether the positive or negative end of the dipole is nearer the surface.

A weakness of the spheroid calculations is that the spheroid would partake of the heat motion with rotations. These rotations would be of such a high frequency that the ionic atmosphere, owing to its relatively long time of relaxation, would not be able to follow them. These calculations do, however, indicate that θ_0 and r_0 may be chosen as *critical average values*. It is in this sense that they are used in Eq. (8.33). In Eq. (8.33), $\cos \theta$ is chosen as $+1$ for the equation to agree with empirical data, i.e., for $\ln k'$ to increase with an increase of $1/D$ for positive ions and vice versa for negative ions. This means, in the spheroidal model, that the negative charge of the dipole must be nearer the surface if the ion is positive. Furthermore, we shall let the critical distance r_0 coincide with the radius a.

Adaptation of the equation for practical use

Using Eq. (8.20), (8.25), and (8.28), Eq. (8.33) can be written

$$\ln k' = \ln k'_{\varkappa = 0} + \frac{\epsilon z_\mathrm{B} \cos \theta_0}{DkT r_0^2}\left(\mu_0^* - \frac{\mu^*(1 + \varkappa r_0)}{e^{\varkappa r_0}}\right) \qquad (8.35)$$

In Eq. (8.35) since $\mu_0^* > \dfrac{\mu^*(1 + \varkappa r^0)}{e^{\varkappa r_0}}$ and since the term $\mu^*(1 + \varkappa r_0)/$

$e^{\varkappa r_0}$ decreases at a decreasing rate while μ_0^* remains constant with increasing ionic strength, then for positive ionic reactants (z_B positive), k' should increase with decreasing rate as the ionic strength is increased. For negative ionic reactants, however, k' should decrease with decreasing rate as ionic strength increases. Also k' should increase, but to a progressively less extent, with decreasing dielectric constant of the medium for positive ion reactants, since although the term μ_0^*/D increases, $\mu_-^*(1 + \varkappa r_0)/e^{\varkappa r_0} D$ decreases faster proportionally with decreasing dielectric constant. For negative ion reactants, k' should decrease with decreasing rate as the dielectric constant decreases.

Taking the dimensionless quantity

$$z = \varkappa a = \varkappa r_0 \tag{8.36}$$

and the dimensionless quantity

$$W = \frac{(\ln k' - \ln k'_{\varkappa=0}) 2DkTr_0^2}{\epsilon z_B \mu_0^* \cos\theta} \tag{8.37}$$

we can write Eq. (8.34) in the form

$$W = \frac{z^2}{1 + z + z^2/2 + (n^2/2D)(1 + z)} \tag{8.38}$$

This formula brings out the dependence of k' on concentration in a general way, and it is in this form that we will use the equation later when applying it to data.

In the case of ion-ion reactions it has proved successful to measure the dielectric constant dependence of k' from a point of reference defined by the double transition $\varkappa = 0$ and $D = \infty$. Such double transition in the case of ion-dipole reactions leads to a change in k' with $1/D$ opposite in sense to the change in k' with $\varkappa$. But data indicate that the change of k' should be in the same sense in both cases. In the case of ion-ion reactions the electric forces, attractions or repulsions, tend toward zero as D is increased indefinitely. However, the *external moment* of a dipolar molecule increases with increasing D, and though $\lim_{D=\infty} \mu_j^*$ exists, the point $D = \infty$ is certainly not an adequate point of reference, since it accentuates rather than eliminates the effect of D. For ion-dipole reactions, therefore, the point $\varkappa = 0$ can be interpreted as the ideal limiting case in which all electrostatic actions have disappeared. In any case we shall make the assumption that $\varkappa = 0$ is an adequate point of reference. Then Eq. (8.33) expresses the dependence of k' on both D and concentration.

Let us again introduce dimensionless variables. If we set

$$x^2 = \lambda^2/D \tag{8.39}$$

λ will be of the dimension cm^{-1}, but free of D.
Then if

$$\zeta = \lambda a = \lambda r_0 \tag{8.40}$$

and

$$W' = \frac{(\ln k' - \ln k'_{x=0})(2kT)}{\epsilon z_B \mu_0^* \lambda^2 \cos \theta} \tag{8.41}$$

We have the general relation

$$W' = \frac{1}{D^2} \frac{1}{1 + \zeta/D^{\frac{1}{2}} + \zeta^2/2D} \tag{8.42}$$

Equation (8.42) shows that in the limit $\lambda = 0$, W' will change as $1/D^2$. For larger concentrations the increase will become less and will depend on the parameter ζ.

It should be pointed out that both z^2 and ζ^2 are by their definitions (Eq. 8.36 and 8.40) proportional to the ionic strength.

Application of theory to dipolar-positive ion reactants

An application of this theory using Eq. (8.38) and (8.42) was made by Amis and Jaffé (*J. Chem. Phys.*, **10**, 598, 1942) for positive hydrogen ion reacting with sucrose, ethylene acetal, and glucose. The reactions involving sucrose and glucose were applied with respect to ionic strength upon ion-dipolar molecule reactions. In these tests the term $(n^2/2D)(1 + z)$ was omitted in Eq. (8.38) since this term is very small and has only slight influence on the theoretical curve, as can be seen in Fig. 1. (Amis and Jaffé, *loc. cit.*). In Fig. 1 of the reference referred to, the solid line is the theoretical curve for $n^2 = 0$ and the broken line that for $n^2 = 9$. Even these extreme values of n^2 do not cause a great variation in the plots.

In Fig. 1 given here are plotted on curve 1 the data of Fales and Morrell (*J. Am. Chem. Soc.*, **44**, 2071, 1922) for the inversion of sucrose in various concentrations of HCl and the data of Kautz and Robinson (*J. Am. Chem. Soc.*, **50**, 1022, 1928) for the inversion of sucrose in $0.1M$ HCl containing various concentrations of different salts. In curve 2 of Fig. 1 the part of curve 1 up to an ionic strength of 0.1 has been reproduced and enlarged. In curve 2 the data of Brönsted and Grove (*J. Am. Chem. Soc.*, **52**, 1397, 1930) for the hydrolysis of ethylene acetal by perchloric acid has also been plotted. Below about $0.01M$ C_{H^+}, the data of Fales and Morrell were omitted from the graph since they were inconsistent with the rest of the data. The data for Kautz and Robinson for the inversion of sucrose in the presence of NaCl show two points which are evidently in error.

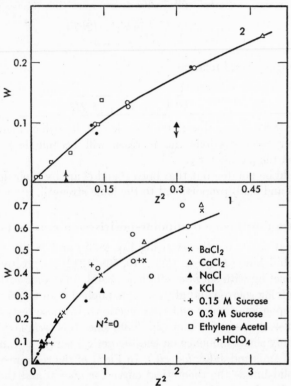

Figure 1   Plot of W versus Z^2 for sucrose inversion and ethylene acetal hydrolysis.

In column 2 of Table I are given r_0 values used in fitting the various data to the theoretical curves in Fig. 1. These values are reasonable and, in these cases, are the same for the same type of atmosphere. In column 3 of this table are given the modified moments calculated according to the equation

$$\mu_0^* = \frac{4.606 DkTr_0^2 \, \Delta \log k'}{\epsilon z_B \cos \theta \, \Delta W} \tag{8.43}$$

Column 4 contains the value of n^2 (the internal refractive index) necessary to reduce the modified moment to 3.4×10^{-18} in the case of sucrose (E. Landt, *Naturwiss*, **22**, 109, 1934) and to 4×10^{-18} (chosen arbitrarily since no value was found in the literature) in the case of acetal. Column 5 of this table gives an indication as to the value of the ionic strength to which this theory held for each charge type of ionic atmosphere. For sucrose inversion, when the atmosphere was made up of univalent ions, the theory held up to an ionic strength greater than 3, which is as far as the data extended. However, when there were bivalent ions in the atmosphere, the theory applied up to a value of the ionic strength of about 0.6. This is comparable to the case of reactions between ions where the presence of the higher valence ions in the ionic atmosphere causes a departure from theory at lower ionic strengths than is the case for an ionic atmosphere of univalent ions. For the hydrolysis of ethylene acetal the data extended only to an ionic strength of about 0.08.

TABLE I Constants used in plotting the curves of Fig. 1

(1) Substances	(2) $r_0(\text{Å})$	(3) $10^{18}\mu_0^*$	(4) n^2	(5) z^2 at ionic strength = 1 for curve 1	(6) $k_{x=0}$
Sucrose + HCl + BaCl$_2$	6.0	6.65	1.91	3.867	4.02×10^{-4}
Sucrose + HCl + CaCl$_2$	6.0	9.05	3.32	3.867	4.02×10^{-4}
Sucrose + HCl + KCl	2.5	14.0	6.24	0.670	3.95×10^{-4}
Sucrose + HCl + NaCl	2.5	10.5	4.18	0.670	4.30×10^{-4}
Sucrose (0.15M) + HCl	3.5	10.3	4.06	1.35	2.17×10^{-4}
Sucrose (0.3M) + HCl	3.5	7.15	2.21	1.35	2.16×10^{-4}
Ethylene acetal + HClO$_4$	4.0	18.6	7.3 ($\mu_0 = 4 \times 10^{-18}$)	1.70	4.15×10^{-1}

In the case of positive ion reactants the influence of the dielectric constant of the solvent upon the reaction rate can be illustrated by two sets of data. Amis and Holmes (*J. Am. Chem. Soc.*, **63**, 2231,

1941) have studied the inversion of $0.1000N$ HCl catalyzed sucrose in ethyl alcohol-water and in dioxane-water. The data for alcohol-water media were shown from energy considerations to be in opposition to the predictions of electrostatics and hence cannot be used to check this theory. The data for dioxane-water does illustrate the influence of the dielectric constant upon a reaction rate when electrostatic forces are the governing factors. Dyas and Hill (*J. Am. Chem. Soc.*, **64,** 236, 1942) investigated the mutarotation of glucose by HCl in methyl alcohol-water media. That part of the mutarotation brought about by oxonium ion meets the requirements of being an ion-dipole type of reaction and that part of the data is pertinent here. The results of these authors are reduced to unit normality.

In Fig. 2 are plotted the data of Amis and Holmes and of Dyas and Hill. The theoretical curve for $\zeta = 3.2$, corresponding to a value of r_0

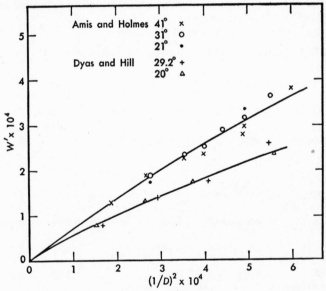

Figure 2   Plot of $W' \times 10^4$ versus $\dfrac{10^4}{D^2}$ for the inversion of sucrose and the mutarotation of glucose.

of about 3.5Å used in calculations on atmosphere effects, average the Amis and Holmes data very well except that the values for pure water as the solvent at 21° C and 31° C were omitted from the graph since they were so inconsistent with the rest of the data that they must be greatly in error. The Dyas and Hill data fitted the same line well but gave an r_0 value of only slightly greater than 1Å. The difference between 1.0Å and 3.5Å for the glucose-oxonium ion reaction as compared to the sucrose-oxonium ion reaction seemed rather large. Choosing, therefore, r_0 as 2.0Å gave the very satisfactory results shown by the curve for $\zeta = 6.0$ in Fig. 2.

TABLE II Constants used in plotting the curves of Fig. 2

Substances	r_0(Å)	$10^{18}\mu_0^*$	n^2	Temp. °C	$k_{\kappa=0}$
Sucrose + HCl	3.5	14.6	6.59	21	4.95×10^{-4}
Sucrose + HCl	3.5	14.7	6.65	31	2.00×10^{-3}
Sucrose + HCl	3.5	14.3	6.42	41	6.67×10^{-3}
Glucose + HCl	2.0	8.07	2.04 ($\mu_0 = 2 \times 10^{-18}$)	20	2.95×10^{-1}
Glucose + HCl	2.0	8.13	2.07 ($\mu_0 = 2 \times 10^{-18}$)	29.2	7.59×10^{-1}

In Table II, column 3, are given the modified moments calculated for sucrose and glucose molecules. The values of μ_0^* for sucrose are of the same order of magnitude and compare favorably in actual value with those obtained from concentration data of entirely different authors when the same value of r_0 is used in the two cases. Here an approximation $n^2/2D \ll 1$ is used and since the ratio μ_0^*/μ_0 depends only on n^2 this ratio should be independent of temperature. It is seen that, in accordance with this theory, the μ_0^* values for both sugars are consistent at the different temperatures.

In column 4 of Table II are given the values of n^2 required to make the moment of sucrose 3.4×10^{-18}, and that of glucose 2×10^{-18} (2×10^{-18} was chosen arbitrarily since a moment for glucose was not found in the literature). The values of n^2 for either molecule are consistent, and those values for sucrose compare favorably with values found by the rate dependence upon ionic strength.

Application to dipolar-negative ion reactants

This theory was tested by Amis, Jaffé and Overman (*J. Am. Chem. Soc.*, **66**, 1823, 1944) using the data of Åkerlöf (*J. Am. Chem. Soc.*, **48**, 3046, 1926; *ibid.*, **49**, 2960, 1927; *ibid.*, **50**, 1272, 1928) for the decomposition of diacetone alcohol by the negative hydroxide ion. Åkerlöf studied the reaction in various alkali metal hydroxides alone and in the presence of their uni-univalent and uni-bivalent salts. He also studied the same reaction using sodium hydroxide in various mixed solvents. These data are ideal for testing the ion-dipole theory of reaction rates. As the theory predicts, there is not only a change in the sign of the slope but also an inversion of the curvature of the empirical curves (ln k' vs ionic strength and ln k' vs $1/D^2$), in the majority of the data. The ionic strength data are plotted according to Eq. (8.38) and the dielectric constant data according to Eq. (8.42).

TABLE III Uni-univalent salts: $r_0 = 3.05$Å.; $\mu_0 = 4 \times 10^{-18}$

Salt	$10^4 k_{x=0}$	$\mu_0^* \times 10^{18}$	n^2
POTASSIUM	HYDROXIDE-POTASSIUM	SALTS	
KNO$_2$	212	6.15	1.08
KNO$_3$	213	7.35	1.68
KCl	214	8.30	2.15
KBr	217	10.34	3.17
KI	222	14.6	5.30
KCN	215	8.79	2.40
KSCN	225	16.4	6.20
SODIUM	HYDROXIDE-SODIUM	SALTS	
NaNO$_2$	209	10.04	3.02
NaNO$_3$	210	10.60	3.30
NaCl	211	11.2	3.60
NaBr	213	13.4	4.70
NaI	217	17.5	6.78
NaCN	205	7.27	1.64
NaSCN	220	19.4	7.70
NaClO$_3$	210	10.98	3.49

In Fig. 3 are plotted data for the decomposition of diacetone alcohol in potassium hydroxide-uni-univalent salt solutions of various ionic strengths, and also similar data for sodium hydroxide-uni-univalent salt solutions. The solid line is the theoretical curve from Eq. (8.38) (neglecting the insignificant term $n^2/2D$), and the data for the seven potassium and eight sodium salts fall within the vertical ellipsoid at each specified value of z^2. The range of ionic strength from zero to 3.6 given in this graph is very much wider than is given for ion-ion reactions on the basis of the Debye-Hückel limiting law. This range is included to indicate to what region of ionic strengths the ion-dipole theory may be applied. Table III contains the constants used in fitting the data to the theoretical curve in Fig. 3.

In practically all cases Åkerlöf (*loc. cit.*) found the rate was slowed down to a less extent by a potassium salt than by the corresponding sodium salt at like concentrations. This is reflected in the smaller μ_0^* and n^2 values. In the case of the cyanides the relative rate of the decrease was inverted for the potassium and sodium salts and here also the magnitudes of μ_0^* and n^2 were inverted. In most instances $k'_{x=0}$ is larger in the case of the potassium salts. The actual values of all

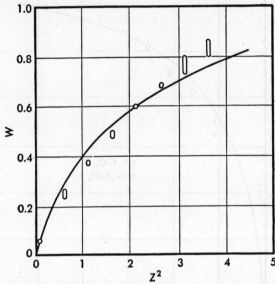

Figure 3 Plot of W versus Z^2 for the decomposition of diacetone alcohol in the presence of potassium hydroxide-uni-univalent salts.

three constants (μ_0^*, n^2, and $k'_{x=0}$) correspond closely to the values used in fitting data for the positive hydrogen reactant to the theoretical curve.

Åkerlöf found that the four salts, potassium fluoride, potassium carbonate, sodium carbonate, and sodium sulfate gave data which do not conform to theory. Even in these data the curvature of the log k' vs ionic strength curves is that predicted by theory though the sign of the slope of the curves is positive with increasing ionic strength in opposition to the predictions of Eq. (8.35). Åkerlöf discusses the anomalous effect of these salts upon the rate constant but reaches no definite conclusion as to the causes. In the case of the carbonates which are hydrolyzed to give hydroxide ions, Åkerlöf points out that full correction for the influence of hydrolysis will not eliminate the marked increase of rate with increasing ionic strength. These few

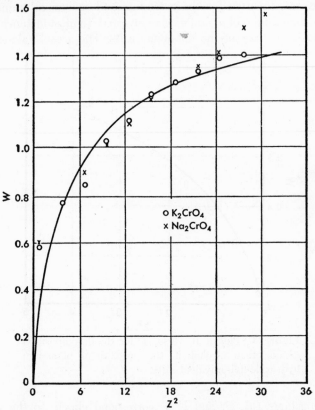

Figure 4 Plot of W versus Z^2 for the decomposition of diacetone alcohol in the presence of $KOH - K_2CrO_4$ and $NaOH - Na_2CrO_4$.

salts exert specific effects upon the rate which are inexplicable on the basis of the present theory. Fluorides are notoriously abnormal in many of their properties.

Figure 4 contains a plot of the data for the reaction rate in solutions of alkali hydroxide-uni-bivalent chromates up to an ionic strength of 13.6. The data showed no marked departure from theory up to this high value of ionic strength. The constants used in fitting data to theory are given in Table IV. Except for the values of $k'_{x=0}$, the relative values of the constants for the potassium and sodium chromates were in the same direction as for the majority of uni-univalent salts, and the actual magnitudes of the constants agree well with the values found for uni-univalent salts. The relative values of the constants for the potassium and sodium chromates correspond to he potassium salt slowing down the rate of reaction less than does sodium chromate for like concentrations of the two salts.

In fitting the data for the rate of diacetone-alcohol decomposition to theoretical curves, μ_0 was taken as 4×10^{-18} for the alcohol, since no value of the moment was found recorded in the literature. The other constants were determined by trial and error after fixing the value of μ_0.

TABLE IV Uni-bivalent salts: $r_0 = 4.56$Å.; $\mu_0 = 4 \times 10^{-18}$

Salt + Base	$10^4 k'_{x=0}$	$\mu_0^* \times 10^{18}$	n^2
K_2CrO_4 + KOH	235	6.76	1.38
Na_2CrO_4 + NaOH	260	12.91	4.46

TABLE V Uni-univalent bases: $r_0 = 4.82$Å.; $\mu_0 = 4 \times 10^{-18}$

Base	$10^4 k'_{x=0}$	$\mu_0^* \times 10^{18}$	n^2
KOH	212	5.20	0.600
NaOH	207	6.23	1.11
LiOH	208	10.0	3.00

TABLE VI Mixed solvent: $r_0 = 1$Å.; $\mu_0 = 4 \times 10^{-18}$

Solvent	$10^4 k'_{x=0}$	$\mu_0^* \times 10^{18}$	n^2
$C_2H_5OH - H_2O$	213	9.84	2.92
$n\text{-}C_3H_7OH - H_2O$	219	23.9	9.95

A plot of the logarithm of the rate constants for the decomposition of diacetone alcohol in alkali metal hydroxides as a function of the concentrations of these hydroxides is given in Fig. 5. The plot extends to an ionic strength of 1.2, and there is agreement between theory and data only to an ionic strength of about 0.8. The departure of the data from theory is reminiscent of that for ion-ion reactions, which generally fall off sharply from the limiting law at ionic strengths of roughly greater than 0.1. The points for $0.1N$ KOH and NaOH are omitted from Fig. 5 since they fall considerably below the theoretical curve. These k' values would have to be 2.5 per cent and 4 per cent lower, respectively, than measured by Åkerlöf in order to fall on the theoretical curve. French, Murphy, and also Sturtevant (French, *J. Am. Chem. Soc.*, **51**, 3215, 1929; Murphy, *ibid.*, **53**, 477, 1931; Sturtevant, *J. Am. Chem. Soc.*, **59**, 1528, 1937) confirm Åkerlöf's value of k' at $0.1N$ NaOH. There seems to be a discrepancy between observation and theory at these low concentrations, unless the devia-

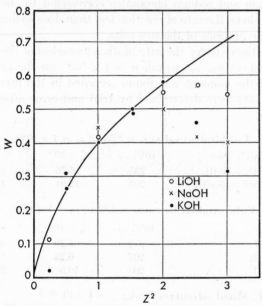

Figure 5　Plot of W versus Z^2 for the decomposition of diacetone alcohol in the presence of different alkali metal hydroxides.

tions are due to acid impurities. These had been suggested to Sturtevant as possible sources of error. The values of the constants recorded in Table V show the increased effect of like concentrations of the alkalis in decreasing the rate in the order potassium hydroxide, sodium hydroxide, lithium hydroxide.

Amis, Jaffé, and Overman (*loc. cit.*) presented a plot of logarithms of the rate constants versus $1/D^2$ in 0.1 normal sodium hydroxide for the mixed solvents ethyl alcohol-water and *n*-propyl alcohol-water down to a dielectric constant of 50. The values of the constants used in fitting these data to the theoretical curve are recorded in Table VI.

The values of these constants are fairly consistent with the values found for the ionic strength dependence. These constants also compare favorably in value with those determined by Amis and Jaffé (*loc. cit.*) for the dielectric constant dependence of rates when positive ionic reactants were involved.

The mixed solvents methyl alcohol-water, glycol-water, and glycerol-water give data in agreement with theory as to the direction and shape of the ln k' vs $1/D^2$ curves. To make these data fit the theoretical curve however, μ_0^* and n^2 must be unreasonably large or r_0 must be unreasonably small. The acidity of the glycol-water and glycerol-water solvents might account for the abnormal slowing down of the alkali-diacetone alcohol reaction. Glycerol-water media were found by Amis and Cook (*J. Am. Chem. Soc.*, **63**, 2621, 1941) to slow down the alkaline fading of brom phenol blue proportional to the amount of glycerol. This abnormal effect was attributed to the acidic nature of the glycerol. In the case of the diacetone alcohol-hydroxide ion reaction, however, the abnormal effect upon the rate of methyl alcohol and of iso-propyl alcohol, the latter of which actually increases the rate, must be due to specific solvent effects the nature of which is not yet clear. Such specific solvent effects in the case of ion-dipolar molecule reactions have been noted previously by Amis and Holmes (*J. Am. Chem. Soc.*, **63**, 2231, 1941).

The Laidler-Eyring equation for reaction rates between ions and neutral molecules

These authors (*Ann. New York Acad. Sci.*, **39**, 303, 1940) take the type reaction

$$A^{z_A} + B^0 \longrightarrow M^{*z_A} \longrightarrow X + Y$$

where z_A is the charge on A and M*. Laidler and Eyring also express the activity coefficients of the ions A and M* as being given by the equations

$$\ln f_A = \frac{z_A^2 \epsilon^2}{2 r_A k T}\left(\frac{1}{D} - 1\right) - \frac{z_A^2 \epsilon^2}{2 D k T}\frac{\varkappa}{1 + a_A \varkappa} + b_A \mu + \frac{\phi_A}{kT} \quad (8.44)$$

and

$$\ln f_{M*} = \frac{z_A^2 \epsilon^2}{2 r_{M*} k T}\left(\frac{1}{D} - 1\right) - \frac{z_A^2 \epsilon^2}{2 D k T}\frac{\varkappa}{1 + a_{M*} \varkappa} + b_{M*} \mu + \frac{\phi_{M*}}{kT} \quad (8.45)$$

where $b\mu$ represents the semiempirical Hückel term (*Physik. Z.*, **26**, 93, 1925) and ϕ is a nonelectrostatic term. To obtain an expression for f_B we will use the expression for the free energy of transfer of a neutral molecule from the vapor to a medium of dielectric constant D_0, which is that of the medium containing B but having no ions present. To this must be added the increase of free energy brought about by the addition of the ions. For the first of these quantities we will employ the Kirkwood formula (*J. Chem. Phys.*, **2**, 351, 1934), modified by nonelectrostatic terms, and for the second the approximate expression of Debye and McAulay (*Physik. Z.*, **26**, 22, 1925). This latter expression gives the relationship between the free energy of the process and the extent to which the dielectric constant is altered by the nonelectrolyte added.

The Kirkwood formula modified by nonelectrostatic corrections is

$$\Delta F_1 = - \frac{\mu_B^2}{r_B^3} \frac{D_0 - 1}{2D_0 + 1} + \frac{\phi_B}{kT} \tag{8.46}$$

and the Debye-McAulay expression is

$$\Delta F_2 = \frac{\epsilon^2 \delta}{2D} \sum_i \frac{n_i z_i^2}{r_i} \tag{8.47}$$

where n_i is the number of ions of the ith kind per cubic centimeter; z_i is the valence; and r_i the radius of this species of ions. The quantity δ is defined by the equation

$$D = D_0(1 - \delta n_B) \tag{8.48}$$

In Eq. (8.48), D_0 is the dielectric constant of the pure solvent, and D that of the solution containing n_B molecules of B per cubic centimeter. But the total free energy change is given by

$$\Delta F = kT \ln f_B = \Delta F_1 + \Delta F_2 \tag{8.49}$$

from which the expression for the activity coefficient f_B of the molecule becomes

$$\ln f_B = - \frac{1}{kT} \frac{D_0 - 1}{2D_0 + 1} \frac{\mu_B^2}{r_B^3} + \frac{\epsilon^2 \delta}{2DkT} \sum_i \frac{n_i z_i^2}{r_i} + \frac{\phi_B}{kT} \tag{8.50}$$

The expression for the rate of the reaction from substituting Eq. (8.44), (8.45), and (8.50) into the equation

$$k' = k_0' \frac{f_A f_B}{f_{M*}} \tag{8.51}$$

becomes

$$\ln k' = \ln k_0' + \frac{\epsilon^2 z_A^2 N}{2RT} \left(\frac{1}{D} - 1 \right) \left(\frac{1}{r_A} - \frac{1}{r_{M*}} \right) - \frac{N}{RT} \frac{\mu_B^2}{r_B^3} \frac{D_0 - 1}{2D_0 + 1}$$

$$+ \left(b_A + b_{M*} + \frac{\epsilon^2 \, \delta N}{DrRT}\right) + N \left(\frac{\phi_A + \phi_B - \phi_{M*}}{RT}\right) \quad (8.52)$$

In Eq. (8.52) the Debye-Hückel term has disappeared under the assumption that the mean distance of closest approach a is the same for the ion A and the complex M*. In this equation a mean value r of the r_i terms in Eq. (8.50) has been used. The dependence of log k' is now upon μ instead of upon the $\sqrt{\mu}$ as in the ion-ion case. The equation predicts a linear dependence of log k' upon μ when the dielectric constant is unvarying and concentrations are appreciable. Such a relationship was found by Brönsted and Wynne-Jones (*Trans. Faraday Soc.*, **25**, 59, 1929) for the hydrolysis of acetals by hydrogen ions.

The equation can be further tested by plotting ln k' extrapolated to zero ionic strength vs $1/D$, choosing reactions in which the dipole moment μ_B of molecule B is zero and from which the Kirkwood term in Eq. (8.50) therefore disappears. Thus straight lines having a slope

$$\frac{\epsilon^2 z_A^2 N}{2RT} \left(\frac{1}{r_A} - \frac{1}{r_{M*}}\right)$$

should result. Fair results may be obtained by plotting ln k' at any ionic strength vs $1/D$ owing to the cancellation of Hückel and Debye-McAulay terms in Eq. (8.50). In Fig. 6 is given a plot of log k' vs $1/D$ for the hydrochloric acid-catalyzed conversion of *n*-chloranilides into the *p*-chloranilides at 25° C. The data are those of Fontein (*Rec. Trav. Chim.*, **47**, 635, 1928). The data yield good straight lines.

For reactions where the reactant molecule is polar, the complete form of Eq. (8.50) would have to be applied.

Thus two equations predicting somewhat different results are extant for reactions between ions and dipolar molecules. Both equations have been supported by kinetic data. The principal difference in the conclusions drawn by the two sets of authors for the influence of neutral salts and dielectric constant of the solvent upon ion-dipolar molecule reaction rates may be summarized as shown in Table VII.

It is evident from both data and theory that there is both an ionic strength and dielectric constant dependence of rate for ion-dipolar molecule reactions. The whole question of reaction rates, and especially for ion-dipolar molecule reactions in solution, is in its swaddling clothes, and much experimental and theoretical work must yet be done to put this branch of physical chemistry upon a sound basis.

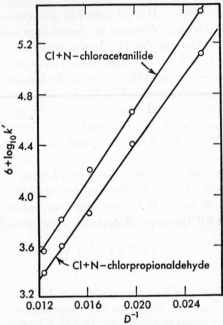

Figure 6 Plot of log k' versus D^{-1} for the hydrochloric acid-catalyzed conversion of n-chloranilides into the p-chloranilides at 25° C.

TABLE VII

Author	FOR POSITIVE ION EFFECT OF INCREASING		FOR NEGATIVE ION EFFECT OF INCREASING	
	Dielectric constant	Ionic strength	Dielectric constant	Ionic strength
Amis and Jaffé	Decrease	Increase	Increase	Decrease
Laidler and Eyring	Decrease	Increase	Decrease	Increase

Reactions between dipolar molecules

While this chapter deals largely with reactions between ions and dipolar molecules, reactions between dipolar molecules should be mentioned at some point in a discussion of reactions in solution. In the case of dipolar substances, van der Waals forces cannot, except as a very rough approximation, be neglected. However, Laidler and Eyring, believing that for strongly polar molecules, dipolar forces are somewhat stronger than nonelectrostatic ones, treated certain reactions involving fairly strong dipoles in terms of the electrostatic dipolar forces. Kirkwood's (*J. Chem. Phys.*, **2**, 351, 1934) formula for the free energy of transfer of a strong dipole of moment μ and having a symmetrical charge distribution within the molecule from a vacuum to a medium of dielectric constant D is

$$\Delta F = kT \ln f = \frac{\mu^2}{a^3} \frac{D - 1}{2D + 1} \tag{8.53}$$

where a is the radius of the molecule. Laidler and Eyring corrected this for a nonelectrostatic potential and obtained

$$\Delta F = kT \ln f = \frac{\mu^2}{a^3} \frac{D - 1}{2D + 1} + \phi \tag{8.54}$$

which they applied to the bimolecular reaction

$$A + B \longrightarrow M^* \longrightarrow X + Y$$

using the rate expression Eq. (8.51) and obtained

$$\ln k' = \ln k_0' - \frac{N}{RT} \frac{D - 1}{2D + 1} \left[\frac{\mu_A^2}{a_A^3} + \frac{\mu_B^2}{a_B^3} - \frac{\mu_{M*}^2}{a_{M*}^3} \right] + N \left(\frac{\phi_A + \phi_B - \phi_{M*}}{RT} \right) \tag{8.55}$$

where D is the dielectric constant of the final solution formed. Provided the nonelectrostatic terms in Eq. (8.55) are small enough to be neglected, a plot of $\ln k'$ versus $\frac{D - 1}{2D + 1}$ should as an approximation yield a straight line. Since the dielectric constants of the dilute solutions do not differ greatly from those of the pure solvents, the dielectric constants of the latter may be used in making the plots. Laidler and Eyring make such plots for two quaternary ammonium salt formations in alcohol-benzene mixtures, and for the water hydrolysis of tertiary butyl chloride, for the acid-catalyzed hydrolysis of orthoformic ester, and for alkaline hydrolysis of ethyl benzoate, the last three in alcohol-water mixtures. In these five cases agreement of data and theory is all that can be expected. The plot for the two quaternary ammonium salt formations is reproduced in Fig. 7. When the quaternary ammonium salt formation is studied in benzene-nitrobenzene solvents, considerable deviation is found. A plot of these data is given in Fig. 8. Laidler and Eyring attribute these variations to specific solvent effects, and formulate these effects in terms of the nonelectrostatic potentials ϕ. In the formation of quaternary ammonium salts the activated complex has a considerable dipole moment and approaches the salt in general properties. Thus in nitrobenzene

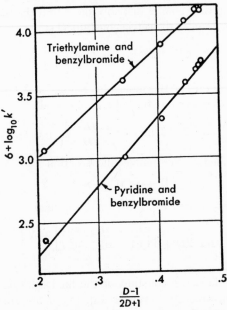

Figure 7 Plot of log k' versus $\dfrac{D-1}{2D+1}$ for quaternary ammonium salt formation in alcohol-benzene mixtures at 29° C.

the activated complex is solvated, has a low activity coefficient, and thus causes the reaction velocities to be high. In terms of the ϕ terms, even in nitrobenzene ϕ_A and ϕ_B are fairly normal, but owing to solvation ϕ_{M*} is very small. In benzene the converse is true. The product of the reaction is only slightly soluble in benzene and the solubility of the activated complex is likewise probably low in this solvent. Hence, for benzene solvent, ϕ_{M*} and f_{M*} will be large and the reaction therefore slow.

In the case of dipolar molecule-dipolar molecule reactions the data are again meager, and much more experimental work needs to be done

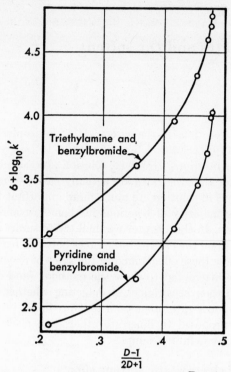

Figure 8 Plot of log k' versus $\dfrac{D-1}{2D+1}$ for quaternary ammonium salt formations in benzene-nitrobenzene mixtures at 29° C.

both upon activity coefficients of molecules in solution and upon rates of reactions between molecules in the liquid phase.

CHAPTER IX

Reaction rates and the solvent

The theory of reactions in the gaseous state is simpler than that for the solution state because of fewer variables to be accounted for in case of gaseous reactions. However, solution processes have the compensating factor that the rates are actually easier to measure. Practically, reactions in solution are much more important than gas reactions since the majority of reactions in chemistry and biology take place in solution. In this chapter we shall try to summarize the effect of the solvent upon the electrostatic forces between reactant particles and to show how these effects modify the rates of chemical reactions. Also it will be attempted to show the methods (and evaluate these methods as to their sensitivity) of detecting whether a solvent has an influence upon a rate other than that predicted by electrostatics. Further it is proposed to illustrate other than electrostatic effects of the solvent by definite examples.

Summary of electrostatic solvent effects

In Chapter IV we learned that for reactant ions of like sign there will be an increase of reaction rate with increasing dielectric constant of the solvent and vice versa with decreasing dielectric constant. Also that for reactant ions of unlike sign the rate of reaction will decrease as the dielectric constant of the solvent is increased and vice versa. The linear relationship between $\ln k_0'$ and $1/D$ predicted by Eq. (4.27) seems to hold strictly for electrostatic effects only down to dielectric constant values of about 40. Laidler and Eyring (*Ann. New York Acad. Sci.*, **39,** 303, 1940) explain this divergence of data from theory at low dielectric constants as probably due to preferential adsorption of water from a mixed solvent upon the ions, with the result that when lower dielectric constant solvents are added, their effect will not be as great as if the solvent molecules were randomly distributed. Deviations at low dielectric constants, probably due to the same cause, were observed in acid-base equilibria by Minnick and Kilpatrick (*J. Phys. Chem.*, **43**, 259, 1939), and in the dissociation constant of acetic acid by Harned and Embree (*J. Am. Chem. Soc.*, **57**, 1699, 1935) and by Harned and Kazanjian (*J. Am. Chem. Soc.*, **58**, 1912, 1936). In general it might be supposed that the higher dielectric constant component of a solvent mixture would be preferentially adsorbed and that the deviations from predicted electrostatic effects at low dielectric constants are in the direction of the effects at higher dielectric constants, since the ions are surrounded by an envelope of the high dielectric solvent component, i.e., the distribution of the solvent molecules is less random.

From Eq. (8.35) we learn that for a positive ion reacting with a dipolar molecule, the specific reaction rate constant k' would increase, but to a progressively less extent, with decreasing dielectric constant of the medium. For a negative ion reacting with a dipolar molecule k' should decrease with decreasing rate as the dielectric constant decreased. Here again deviations at low dielectric constants toward the electrostatic effects at higher dielectric constants are probably due to preferential adsorption of the higher dielectric solvent component with a consequent less random distribution of solvent molecules. This effect of lack of randomness becomes pronounced after the dielectric constant has been lowered to within a certain region, roughly between 40 and 50. In the case of ion-dipolar molecule reactants $\ln k'$ is related theoretically to $1/D^2$.

Equation (8.55) indicates a linear relationship between $\ln k'$ and the function $\dfrac{D-1}{2D+1}$ when the reactants are both dipolar molecules so that in the case of these reactants forming a polar product the rate of reaction increases with increasing dielectric constant of the solvent. Laidler and Eyring (*loc. cit.*) attribute the deviations from theory in these cases to the influence of the solvating power of the solvent upon nonelectrostatic terms in the rate equation. Thus when the activated complex is relatively polar and therefore highly solvated, its activity coefficient is very low. Hence, the reaction rate will be relatively high, especially in polar solvents, since the nonelectrostatic term for the complex in Eq. (8.55) is very small while the same terms for the reactants remain about normal. Solubility of reactants and products likewise influences these deviations. Thus in a solvent in which the activated complex is only slightly soluble (this can be inferred if the product of the reaction is slightly soluble), the nonelectrostatic term of the complex in the rate equation is large and the reaction will be slow.

Ion-ion reactions and the solvent

Equation (5.6), namely

$$\Delta E_C = -329.7 \frac{z_A z_B}{D_1 D_2 r} \Delta D \tag{9.1}$$

is the most sensitive test for obedience of an ion-ion reaction to the requirements of electrostatic theory with respect to the influence of the solvent upon the rate. This is true because the coulombic energies involved are only a few hundred calories at the most (see Table V, Chapter I). Therefore for reasonable values of r (the distance of approach of the reactant ions), if there is obedience to this equation when the rates are measured at different dielectric constants, then the reaction is being influenced very little, if at all, by specific solvent effects. Amis and Cook (*J. Am. Chem. Soc.*, **63**, 2621, 1941) found that the alkaline fading of brom phenol blue in glycerol-water solvents did not conform to the expectations of Eq. (9.1), though it did agree with the predictions of the Brönsted-Christiansen-Scatchard equation (Eq. 4.28) with respect to the effect of the dielectric constant of the solvent. There was agreement also with the predictions of Eq. (5.21) and (6.32).

Equations (4.27) or (4.28), (5.22), and (6.33) are about of equal sensitivity in predicting electrostatic effects of the dielectric constant of the solvent upon reaction velocities. If a reaction is studied at several dielectric constant values and $\ln k'$ is plotted against $1/D$ according to Eq. (4.27), namely

$$\ln k_0' = \ln k_{\substack{\varkappa=0 \\ D=\infty}}' - \frac{z_A z_B \epsilon^2}{D k T r} \tag{9.2}$$

a straight line should result. The slope of the line should be positive for unlike sign of reactants and negative for like sign of reactants. A required line of the expected slope is not a very sensitive test for other than electrostatic effects. However, if the radius of the complex is calculated from the data according to Eq. (4.30), that is from

$$r = -\frac{z_A z_B \epsilon^2}{2.303 S k T} \tag{9.3}$$

then the test is much more sensitive since not only the sign of the slope but also, within limits, its magnitude is established. This is true since r must be of the order of the radius of a molecule.

If Eq. (5.21) or (5.22)

$$\Delta E'_{f.c.} - \Delta E'_{D} = \frac{z_A z_B \epsilon^2 N T}{D^2 J} \left(\frac{1}{r} - \frac{3\epsilon}{10} \sqrt{\frac{2\pi N \mu}{10 D k T}} \right) \frac{dD}{dT} \qquad (9.4)$$

or Eq. (6.33)

$$\log Z_C - \log Z_D = \frac{z_A z_B N \epsilon^2}{2.303 D^2 R} \left(\frac{1}{r} - \frac{3\epsilon}{10} \sqrt{\frac{2\pi N^2 \mu}{10 D k T}} \right) \frac{dD}{dT} \qquad (9.5)$$

is used, then measured values of the difference in energy of activation or the Arrhenius frequency factor in constant composition media as contrasted with constant dielectric media should be reproduced by Eq. (9.4) and (9.5) respectively when reasonable values of r are employed. As pointed out, these tests will be of the same order of sensitivity for checking electrostatic effects as that resulting from the use of Eq. (9.2) in combination with Eq. (9.3). The predictions of Eq. (9.2) to (9.5) have been checked by various investigators. Amis and LaMer (*J. Am. Chem. Soc.*, **61,** 905, 1939) applied Eq. (9.2) and (9.3) to the reaction between the negative bivalent brom phenol blue ion and the negative univalent hydroxide ion in methyl alcohol-water and in ethyl alcohol-water media and obtained expected results, although the r values were somewhat small. These data were tested by Amis (*J. Am. Chem. Soc.*, **63,** 1606, 1941) using Eq. (9.1), and good agreement with theory was found. Svirbely and Warner (*J. Am. Chem. Soc.*, **57,** 1883, 1935) and Svirbely and coworkers (*J. Am. Chem. Soc.*, **60,** 330, 1938; *ibid.*, **60,** 1613, 1938) have studied the reaction of the positive ammonium ion reacting with the negative cyanate ion in various mixed solvents of constant composition and of constant dielectric constant. These data gave results in conformity with the above equations. Amis and Potts (*J. Am. Chem. Soc.*, **63,** 2883, 1941), studying the iodide-persulfate reaction in ethyl-alcohol-water media obtained data in agreement with Eq. (9.2), (9.4), and (9.5). A more recent application of Eq. (9.2), (9.4), and (9.5) to data was made by King and Josephs (*J. Am. Chem. Soc.*, **66,** 767, 1944) who studied the catalyzed decomposition of the azodicarbonate ion in dioxane-water mixtures. The rate-controlling process is second-order, presumably

$$N_2(COO)_2^= + H_3O^+ \longrightarrow X^-$$

while the stoichiometric equation is

$$2N_2(COO)_2^= + 4OH^- \longrightarrow N_2 + N_2H_4 + 4CO_3^=$$

The data for this reaction in these solvent mixtures were reasonably in agreement with theory.

Ion–dipolar molecule reactions and the solvent

The most sensitive test as to whether ion-dipolar molecules are being influenced in their rate processes practically exclusively by electrostatic effects is Eq. (5.9) which can be written

$$\Delta E_C = \frac{69.1z\mu}{D_1D_2r^2} \Delta D \tag{9.6}$$

where 69.1 is the kilocalories per mole for univalent ions reacting in a vacuum with molecules having a dipole moment of 1 Debye unit, r having a value of 1Å. The energies involved here are ordinarily less than one-half kilocalorie and hence the solvent must in no way sensibly affect the reaction except through the electrostatic effect of its dielectric constant if the expectations of theory are to be fulfilled. Amis and Holmes (*J. Am. Chem. Soc.*, **63**, 1606, 1941) found that inversion of sucrose by hydrochloric acid met these stringent requirements of electrostatic theory. Table II of Chapter V gives the calculated and observed values of ΔE_C reported by these authors.

Equation (8.35) permits the testing of kinetic data in the case of ions reacting with dipolar molecules for electrostatic influence of the solvent. The equation is

$$\ln k' = \ln k'_{x=0} + \frac{\epsilon z_B \cos \theta}{DkTr_0^2} \left(\mu_0^* - \mu^* \frac{(1 + xr_0)}{e^{xr_0}} \right) \tag{9.7}$$

and is quite sensitive in its predictions of the effect of the dielectric constant of the medium upon a reaction rate. Not only must the data yield a reasonable value of r_0 but also of μ_0^*. That this equation does predict electrostatic influence of the solvent in so far as its dielectric constant is concerned is illustrated for several reactions in different solvents in Chapter VIII.

Dipolar molecule–dipolar molecule reactions and the solvent

Moelwyn-Hughes and Sherman (*J. Chem. Soc.*, **1936,** 101) give the potential energy of two molecules held together in a head-on position by the mutual interaction of two dipoles (μ_A and μ_B) in a medium of unvarying dielectric capacity D as

$$E_C = \frac{2\mu_A\mu_B}{Dr^3} \tag{9.8}$$

This comes from the general equation

$$E_C = \frac{2\mu_A\mu_B \cos\theta_1 \cos\theta_2}{Dr^3} + \frac{\mu_A\mu_B \sin\theta_1 \sin\theta_2}{Dr^3} \tag{9.9}$$

for the potential between two dipoles (see Oscar Kneffler Rice, *Electronic Structure and Chemical Binding*, New York, McGraw-Hill Book Company, Inc., 1940, p. 465), for when the two dipoles are aligned head-on, angles θ_1 and θ_2 become zero and consequently the cosines of these angles become unity and their sines zero. With r in Å and μ in Debye units Eq. (9.8) becomes

$$E_C = \frac{28.9\mu_A\mu_B}{Dr^3} \tag{9.10}$$

kilocalories per mole. Then

$$\Delta E_C = -\frac{28.9\mu_A\mu_B}{D_1D_2r^3}\Delta D \tag{9.11}$$

The electrostatic energies given by Eq. (9.11) are perhaps the most precise method of testing the electrostatic influence of the solvent, provided methods of measuring the kinetic data are sufficiently accurate. In addition Eq. (8.55) can be used as a check on the electrostatic influence of the solvent upon reaction rates between dipolar substances. This equation neglecting the nonelectrostatic terms (assumed small) can be written

$$\ln k' = \ln \frac{kT}{h}K_0^* - \frac{1}{kT}\frac{D-1}{2D+1}\left[\frac{\mu_A^2}{a_A^3} + \frac{\mu_B^2}{a_B^3} - \frac{\mu_{M*}^2}{a_{M*}^3}\right] \tag{9.12}$$

and if the moments μ_A, μ_B, and μ_{M*} remain constant while the dielectric constant changes, then as an approximation a plot of the logarithm of the specific rate versus $\frac{D-1}{2D+1}$ should yield a straight line. This was proven to be the case in Chapter VIII for several reactions between dipolar substances.

Specific solvent effects

Verhoek (*J. Am. Chem. Soc.*, **61,** 186, 1939) gives as the rate-determining step for the decomposition of 2,4,6-trinitrobenzoic acid, the reaction

$$(NO_2)_3C_6H_2COO^- \longrightarrow (NO_2)_3C_6H_2^- + CO_2$$

In support of this mechanism Verhoek cites the observation of Moelwyn-Hughes and Hinshelwood (*Proc. Roy. Soc.* (London) *A*, **131,** 177, 1931) that trinitro-benzoic acid decomposed to trinitrobenzene and carbon dioxide more rapidly in moist solvents than in solvents which had been carefully dried. The decompositions of the lithium and sodium tribenzoates in ethyl alcohol were found by Verhoek to be of the first order, but in support of the theory that the step governing the rate was the one given above, the decomposition of trinitrobenzoic acid in alcohol in the presence of aniline and substituted anilines was found to be of the one-half order with respect to both acid and base when the ratio of acid to base was not too different from unity. That the rate should be one-half order with respect to both acid and base provided that the decomposing substance is trinitrobenzoate ion can be shown as follows.

If the decomposing substance is the trinitrobenzoate ion, the concentration of that ion and hence its decomposition rate may be changed by adding varying amounts of a weak base such as aniline to a solution containing trinitrobenzoic acid. In this case the behavior of the reaction is determined by the following equilibrium and decomposition:

$$HA + B \overset{K}{\underset{\nu}{\rightleftharpoons}} BH^+ + A^-$$
$$A^- \overset{}{\longrightarrow} products$$

From the above equilibrium

$$[A^-] = \sqrt{K}\sqrt{[HA]}\sqrt{[B]} \tag{9.13}$$

and from the equilibrium decomposition expression and Eq. (9.13)

$$-\frac{d[HA]}{dt} = k'[A^-] = k'\sqrt{K}\sqrt{[B]}\sqrt{[HA]} \tag{9.14}$$

Expressing the equilibrium constant K in terms of the dissociation constant of the acid K_{HA} and of the cation K_{BH} gives

$$-\frac{d[HA]}{dt} = k'[A^-] = k'\sqrt{\frac{K_{HA}}{K_{BH^+}}}\sqrt{[B]}\sqrt{[HA]} \tag{9.15}$$

Integration for a given experiment for which the concentration of the base is a constant b, since no base is used in the reaction, gives

$$\sqrt{[\text{HA}]} = -k''\sqrt{b}\,t + \text{constant} \qquad (9.16)$$

where

$$k'' = \frac{k'}{2}\sqrt{\frac{K_{\text{HA}}}{K_{\text{BH}^+}}} \qquad (9.17)$$

Equation (9.15) predicts that the velocity of the reaction should be of the one-half order with respect to the concentration of trinitrobenzoic acid HA and with respect to the concentration of base. Equation (9.16) shows that a plot of the square root of the trinitro-

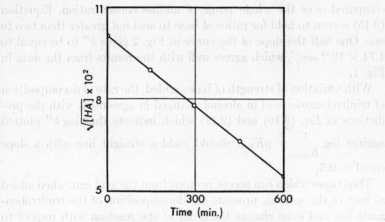

Figure 1 Decomposition of trinitrobenzoate ion at 35° C when $a = 0.01002M$, and $b = 0.00503\ M$. a is the total trinitrobenzoate (acid and salt) concentration, and b is the anilinium trinitrobenzoate (salt) concentration.

benzoic acid concentration versus time should give a slope of $-k''\sqrt{b}$. Figure 1 shows such a plot at 35° C for a solution $0.00503M$ in anilinium trinitrobenzoate and $0.00499M$ in excess trinitrobenzoic acid.

The slope of the curve divided by 0.00503 gives the value $k'' = 1.77 \times 10^{-5}$. Good straight lines show the one-half order course of the reaction so long as the concentration of the base does not exceed twice the concentration of the acid. At higher ratios of base to acid the order increases and becomes first order with very large excess of base over acid since the equilibrium shifts far to the right, and the approximation that the concentration of anion may be expressed in terms of the stoichiometric concentrations of HA and B will no longer be a good one. Equation (9.15) also indicates that the reaction velocity should increase as the square root of the base concentration b, at constant initial acid concentration a. In Fig. 2 is a plot of initial rate in moles per liter per second versus $\sqrt{a \times b}$ in moles per liter for the base aniline at initial concentrations of trinitrobenzoic acid near $0.01M$. The values plotted are initial rates since the order changes as excess aniline over acid increases, and only thus can the data be compared over the whole range of aniline concentration. Equation (9.15) is seen to hold for ratios of base to acid not greater than two to one. One half the slope of the curve in Fig. 2 gives k'' to be equal to 1.74×10^{-5} sec^{-1}, which agrees well with the results from the data in Fig. 1.

With variation of strength of bases added, the rate of decomposition of trinitrobenzoic acid in alcohol changed in agreement with the predictions of Eq. (9.16) and (9.17) which indicate that $\log k''$ plotted against $\log \dfrac{1}{K_{BH^+}} = pK_{BH^+}$ should yield a straight line with a slope equal to 0.5.

Thus bases which can accept protons from the acid can, when added as part of the solvent, promote the decomposition of the trinitrobenzoate ion and even change the order of the reaction with respect to the concentration of the unionized acid.

Further, Verhoek found an energy of activation for the trinitrobenzoate ion decomposition in ethyl alcohol to be 27,000 calories per mole, whereas Moelwyn-Hughes and Hinshelwood (*loc. cit.*) found an energy of activation for the reaction in water to be 29,970 calories per mole. This difference of energies of activation Verhoek attributes to the stabilizing effect of solvation on the ion.

Trivich and Verhoek (*J. Am. Chem. Soc.*, **65**, 1919, 1943) studied the decomposition of the trinitrobenzoate ion in dioxane-water mixtures. The increase of reaction velocity and consequent decrease in energy of activation with increasing dioxane content are presumed to be due to the changing character of the solvation of the ion. The reaction velocity increases about 2.5 times in going from pure water to 60 per cent dioxane and then decreases again with further increase of dioxane. The energy of activation decreases from 36,000 calories per mole in pure water to 22,000 calories per mole in 90 per cent dioxane.

In water, hydration stabilizes the trinitrobenzoate ion so that a greater amount of energy is required to decompose the hydrated ion than would be required if the ion were not hydrated. As the dioxane

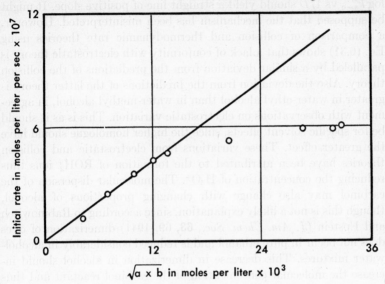

Figure 2 Change at 35° C of initial rate with aniline concentration.

content of the solvent is increased, the degree of hydration of the ions is decreased, resulting in the decreased activation energy and the corresponding increase in reaction rate.

An outstanding example of a specific solvent effect which was so large as to dominate all electrostatic effects of the solvent in the case of an ion-ion reaction is the regeneration in acid solution of alkali-faded brom phenol blue studied by Amis and Price (*J. Phys. Chem.*, **47**, 338, 1944) in water-ethyl alcohol and water-methyl alcohol media. The mechanism was presumed to be

$$(B\phi BOH^-)_x + H_2O \longrightarrow XB\phi B + XOH^- + H_2O$$
$$(B\phi BOH^-)_x + XH_3O^+ \longrightarrow XB\phi B + 2XH_2O$$

When the rate due to the water reacting with the carbinol is eliminated by extrapolating the rate constants to zero concentration of hydrochloric acid, and subtracting this value of k' for each temperature from the total k' at each concentration of acid and at each temperature, the resulting differences, k'' values, should be the specific rate constants of the oxonium ion reacting with the colorless carbinol ion. Since the reaction is one between ions of unlike sign, a plot of $\log k''_{x=0}$ vs $1/D$ should yield a straight line of positive slope. It might be supposed that the mechanism has been misinterpreted. However, a comparison of collision and thermodynamic rate theories using Eq. (6.31) shows that a lack of conformity with electrostatic theory is paralleled by a similar deviation from the predictions of the collision theory. Also the deviation from the predictions of the latter theory is greater in water-ethyl alcohol than in water-methyl alcohol, in agreement with observations on electrostatic variation. This is as it should be for specific solvent effects, since the higher homologue should have the greater effect. These variations from electrostatic and collision theories have been attributed to the formation of ROH_2^+ ions thus reducing the concentration of H_3O^+. The molecular dispersion of the carbinol may also change with changing proportions of alcohol, though this is not a likely explanation, since according to Rabinowitch and Epstein (*J. Am. Chem. Soc.*, **63**, 69, 1941) dimerization of dyes does not occur in pure ethanol and is reduced considerably in alcohol-water mixtures. This decrease in dimerization in alcohol should increase the molecular concentration of the carbinol reactant and thus enhance the expected increase of rate expected from electrostatics as alcohol is added and the dielectric constant of the medium consequently lowered. Instead a decrease of rate follows the addition of alcohol. However, here we are dealing with a carbinol or faded dye and possibly the solvent would exert a different influence from what it would upon the colored form of the dye.

An example of a reaction rate which did not stand the most sensitive electrostatic requirements of Eq. (9.1) for ion-ion reactions but which met the requirements of other electrostatic equations is the alkaline fading of brom phenol blue in glycerol-water solvents mentioned above.

Reaction rates between ions which in different solvents meet all electrostatic requirements are numerous. Some of these have been listed above when the equations were given and are: the fading of brom phenol blue in water-ethyl alcohol and water-glycol; and the iodide-persulfate reaction in ethyl alcohol-water. Even though these reactions meet the requirements of electrostatics in the different solvents, yet there is a slight specific solvent effect for the same reaction in different solvents resulting in the log $k'_{\varkappa=0}$ vs $1/D$ curves for these different solvents not coinciding and hence yielding differences for the parameter r in Eq. (3.9), and for the energies and entropies of activation. A plot of Svirbely and Schramm's (*J. Am. Chem. Soc.*, **60**, 330, 1938) data and of Lander and Svirbely's data (*J. Am. Chem. Soc.*, **60**, 1613, 1938) for the ammonium ion-cyanate ion reaction at 30° C in water-methyl alcohol and in water-glycol respectively are given in Fig. 2 of Chapter IV. Amis and Price (*loc. cit.*) show that Eq. (9.3) yields r values of 2.2×10^{-8} and 2.5×10^{-8} centimeter for the water-methyl alcohol and water-glycol data, respectively.

Examples of ion-dipolar molecule reaction rates which are in utter disagreement with the electrostatics of existing equations in so far as the solvent is concerned are the diacetone alcohol-hydroxide ion reaction in isopropyl alcohol studied by Åkerlöf (*J. Am. Chem. Soc.*, **50**, 1272, 1928) and the inversion of cane sugar by hydrogen ion in ethyl alcohol-water media studied by Amis and Holmes (*J. Am. Chem. Soc.*, **63**, 2231, 1941). The former rate increases with decreasing dielectric constant of the solvent while the latter decreases with decreasing dielectric constant of the solvent, the opposite to what is observed is predicted for the two reactions by Eq. (9.7). Furthermore the electrostatic energy of activation for the sucrose inversion was pointed out by Amis and Holmes to be wrong in sign according to Eq. (9.6). The effect was attributed in the case of cane sugar inversion to the formation of ROH_2^+ ions, thus reducing the concentration of H_3O^+ ion. This is similar to the acid regeneration of brom phenol blue discussed under ion-ion reactions. A reaction between ions and dipolar molecules which obeys partially the requirements of existing equations in so far as the electrostatic influence of the solvent is concerned is the diacetone alcohol-hydroxide ion reaction in methyl alcohol-water, glycol-water, and glycerol-water. The data for this reaction in these solvents are in agreement with the predictions of Eq. (9.7) in so far as the slope and curvature of the log k' vs $1/D^2$ curves are concerned, but either μ_0^* and n^2 must be unreasonably large, or r_0 must be unacceptably small to account for the great effect of these solvents in slowing down the rate. (See Amis, Jaffé, and Overman, *J. Am. Chem. Soc.*, **66**, 1823, 1944.) Again, as was the case for the alkaline fading of brom phenol blue in glycerol-water, the acidity of the glycol and glycerol may have caused the abnormal slowing down of the diacetone alcohol decomposition, since the hydroxide ion reactant would be more or less diminished by reaction with the solvent.

As was said in Chapter VIII, the effects of isopropyl alcohol and of methyl alcohol upon the diacetone alcohol-hydroxide ion reaction cannot be explained on any assumptions known to the author.

Agreement with theory for ion-dipolar molecule reactions in their dependence upon the dielectric constant of the solvent is found, as was pointed out in Chapter VIII, in the inversion of cane sugar by hydrochloric acid in dioxane-water, in the mutarotation of glucose by hydrochloric acid in methyl alcohol-water, and in the diacetone alcohol-hydroxide ion reactions in ethyl alcohol-water and in n-propyl alcohol-water.

From the standpoint of dipolar molecule-dipolar molecule reactions Grimm, Ruf, and Wolff (Z. physik. Chem. B, 13, 301, 1931) have studied the reaction between triethylamine and ethyl iodide in a variety of different solvents. They do not get rates which are even in the same order as the dielectric constant. Their results are, therefore, opposite to the predictions of Eq. (9.12). Laidler and Eyring (Ann. New York Acad. Sci., 39, 303, 1940) mention Menschutkin's (Z. phys. Chem., 6, 41, 1890) conclusion that there is a rough relation between the two, in that the reaction tends to be accelerated by solvents of high dielectric constants. Nonelectrostatic influences, especially solvation, are given by Laidler and Eyring as a probable explanation of this nonconformity to electrostatic theory as represented by Eq. (9.12).

In the rates for quaternary ammonium salt formation in benzene-nitrobenzene mixtures, considerable deviations from theory are found. The straight-line relationship between $\ln k'$ and $\dfrac{D-1}{2D+1}$ as expected from Eq. (9.12) does not hold, as is evident from Fig. 8 of Chapter VIII. However, the trend is in the right direction.

In Chapter VIII several reactions in various solvents were discussed which did give kinetic data in agreement with the requirements of Eq. (9.12).

Reactions involving reactants of various charge types range all the way from complete disobedience, through slight disobedience, to expected obedience with regard to the present theoretical expectations of the electrostatic effect of the solvent in so far as the dielectric constant of the solvent is concerned.

Other solvent effects

Glasstone, Laidler, and Eyring (*The Theory of Rate Processes*, New York, McGraw-Hill Book Co., Inc., 1941) point out that solvation of the activated complex will tend to bring about an increased rate of reaction, whereas solvation of one or more of the reactants will retard the reaction.

The internal pressure or cohesion of the liquid solvent influences rates of reaction. Glasstone, Laidler, and Eyring (*loc. cit.*) and Richardson and Soper (*J. Chem. Soc.*, **1929**, 1873) discuss this effect. Harkins, Davis, and Clark (*J. Am. Chem. Soc.*, **39**, 555, 1917) evaluated the cohesion of a medium by use of the expression $E_\sigma/v^{\frac{1}{3}}$, where E_σ is the total surface energy in dynes per centimeter and v is the molar volume in cubic centimeters. Stefan (*Wied. Ann.*, **29**, 655, 1886) calculated the cohesion using the expression L/v, where L is the latent heat of evaporation in joules per mole. Richardson and Soper (*loc. cit.*) state the following rules:

1. "If the reaction is one in which the products are substances of higher cohesion than the reagents, then it is accelerated by solvents of high cohesion."

2. "If the reaction is one in which the products are substances of lower cohesion than the reagents, then it is retarded by solvents of high cohesion."

3. "When the products and reagents are substances of like cohesion, the solvent has little influence on the reaction velocity."

Thus in the formation of quaternary ammonium salts, substances of high polarity and high cohesion are being formed from substances

TABLE I Influence of the cohesion of the solvent on quaternary ammonium salt formation

Solvent	$E_\sigma/v^{\frac{1}{3}}$	L/v	Triethylamine and ethyl iodide	Triethylamine and ethyl bromide
Hexane	9.45	243.3	0.000180	
p-xylene	12.12	292.5	.00287	0.000103
Benzene	15.29	275.0	.00584	.000228
Chlorobenzene	14.68	360.8	.00231	.000843
Acetone	14.46	408.3	.0608	.0024

of relatively low cohesion. From rule 1 the reaction should be accelerated by solvents of high cohesion. Table I contains Richardson and Soper's data for two such reaction rates in various solvents.

In general rule 1 is obeyed.

For the reaction of acetic anhydride with isopropyl alcohol, a reaction in which alcohol molecules of high cohesion form esters of low cohesion, rule 2 should be applicable. In Table II are listed data from the same authors on these two reaction rates.

TABLE II   Influence of the cohesion of the solvent upon the esterification of isopropyl and isobutyl alcohols by acetic anhydride

Solvent	$E_\sigma/v^{\frac{1}{3}}$	L/v	Acetic anhydride with isopropyl alcohol	Acetic anhydride with isobutyl alcohol
Hexane	9.45	243.2	0.0855	0.0307
Xylene	12.12	292.5	.0510	.0196
Benzene	15.29	275.0	.0401	.0148

Thus rule 2 fairly accurately predicts results.

In the illustration of the third rule, Richardson and Soper point out that there is relatively little solvent effect for the conversion in the presence of ethyl tartrate of anis*syn*aldoxime into *anti*aldoxime, in which case the cohesions of the products and of the reagents are probably nearly the same.

Moelwyn-Hughes (*J. Chem. Soc.*, **1932**, 95) derives the collision number z in the form

$$z = 2.9 \times 10^{24} \sigma \eta / M_1 \qquad (9.18)$$

where z is the number of solvent molecules encountered per second by each solute molecule, σ is the diameter of the solute molecule, M_1 is the mass of the solute molecule, and η is the viscosity of the solvent. From the proportionality between the collision rate and the viscosity of the medium this author writes

$$k' = K\eta e^{-\Delta E'/RT} \qquad (9.19)$$

where K is a constant, and $\Delta E'$ differs from the Arrhenius ΔE since it is obtained from the slope of the curve obtained by plotting $\ln k'/\eta$ against $1/T$, and not $\ln k'$ against $1/T$. Moelwyn-Hughes checked this theory with the hydrolysis of monochloroacetic acid among other reactions. The Arrhenius critical increment of 26,310 calories is reduced by 3,370 calories to allow for the variation of collision number with temperature due to change in viscosity. σ is taken as 5.4×10^{-8} centimeters. The data are given in Table III for the agreement between observation and calculation using Eq. (9.18) to calculate z and Eq. (9.19) to calculate k'.

TABLE III **Calculated and observed unimolecular velocity constants for the hydrolysis of monochloroacetic acid**

Temp.° C	$\eta \times 10^3$	Observed	Calculated
80	3.56	8.52×10^{-7}	2.30×10^{-6}
90	3.16	2.31×10^{-6}	6.00×10^{-6}
100	2.84	6.64×10^{-6}	1.63×10^{-5}
110	2.56	1.67×10^{-5}	4.23×10^{-5}
120	2.32	4.03×10^{-5}	1.03×10^{-4}
130	2.14	9.10×10^{-5}	2.50×10^{-4}

Thus the reaction velocity is approximately that expected from the simple collision theory of activation. Other data given by Moelwyn-Hughes are similar in their trends.

It can be seen, however, that solvation, acid or basic nature of the solvent, effect of solvent upon molecular dispersion, nonrandom distribution of the components of a mixed solvent, and perhaps many other factors some of which are not yet fully understood, enter into specific solvent effects. Hence only the more sensitive tests can indicate in some cases that such effects are existent, and even these most sensitive tests may fail to indicate a very minor influence of such solvent effects. In other instances even the roughest approximation will indicate a solvent effect other than purely an electrostatic one. In some cases the tests will indicate a specific effect so great as to overcome all electrostatic forces and cause a trend in reaction rate opposite to that predicted by theory.

What is particularly needed is more and accurate data on reactions between various charge types of reactants. The theorist can be more confident when he has ample data to work with and to check his predictions against. In many cases the explanation of an anomalous result on the basis of specific solvent effect is merely a confession that we are ignorant of the cause of the observed effect.

Mole fraction and volume molar rate constants

Scatchard (*J. Chem. Phys.*, **7**, 657, 1939; *Ann. New York Acad. Sci.*, **39**, 341, 1940) points out that in a mixture of nonpolar molecules of different sizes but of the same cohesive energy density, the activities are proportional to the mole fractions and not to the volume concentrations; in other words, theories of solution make activity coefficients equal to the ratio of activity to mole fraction, and not the ratio of activity to relative volume concentration. To correct rate constants in terms of concentrations to rate constants in terms of mole fractions, the former must be multiplied by the factor $(\Sigma N/V)^{\nu-1}$. Here ΣN is the total number of moles, including solvents, in volume V, and ν is the order of the reaction. Davis and LaMer (*J. Chem. Phys.*, **10**, 585, 1942) divide the mole fraction constant by $(\Sigma N/V)^{\nu-1}_{\text{std.}}$ for a standard solvent to obtain a normalized rate constant, k^N, thus

$$k^N = \frac{k'(\Sigma N/V)^{\nu-1}}{(\Sigma N/V)^{\nu-1}_{\text{std.}}} \tag{9.20}$$

where k' is the volume molar constant. In Fig. 3 and 4 are given plots of $\log k'_{x=0}$ vs $10^2/D$, and of $\log k^N_{x=0}$ vs $10^2/D$, respectively, for the bromacetate-thiosulfate reaction in various mixed solvents, taken from the paper of Davis and LaMer, who used water as the standard solvent. The points for glycine-water solutions lie on a straight line in both plots. For solvents of dielectric constant lower than that of water, linear plots were not always obtained. The data for methanol-water obeyed the requirements, within experimental error, of the Brönsted-Christiansen-Scatchard equation, while the data for butanol-water showed a slight upward curvature.

Comparison of Fig. 3 and 4 demonstrates that use of a mole fraction scale eliminates many of the specific solvent effects evident in Fig. 3. The data for water, water-glycine, water-sucrose, water-mannitol, and water-methanol are collinear after normalization; the data for water-ethanol, water-glycol, and water-glycerol show slight deviation. However, the data for water-t-butanol lie appreciably above the others, but are much closer to the extrapolated high dielectric curve than when plotted on a volume molar scale. The correction for the urea points is too large, and these therefore lie below the common linear plot of Fig. 4.

Davis and LaMer found that for some solvents there is a temperature dependence of the radius of the intermediate complex. Such a temperature dependence suggests a solvent effect upon ion-ion reactions not entirely accounted for by Eq. (4.28) and not entirely removed by use of k^N. Further these authors pointed out that a linear relationship between $\ln k_{\kappa=0}^N$ and $1/D$ does not disprove the existence of nonelectrostatic effects. Especially is this true since $1/D$ is nearly linear in mole fraction for many common solvents, and if there is a specific solvent effect also linear in mole fraction of added solvent, the plot of $\ln k_{\kappa=0}^N$ vs $1/D$ may still be a straight line. However, in these cases the values of $\ln k_{D=\infty}^N$ and the radius of the complex r will

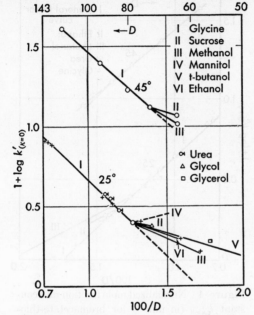

Figure 3 Volume molar rate constant $k'_{\kappa=0}$ (in min^{-1}) for bromacetate-thiosulfate reaction as a function of temperature and dielectric constant.

generally be in error and dependent upon both solvent and temperature. Thus the small and temperature dependent values of r found in the alkaline fading of dye ions to carbinol are perhaps due partly to linear solvent effects.

Svirbely and Peterson (*J. Am. Chem. Soc.*, **65**, 166, 1943) studied the ammonium ion-cyanate ion reaction in various nonaqueous solvents. They concluded from the behavior of $k'_{\kappa=0}$ calculated on the mole fraction basis, that salting-out is not the explanation for the deviations from linearity of $\ln k'_{\kappa=0}$ vs $1/D$ predicted by Scatchard's theory. Apparently specific solvent influences are more important than salting-out effects. These authors also observed that the Arrhenius frequency factors obtained from the corrected rate constants are lower than the values obtained from rate constants based

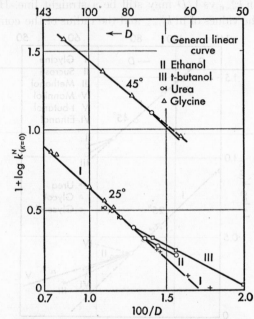

Figure 4 Normalized mole fraction rate constant $k_{\varkappa=0}^N$ (in min^{-1}) for bromacetate-thiosulfate reaction as a function of temperature and dielectric constant.

on volume concentrations, while the energies of activation are essentially the same. The plot of ln $k_{\varkappa=0}'$ vs $1/D$ based upon mole fractions was less linear than a like plot based upon volume molar concentrations.

King and Josephs (*J. Am. Chem. Soc.*, **66**, 767, 1944) investigated the acid-catalyzed decomposition of azodicarbonate ion in dioxane-water solvents. They found very low values of the entropy of activation, the largest being −3.5 entropy units. They suggested that these small values may indicate a small or even negligible entropy of activation. They also suggested that the negative values actually found could be due to fractional *transmission coefficients* or other factors. The use of *normalized* or mole fraction rate constants as compared with volume concentration rate constants made little difference in the results obtained.

Thus the results of Svirbely and Peterson and of King and Josephs indicate little advantage in the use of mole fraction rate constants as compared to volume concentration ones.

CHAPTER X

Photochemistry; chain reactions

Even as far back as the seventeenth century the influence of light in
promoting certain chemical reactions was recognized. To understand
photochemical processes, it is necessary to have in mind a few of the
fundamental principles involved. Thus the quantum theory as applied
to spectra, the laws of light absorption, absorption in liquids, the
existence of free atoms and radicals, the idea of chain reactions, etc.,
are involved in photochemistry. While space will not permit an
extensive presentation of these topics, it will be necessary to discuss
briefly these subjects, some in more detail and some in less. The
order of presentation will be somewhat as mentioned above, except
that some of the topics and others not mentioned will be discussed
when examples of photo-chemical reactions are given.

Quantum theory and spectra

Quantization of energy (stationary energy states)

According to Bohr an atom or molecule can exist only in certain
discrete energy states called stationary states. Quantum conditions
determine these states, from the classically possible continuous range
of energy states. The energy of the atom or molecule varies by units,
which Planck called *quanta*. Bohr (*Phil. Mag.*, **26**, 476 and 857, 1913)
postulated that the energy of an atom varies only in conformity with
the existing stationary states within the atom, and that the quantum
variation between two stationary states is $h\nu$, where h is Planck's
constant and ν is the radiation frequency associated with the energy
change between the two states. Mathematically the latter postulate
may be stated as follows:

$$h\nu = E_2 - E_1 \qquad (10.1)$$

where E_2 is the energy of the final state and E_1 that of the initial

198

state of the atom. These postulates also apply to molecules. It had
been noted in the photoelectric effect that the number of photoelectrons emitted was proportional to the intensity of the incident
light and that the kinetic energy of the photoelectrons is directly proportional to the frequency of the incident light. Einstein (*Ann.
Physik.*, **17**, 132, 1905) explained these facts on the basis of quantization of light. The relationship between the kinetic energy of the
electron and the frequency of the light absorbed was given by the
equation

$$\tfrac{1}{2}mv^2 = h\nu - h\nu_0 \tag{10.2}$$

where $h\nu$ is the energy given to the electron when it absorbs a quantum of light having a frequency ν, and $h\nu_0$ is the quantum of energy
necessary to bring the electron out of the particle. Thus $h\nu - h\nu_0$ is
the kinetic energy which the electron possesses when freed from the
particle. By determining the frequency which will just expel an electron from a particle (i.e., by determining the photoelectric threshold),
ν_0 can be determined.

Empirical formulae for spectra series

Lyman, Balmer, Paschen, Brackett, and Pfund series are given by
the formula

$$\nu = R\left(\frac{1}{n_1^2} - \frac{1}{n_2^2}\right) \tag{10.3}$$

where n_1 is, respectively, 1, 2, 3, 4, and 5 for the five series and n_2
always has a range of values, of which the minimum value is one
greater than the corresponding n_1 value. Thus in the Lyman formula
$n_1 = 1$ and $n_2 = 2, 3, 4 \cdots$.

Rydberg gave the equation

$$\nu = \nu_\infty - \frac{R}{(n - \mu')^2} \tag{10.4}$$

to express the frequencies of the lines in a series. In this equation R
and μ' are constants for any series, and n is a running number having
a characteristic minimum value for each series. ν_∞ is the limiting frequency for a series, i.e., the value for which n is infinite. R, the Rydberg constant, is a universal constant. Its value can be determined
from the hydrogen series and is equal to 109721.6.

Now from Eq. (10.3), the fixed terms in the second, third, fourth,
and fifth series, are the first, second, third, and fourth running terms

in the Lyman series. Also the fixed terms in the third, fourth, and fifth series are the first, second, and third running terms of the Balmer series; etc. This is the Ritz combination principle as applied to hydrogen. The same principle predicted new series in the spectra of elements other than hydrogen. These series have been found in the spectra of several elements. It is found that if the atoms of greater atomic number are made hydrogen-like by removal of all extranuclear electrons save one, then the lines of series can be represented by an equation like Eq. (10.3) except that a multiple (equal to the square of the atomic number) of R must be substituted for R. Thus if beryllium with an atomic number of 4 is made hydrogen-like by the triple ionization of the atom, the value of R in Eq. (10.3) must be multiplied by 16. Lines of different series of the same atom are reproduced by changing the characteristic constants ν_∞ and μ' in Eq. (10.4). Characteristic term values μ' were designated by S, P, D, etc., and the fine structures of these term values were designated by subscripts as S_1, S_2, P_1, P_2, P_3.

These empirical formulas and rules were good since nothing better was known, but the quantum theory, with its tested answers to the question, *Why?*, has now superseded these workable but unexplained laws. We now present a brief introduction to the quantum theory as applied to spectra.

Quantum numbers of individual electrons

To Niels Bohr belongs the credit of first suggesting that an atom or a molecule can exist only in certain discrete energy states called stationary states. These stationary states result when, from a continuous range of classically possible states, certain states are selected by means of specified quantum conditions. The major half-axis of the permissible elliptical orbits of an electron moving around an atomic nucleus is proportional to the square of the principal quantum number n, where n is a whole number and has the values given by the equation

$$n = 1, 2, 3, 4, \cdots \tag{10.5}$$

The quantum number determines the extent of the *electron cloud* at a given distance from the nucleus. For each value of n, the minor half-axis is proportional to a whole number l, designated as the *azimuthal quantum number*, and which can have the values

$$l = 0, 1, 2, 3, \cdots, n - 1 \tag{10.6}$$

For $l = 0, 1, 2, \cdots$, subgroups are designated $s, p, d, \cdots$. The azimuthal quantum number gives the angular momentum of an electron in its orbit. The *magnetic quantum number* m_l gives the component of l in a given direction. It ranges in integral values from $+1$ through zero to -1. Thus there are $2l + 1$ values of m_1. The remaining quantum number is called the *spin quantum number* m_s, which gives the component of the spin s in a given direction and is limited to the values $+\frac{1}{2}$ and $-\frac{1}{2}$.

The number of electrons in a given shell represented by a given value of the principal quantum number n, is limited by Pauli's exclusion principle which can be stated as follows: No two electrons in the same atom can have all four quantum numbers alike. Thus for quantum number $n = 1, 2, 3, 4, \cdots$ shells are designated as $K, L, M, N, \cdots$, respectively, and for the L shell, where $n = 2$, $l = 0, 1$, and $m_l = 1, 0, -1$. Since $m_s = +\frac{1}{2}, -\frac{1}{2}$, the L shell can contain only eight electrons as is shown in the following table.

TABLE I

n	l	Subgroup	m_l	m_s	Combinations
2	0	s	0	$+\frac{1}{2}, -\frac{1}{2}$	2 $\Big\}$ 8
2	1	p	$+1, 0, -1$	$+\frac{1}{2}, -\frac{1}{2}$	6

In like manner the K shell is filled with 2 electrons, the M shell with 18 electrons, etc. Thus the maximum number of electrons for any shell is $2n^2$.

Angular momenta of the whole atom; term notation

From the quantum numbers, the angular momentum of the whole atom may be found, since for a given quantum number x the quantum theory allows the calculation of the magnitudes of the angular momentum vector x by means of the term $\sqrt{x(x + 1)}\ (h/2\pi)$, or approximately $x(h/2\pi)$. The quantum number may be integral $1, 2, 3, \cdots$, or half-integral $\frac{1}{2}, \frac{3}{2}, \frac{5}{2}, \cdots$. For another quantum number y which may be either integral or half-integral, we would have the magnitude of the angular momentum vector y given by $\sqrt{y(y + 1)}\ (h/2\pi)$, or approximately by $y(h/2\pi)$. The resultant z of x and y is obtained by vector addition of vectors x and y, and can also take only the values $\sqrt{z(z + 1)}\ (h/2\pi)$ or approximately $z(h/2\pi)$, where z is integral when both x and y are integral or half-integral, but is half-integral when only x or only y are half-integral. The values of z are limited to $(x + y)$, $(x + y - 1)$, $(x + y - 2)$, $\cdots$, $| x - y |$.

For an atom containing several electrons, the orbital angular momenta l_1, l_2, l_3, $\cdots$ of the individual electrons couple strongly among themselves as do the spins s_1, s_2, s_3, $\cdots$. The l's add as vectors to give a resultant orbital angular momentum L. Likewise the s's in the same way add to give a resultant spin S. The magnitude of L is $\sqrt{L(L + 1)}(h/2\pi) \approx L(h/2\pi)$, and that of S is $\sqrt{S(S + 1)}(h/2\pi) \approx S(h/2\pi)$. L will always be integral since the various l's are integral, but S will be integral for an even number of electrons but half-integral for an odd number, since the s's are all one-half. The resultants L and S then add in the vector manner to give the total angular momentum J of the extranuclear electrons of the atom. The magnitude of J would, like the other vectors, be given by the term $\sqrt{J(J + 1)}(h/2\pi)$, or approximately $J(h/2\pi)$. The quantum number J is integral when S is integral and half-integral when S is half-integral, and is given by

$$J = (L + S), (L + S - 1), (L + S - 2), \cdots, | L - S | \qquad (10.7)$$

The quantum number L determines the letter designation of the term. Thus for $L = 0, 1, 2, 3, \cdots$, the terms are called S, P, D, F, $\cdots$, respectively. Further the number of components of a multiplet term is determined by the quantum number S, and equals $(2S + 1)$ when L is greater than S. This $(2S + 1)$ value is called the multiplicity and is written at the upper left of a term designation, thus ^3F (triplet F). To specify a term further, the J value is given as a lower right index, for example $^1G_4$ is a singlet G with a J value of 4. Let us consider the terms obtainable from an atom containing a d-electron and a p-electron. In this case $l_1 = 2$ and $l_2 = 1$, and thus L can have the values 1, 2, 3. S can be both 0 and 1. For $S = 0$, we will have the singlet terms P, D, and F, and for $S = 1$, we will have triplet terms of the same L designations. The terms are then

$$^1P_1, \; ^1D_2, \; ^1F_3, \; ^3P_{0, 1, 2}, \; ^3D_{1, 2, 3}, \; ^3F_{2, 3, 4}$$

In calculating resultants, closed shells need not be considered, since from Pauli's principle the resultant L and S values are zero for a shell which has its full quota of electrons.

If S is $\frac{1}{2}$, then doublets result, since J can be only $(L + S)$ and $(L - S)$. In similar fashion $S = \frac{3}{2}$ gives quartets since J can have a maximum of four values. Thus for $L = 2$ and $S = \frac{3}{2}$, $J = \frac{7}{2}, \frac{5}{2}, \frac{3}{2}, \frac{1}{2}, (L + S, L + S - 1, L + S - 2, L - S)$. Also for $S = 2$ five terms can result from combinations of L and S and thus quintets are obtained. For example if $L = 3$ and $S = 2$, $J = 5, 4, 3, 2, 1, (L + S, L + S - 1, L + S - 2, L + S - 3, L - S)$. Sextets will result when $S = \frac{5}{2}$. Thus for S fractional, that is, for atoms having an odd number of valence electrons (elements belonging to the odd-numbered groups of the periodic table) we have only even multiplicities. For S integral, that is, for atoms having an even number of valence electrons (elements belonging to the even-numbered groups of the periodic table), there will be only odd multiplicities.

Effect of a magnetic or electric field

When an atom is placed in a field, space quantization takes place, so that the components of the total angular momentum J in the direction of the field have the value $M_J (h/2\pi)$ where M_J can take the $2J + 1$ values given by the equation

$$M_J = J, (J - 1), (J - 2), \cdots, -J \qquad (10.8)$$

and may be $\frac{1}{2}, \frac{3}{2}, \frac{5}{2}$, etc., or 0, 1, 2, 3, etc., depending on whether J is fractional or integral. Further, M is governed by the selection rule $M_J = \pm 1$ or 0, except that $\Delta M_J \pm 0$ if $J = 0$. The splitting of lines in the presence of a magnetic field is called the *Zeeman effect* and can be represented by the splitting of the yellow sodium doublet, D_1 and D_2, into ten lines as shown in Fig. 1.

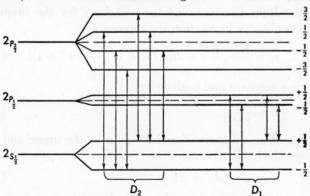

Figure 1 Splitting of the yellow sodium doublet, D_1 and D_2, into ten lines in the presence of a magnetic field.

Molecular spectra; rotation

In molecules, changes in electronic, rotational, and vibrational energy must be considered.

From classical mechanics we have for the rotation of a rigid body the energy E given by

$$E = \tfrac{1}{2}Iw^2 = \frac{(Iw)^2}{2I} = \frac{M^2}{2I} \tag{10.9}$$

where I, the moment of inertia of the rotator about the axis of rotation, is given by

$$I = \sum m_i r_i^2 \tag{10.10}$$

w, the angular velocity, is equal to 2π times the rotational frequency, i.e.,

$$w = 2\pi\nu_{rot.} \tag{10.11}$$

and M is the angular momentum of the system.

To determine the possible quantum states of such a dumbbell type rigid rotator, we have to solve the Schrödinger equation (Eq. 7.25) inserting M', the reduced mass, for the mass m and letting $V = 0$ since there is no kinetic energy of rotation for a perfectly rigid rotator. The solutions ψ are single-valued, finite, and disappear at infinity only for the eigenvalues of E given by

$$E_r = \frac{h^2 J(J + 1)}{8\pi^2 M' r^2} = \frac{h^2 J(J + 1)}{8\pi^2 I} \tag{10.12}$$

where J may assume any positive integral value.

From the Bohr frequency relation, we have for the frequencies arising from changes in rotation the expression

$$\nu_r = \frac{E_r' - E_r''}{h} = B[J'(J' + 1) - J''(J'' + 1)] \tag{10.13}$$

Where B is a constant and is given by

$$B = \frac{h}{8\pi^2 I} \tag{10.14}$$

and the quantum numbers J' and J'' refer to the upper and lower state, respectively. Furthermore

$$J = J' - J'' = \pm 1 \tag{10.15}$$

and since J' for the upper state is greater than J'' for the lower state

$$J = J' - J'' = +1 \tag{10.16}$$

and Eq. (10.13) reduces to

$$\nu_r = 2B(J'' + 1); J'' = 0, 1, 2, \cdots. \tag{10.17}$$

The rotational frequencies of the lines of a simple rigid rotator give rise to a spectrum of equally spaced lines. The first line ($J = 0$) falls at $2B$, and the succeeding lines are spaced at intervals of $2B$. These spectra are associated with dipolar molecules, and the emission and absorption of radiation is associated with change of polar moments.

VIBRATION-ROTATION

The vibrations of a diatomic molecule can be reduced to those of a harmonic oscillator of mass M', and defining the harmonic oscillator by its potential energy ($V = \frac{1}{2}kx^2$) and substituting this in the Schrödinger equation, one obtains

$$\frac{\partial^2 \psi}{\partial x^2} + \frac{8\pi^2 M'}{h^2}(E - \frac{1}{2}kx^2)\psi = 0 \tag{10.18}$$

The solutions ψ of this equation which are single-valued, finite, and continuous, and vanish at infinity obtain only for the E values

$$E_v = hw_e(v + \frac{1}{2}) \tag{10.19}$$

where w_e is the fundamental frequency and v is the vibrational quantum number. Now molecules are usually quite different from harmonic oscillators and the equation for an anharmonic oscillator in which the energy is expressed as a power series is generally applied. Thus

$$E_v = hw_e(v + \frac{1}{2}) - hw_eX_e(v + \frac{1}{2})^2 + \cdots \tag{10.20}$$

In this equation X_e is a factor which is determined experimentally and is dependent upon the departure of the molecule from the purely harmonic oscillator. Again applying the Bohr formula we have, using only the two first terms on the right of Eq. (10.20),

$$\nu_v = \frac{E_v' - E_v''}{h} = w_e(v' - v'') - w_eX_e(v'^2 - v''^2 + v' - v'') \tag{10.21}$$

For actual molecules Δv is not limited to unity, but may be greater than unity. Including changes in rotational energy as well as vibrational energy, we have from Eq. (10.17) and (10.21)

$$\nu = \nu_v \pm 2B(J'' + 1); J'' = 0, 1, 2, \cdots \tag{10.22}$$

Thus there is a series of spectral lines on either side of the frequency

ν_v, but there is no line at ν_v. The lines have a separation of $2B$. Actually there is a deviation from the equal spacing of lines due to rotation and this is allowed for in a more rigid treatment of the frequency.

ELECTRONIC BANDS

For electronic transitions in diatomic molecules, the energy of the minimum of the potential curve is generally taken as the electronic energy of the state. This energy is represented by the symbol E_e. The molecule can have vibrational energy E_v and rotational energy E_r, and very closely the total energy of the molecule is given by

$$E = E_e + E_v + E_r \qquad (10.23)$$

and applying the Bohr principle

$$\nu = \frac{(E_e' - E_e'') + (E_v' - E_v'') + (E_r' - E_r'')}{h} = \nu_e + \nu_v + \nu_r \qquad (10.24)$$

This equation corresponds to bands produced by simultaneous changes in electronic configuration of the molecule, vibration of the molecule, and rotation of the molecule. These bands are more complex than rotation or rotation-vibration bands. Now with the change of electronic state, the moment of inertia of the molecule changes, and hence the B in expressions for ν_r changes (see Eq. 10.14). Thus the frequencies of the bands represented in Eq. (10.24) are also given by

$$\nu = \nu_e + \nu_v + B'J'(J' + 1) - B''J''(J'' + 1) \qquad (10.25)$$

In this equation the single prime terms refer to the upper and the double prime terms refer to the lower state.

In all stable diatomic molecules in their lowest state ΔJ has only the values ± 1. For molecules possessing resultant angular momentum Λ around the axis of rotation, ΔJ can be zero or ± 1 when the value of Λ does not alter in the transition under consideration. Many polyatomic molecules and the diatomic molecule nitric oxide meet these requirements. Now each value of ΔJ gives a corresponding branch to the band, so that there are three bands corresponding to the values of ΔJ. These bands and their frequencies are:

P branch $\Delta J = -1$; $(J' - J'' = -1)$

$$\nu = \nu_e + \nu_v - (B' + B'')J'' + (B' - B'')J''^2; \quad J'' = 1, 2, \cdots \qquad (10.26)$$

Q branch $\Delta J = 0$; $(J' - J'' = 0)$

$$\nu = \nu_e + \nu_v + (B' + B'')J'' + (B' - B'')J''^2; \quad J'' = 0, 1, 2, \cdots \qquad (10.27)$$

R branch $\Delta J = +1$; $(J' - J'' = +1)$

$$\nu = \nu_e + \nu_v + 2B' + (3B' + B'')J'' + (B' - B'')J''^2; J'' = 0, 1, 2, \cdots$$
$$(10.28)$$

According to the above restrictions there will not be a line in the P and R branches at $\nu = \nu_e + \nu_v$. However, the Q branch will start at that point and proceed to higher frequencies. The P branch and R branch begin, respectively, at $\nu = \nu_e + \nu_v - 2B''$ and $\nu = \nu_e + \nu_v + 2B'$, as can be seen if we set J'' equal to 1 in Eq. (10.26) and J'' equal to zero in Eq. (10.28). The R branch will proceed toward higher frequencies and the P branch toward lower frequencies. Also for $B' < B''$ the lines in the R branch have decreasing distances between them, while the lines in the Q branch have increasing spaces between them. For higher values of J if $B' < B''$ the lines progress toward higher frequencies. This is true, since at higher J values the positions of the lines are determined by the sign of the quadratic term, even if the difference between B' and B'' is very small. Fortrat diagrams (Fortrat, *Thesis*, Paris, 1914) are used to illustrate these three branches of the spectra produced by simultaneous changes in vibration, rotation, and electronic configuration.

Most bands have several P, Q, and R branches. This constitutes multiplicity in molecular spectra. The motion of electrons in a diatomic molecule is influenced by a cylindrically symmetrical field. The axis of symmetry of the field is the line joining the nuclei. Due to the strong electric field between the nuclei, a precession of the electronic orbital momentum L takes place about the axis joining the nuclei. This precession has a constant component $M_L(h/2\pi)$ where M_L can take only the values

$$M_L = L, L - 1, L - 2, L - 3, \cdots, -L \qquad (10.29)$$

For molecules, only states with different $|M_L|$ will have different energy. This $|M_L|$ is set equal to Λ, a quantum number corresponding to the angular momentum vector Λ. The vector Λ has a magnitude $\Lambda(h/2\pi)$ and represents the component of the electronic orbital momentum along the internuclear line. For a given value of L the quantum number Λ can have any value from zero to L inclusive. Corresponding to 0, 1, 2, 3, $\cdots$ values of L, there are Σ, π, Δ, ϕ, $\cdots$, terms in molecular spectra. The selection rule for Λ is $\Delta\Lambda = 0$ or ± 1. Thus there can be transitions between Σ and Σ and between π and π terms as well as between Σ and π and between π and Δ terms.

For two identical, or nearly identical nuclei there are even and odd terms. Further, the even terms have positive levels which are symmetric and negative levels which are antisymmetric. The converse is true for odd electronic states. If the electronic eigenfunction is $\psi(x, y, z)$, then the inversion of the electrons at the center of symmetry changes the sign of the coordinates so that the electronic eigenfunction becomes $\psi(-x, -y, -z)$. Now if such a procedure leaves the eigenfunction unchanged, the term is called *even*, and, if the eigenfunction is merely changed in sign, the term is called *odd*. The electronic eigenfunction, if changed at all, merely changes in sign when each coordinate is replaced by its negative value.

We must consider also the case in which the coordinates of the electrons and of the atomic nuclei are reflected about the center of gravity of the molecule. In this instance if the sign of the eigenfunction is not changed, the rotation term is classified as *positive;* if the sign of the eigenfunction is changed the term is designated as *negative*.

Also, if the nuclei are interchanged and this causes no change in sign of the eigenfunction the rotational terms are symmetric; however, if interchanging the nuclei causes a change in sign of the eigenfunction, the terms are antisymmetric.

The general selection rules for molecular spectra are

(1) The change in the total angular momentum J is governed by the condition

$$\Delta J = 0, \pm 1 \tag{10.30}$$

However there can be no transitions between two states in both of which $J = 0$.

(2) Positive terms combine only with negative terms and negative terms with positive terms.

(3) Symmetric terms combine only with symmetric terms, and antisymmetric terms only with antisymmetric terms.

(4) Even electronic states combine only with odd.

The multiplicity of a molecular term is given by $2S + 1$, where S is the vector sum of the electronic spins. This multiplicity is indicated by a number written as a superscript on the left of the term designation, thus $^2\pi$, analogous to ^2P in atomic spectra.

Corresponding to the uncoupled spin quantum number M_S in atoms brought into being when the atom is in the presence of a strong electric field, there is a spin quantum number Σ for molecules, where $\Sigma = S, S - 1, S - 2, \cdots, -S$. Here S is the quantum number for the resultant S of the individual electrons in the atom. This quantum number is used in Hund's case (a) in which the interaction of rotation and electronic motion is very weak, but the latter is strongly coupled with the line joining the nuclei.

Now if we add Λ and Σ we obtain Ω, the total electronic angular momentum about the internuclear axis, and the quantum number Ω for the resultant angular momentum about the internuclear axis is given by

$$\Omega = | \Lambda + \Sigma | \qquad (10.31)$$

But the selection rule for Σ is that $\Delta\Sigma = 0$; and that for Λ is $\Delta\Lambda = 0$, ± 1 as has already been mentioned. Therefore the selection rule for Ω is $\Delta\Omega, = 0, \pm 1$. The Ω value of a term of a multiplet in molecular spectra is written as a subscript, thus distinguishing the terms. The total electronic angular momentum Ω about the internuclear axis combines with the rotational motion to form a resultant J where $J = \Omega, \Omega + 1, \Omega + 2, \cdots$. For $\Omega = 0$, for both electronic states, transitions with $\Delta J = 0$ are forbidden, and only those transitions with $\Delta J = \pm 1$ are found.

Hund's case (b) occurs when Ω is not defined since Σ is no longer required and Λ is zero. Even in certain cases when Λ is not zero, Ω is still not defined. In the cases mentioned above the spin may be only weakly coupled with the internuclear axis, and the orbital angular momentum Λ couples with the rotation to give a resultant K. The possible K values are $\Lambda, \Lambda + 1, \Lambda + 2, \cdots$. K is the total angular momentum, exclusive of spin, and it combines with the total spin S to give the resultant J, where J is the total angular momentum. In general, except when $K < S$, each level with a given value of K is composed of $2S + 1$ components, i.e., has this multiplicity.

VIBRATIONAL STRUCTURE OF ELECTRONIC BANDS

For the transitions between the various vibrational levels of two different electronic states, there is no strict selection rule which limits the change in vibrational quantum number v. From Eq. (10.20) we can obtain the energies of the transitions between the vibrational levels of the two electronic states being considered. Thus

$$E_v' - E_v'' = hw_e'(v' + \tfrac{1}{2}) - hw_e'X_e'(v' + \tfrac{1}{2})^2 - hw_e''(v'' + \tfrac{1}{2}) \\ + hw_e''X_e''(v'' + \tfrac{1}{2})^2 \quad (10.32)$$

The frequency becomes

$$\nu = w_e'(v' + \tfrac{1}{2}) - w_e'X_e'(v' + \tfrac{1}{2})^2 - w_e''(v'' + \tfrac{1}{2}) + w_e''X_e''(v'' + \tfrac{1}{2})^2 \quad (10.33)$$

A large number of lines is obtained in these transitions between the upper and lower vibrational levels of the upper and lower electronic states. This would be expected since there are no definite quantum restrictions limiting the transitions. As the quantum number v increases, the separation of the vibrational levels of any electronic state decreases. The equation usually applied to the band heads is obtained by differentiating Eq. (10.20) with respect to v. (See Rollefson and Burton, *Photochemistry and the Mechanism of Chemical Reactions*, New York, Prentice-Hall, Inc., 1942.) For polyatomic molecules, the spectra have not been interpreted in detail except in a few instances.

Potential energy and stable and unstable molecular states

In photochemistry much can be determined about the behavior of molecules activated by light from the potential energy of the molecule as a function of the separation of the atoms. The electrons move rapidly as compared to the nuclei of a molecule, and the electrons at any moment have an energy corresponding to their positions. The total potential energy which influences the vibrations of the nuclei is composed of the electronic energy plus the repulsive coulombic energy of the nuclei. Stable states of the molecule are those for which the dependence of the potential energy on the internuclear distance shows a minimum. Each electronic state has its own characteristic dependence of electronic energy upon the distance between the nuclei. An approximate expression for these potential energy curves of diatomic molecules has been proposed by Morse. (See Eq. 7.1.) One must resort to the more complex procedures discussed in Chapter VII to represent the potential energies of molecules containing more than two atoms. See Mulliken (*Rev. Mod. Phys.*, **4**, 1, 1932) for the potential curves of the Li_2 molecule in different electronic states. In reality the description of a state is never exact. This fact is according to the Heisenberg uncertainty principle which states that the product of the uncertainties in momentum and in position is equal to or greater than $h/2\pi$. Thus

$$\Delta pi \cdot \Delta q_i \geq h/2\pi \quad (10.34)$$

Where Δpi is the uncertainty in momentum, and Δq_i is the uncertainty in position.

The Lambert-Beer law

For a constant thickness, t, of absorbing layer, the Lambert-Beer law can be written

$$-\frac{dI}{dc} = \epsilon'tI \tag{10.35}$$

where c is moles per liter of absorbing material, I is the intensity of the light and ϵ' is a constant, called the molecular absorption coefficient which is characteristic of the absorbing material and of the wave length of light used. Integrating Eq. (10.35), we obtain

$$I = I_0 e^{-\epsilon'ct} \tag{10.36}$$

where I_0 is the intensity of the light initially and I is the intensity of the light after it has passed through length t of absorbing substance of concentration c. Since ϵ' is a function of the wave length of light, deviations from the Lambert-Beer law can occur when light of more than one wave length is used. Also the change in concentrations of absorbing substances, involving a change in the ratios of their concentrations with respect to each other, will cause a deviation in ϵ' and, hence, in the absorption law. The equation can be tested simply by putting it in the logarithmic form, thus

$$\ln \frac{I}{I_0} = -\epsilon'ct \tag{10.37}$$

and plotting $\ln \dfrac{I}{I_0}$ versus c. A straight line with a slope equal to $-\epsilon't$ should result.

Relationship between the light absorbed and the chemical change which occurs

The Grotthuss-Draper law (1818) states that only radiations which are absorbed by the reacting system are capable of causing chemical transformation. This law must not be interpreted to mean that all light absorbed will produce chemical change. Some of the light may be changed to heat and some of it may be re-emitted as light of the same or of different wave length. This re-emission of light is called fluorescence. If the radiation emitted in fluorescence is of longer wave length than the radiation absorbed, the phenomenon is behaving according to the predictions of G. G. Stokes (1852). Here the incident quantum gave some of its energy to the absorbing molecule. Sometimes the fluorescence exhibits *anti-Stokes* behavior, that is, the emitted radiation is of shorter wave length than the absorbed light. In this case the incident quantum received energy from the absorbing molecule. In the case of resonance fluorescence, re-emitted and absorbed light are of the same wave length.

The Stark-Einstein law, or law of photochemical equivalence, states that each molecule reacting due directly to the absorption of light takes up one quantum of the radiation causing the reaction. The energy absorbed per mole is then $Nh\nu$ which will be in ergs when centimeter-gram-second electrostatic units are used. This amount of energy is called one Einstein of radiation. If the molecules which absorb light react immediately, without the occurrence of successive or of side reactions, one molecule should react for every quantum absorbed, and the quantum efficiency would be unity. The quantum efficiency is defined as the number of molecules reacting chemically per light quantum absorbed. Since one Einstein of radiation absorbed should be equivalent to one mole of reactant being transformed, the quantum efficiency for a given photochemical process can be determined, and the law of photochemical equivalence thus tested. There are generally three classes into which photochemical reactions fall. First, there are those reactions in which the quantum efficiency approaches unity. In these cases the law of photochemical equivalence is applicable. Second, there are those reactions in which the quantum efficiency is a very large number. In these cases secondary processes cause many molecules to react for every quantum of light absorbed. For example a chain may be started by the light activated molecule which will cause many molecules to react. Third, there are the reactions in which the quantum efficiency is a small fraction. These low values can also be accounted for by secondary effects such as deactivation of the excited molecule by collision before it can react, and recombination of the fragments resulting from the initial step in the decomposition. It is commonly accepted that the law of photochemical equivalence is applicable to the primary light absorbing process. These processes occur in the range of wave lengths of approximately 1000Å to 8000Å. Such processes involve electronic transitions and, hence, electronic spectra.

CONTINUOUS AND DISCONTINUOUS ABSORPTION

Continuous absorption occurs beyond the point of convergence of the bands of discrete absorption. No fine structure is discernible.

According to Franck (*Trans. Faraday Soc.*, **21**, 536, 1925), the molecules break up into fragments (atoms, radicals, or molecules) when the continuous spectrum is evidenced, and the energy corresponding to the point at which the continuous absorption begins is just sufficient to bring about dissociation of the molecules in that particular electronic state. The quantum yield for dissociation, however, may be small due to recombination of the fragments. In certain cases these recombinations free excess energy in the form of heat and thus produce the Budde effect, especially if gases are involved. This effect is that of increase of volume at constant pressure when certain gases, e.g. chlorine, are exposed to light. This expansion is due to the increase of temperature of the gas due to the heat evolved in the recombination of the gaseous atoms into molecules.

The electronic spectrum of molecular chlorine gas consists of a series of fine structure bands converging at a wave length of 4785Å into a continuous absorption spectrum. At this wave length the energy of vibration of the chlorine atoms, within the molecule, is such that the molecules dissociate, and the energy of dissociation is, from these spectroscopic data,

$$E = Nh\nu = Nhc/\lambda = \frac{6.023 \times 10^{23} \times 6.6237 \times 10^{-27} \times 2.9977 \times 10^{10}}{4.785 \times 10^{-5} \times 4.187 \times 10^{7}}$$

$$= 59,700 \text{ calories per mole} \qquad (10.38)$$

Now chlorine molecules are each dissociated into one normal and one excited atom. The thermochemical value of the heat of dissociation of chlorine molecules into two normal atoms is 57,000 calories per mole. Therefore, the energy of atomic excitation is 2,700 calories per mole of chlorine dissociated. The calculated value from spectroscopic data of the energy of atomic excitation is 2,500 calories per mole. The two values are in good agreement.

In regions of discontinuous absorption, i.e., where there is discrete fine structure, the molecule is raised from a lower to a higher electronic level at the same time there is a change of vibrational and rotational energy of the molecule. When the excited molecules are present in gases at normal pressures, their average life is such as to allow time for collision with molecules with which they can react. In gases at higher pressures or in solution, the activated molecule may collide with indifferent molecules and dissipate its energy in the form of heat before it can react. This type of collision in which energy of excitation is converted into heat is called a *collision of the second kind*. A *collision of the first kind* is that between an atom or molecule and a fast moving electron, in which the kinetic energy of the particles is converted into electronic energy.

Henri (*Trans. Faraday Soc.*, **25,** 765, 1929) found that there was a common feature appearing on the ultraviolet side of the spectrum of some molecules. Bands which for lower frequencies show a fine structure having quite definite edges and sometimes a well-developed rotation spectrum, become broad and diffuse for higher frequencies. Rotation lines have disappeared and the edges are not sharp. In the case of NO_2 vapor there are two vibration bands: $\lambda = 2491$Å and 2459Å, with many fine rotation lines corresponding to a double rotation of this triangular molecule. There are similar bands toward the visible, corresponding to different vibration states of the molecule. But the next band toward the ultraviolet shows an abrupt change in structure. This change becomes marked at about $\lambda = 2447$Å. The bands are diffuse with no fine structure.

The vibrations are still quantized, but the rotation movements of the molecule are no longer quantized. In the region of broad diffusion bands the molecule is labile and chemically active, and fluorescence is feeble or may disappear. The limit of production of diffuse bands shifts toward the red with increase of temperature. Thus a new state of the molecule preparatory to dissociation is reached. This state is called the *predissociation state* of the molecule and the spectra in the region of diffuse bands are called the *predissociation spectra*. Herzberg (*Z. Physik*, **61,** 604, 1930) explained the absence of rotational fine structure by assuming that the time elapsing between the receipt of the energy by the molecule and its dissociation was less than the time for the molecule to make a complete rotation. The same phenomenon results from heating molecules; that is, at high temperatures, molecules are thermally predissociated.

From the above discussion it is clear that there can be discontinuous absorption with fine structure and also discontinuous absorption with diffuse structure.

ABSORPTION IN THE LIQUID PHASE

The absorption spectra of liquids or solutions are nearly always continuous. However, this cannot be accepted as proof of dissociation as the primary effect of absorption. Franck and Robinowitsch (*Trans.*

Faraday Soc., **30,** 120, 1934) list two explanations of the continuous nature of the spectra: (a) the influence of the electric fields of the surrounding molecules (asymmetrical Stark effect), and (b) the broadening of lines resulting from the shortening of the lifetime of the excited molecules due to collisions with molecules of the solvent. These collisions can cause (a) a return to the ground-state with dissipation of absorbed energy, (b) a chemical reaction with solvent or other surrounding molecules, or (c) a dissociation of the activated molecule. In the case of liquids a molecule probably has a mean interval between collisions of the same order of magnitude (less than the time of one vibration, 10^{-13} second) of the time of dissociation. Thus, unless direct reaction between dissociation products and solvent ensues, primary recombination will play an important role, since third bodies will always be present to act as stabilizers. The apparent quantum yield will be lower, due to primary recombination, in liquids than in gases, except in cases where predissociation is promoted by foreign fields or by collisions. In the latter cases every molecule in a liquid will be subjected to foreign fields and to frequent collisions, so that predissociation and direct dissociation will become practically identical.

While for nonpolar molecules in nonpolar solvents the spectroscopic behavior is quite similar to the gaseous state the situation is altogether different when either solute, solvent, or both are polar. Ionization, polarization, and compound formation make it next to impossible definitely to characterize spectroscopic behavior in such cases.

Chain reactions; free atoms and radicals

A chain reaction is one in which certain steps are repeated over and over again. Chain mechanisms are classified as *energetic* when the chains are propagated by excited molecules. Such chains are sometimes called *hot molecule* chains. In photochemistry, as in many other cases, free atom or free radical chains are preferred. These chain mechanisms are characterized by the formation of free atoms and radicals at required intervals in the chain. Franck and Robinowitsch (*loc. cit.*) discuss at length these free atom and radical chains. A summary of their remarks is given below.

For gases, free atoms or radicals are usually formed as a primary effect of absorption in the continuous region of the spectrum. An exception is the primary dissociation of organic acids into CO_2 and hydrocarbons ($RCOOH + h\nu \longrightarrow RH + CO_2$). This primary dissociation occurs with a quantum efficiency of unity. Even in the band region of the spectrum it is believed that the linear absorption ends in dissociation, though in an indirect way by collision between the excited molecules and other molecules present in the gas.

In general it is believed that in liquids the probability is greater that reactions will proceed through activated molecules. However, it is thought that the rate of formation of free atoms and radicals is generally lower. These statements are true for the first step of photochemical reactions. Since in liquids, excited molecules will be quickly deactivated by collisions with molecules of the solvent, the propagation of reaction-chains even in liquids must take place practically only through the agency of free unsaturated particles. Also, since the rate of formation of these free unsaturated particles is less in liquids and since it is impossible for reaction-chains to be propagated by activated molecules, then the quantum efficiency of chain reactions must be less in liquids than in gases.

There are two possibilities of photochemical reactions not involving free atoms or radicals. They are: (1) Photochemical dissociation into saturated molecules as in the decomposition of formic acid.

$$HCOOH + h\nu \longrightarrow CO_2 + H_2O$$

and (2) chemical chains involving excited molecules as possibly

$$Br_2 + h\nu \longrightarrow Br_2^*$$
$$Br_2^* + RCH = CHR \longrightarrow (RCHBr)_2$$

In solution, photochemical reactions having a quantum efficiency of unity or nearly so, and exhibiting no pronounced influence of temperature, light intensity, or wave length, have a mechanism which does not involve free atoms or radicals. Those mechanisms which do involve free atoms or radicals will show characteristic variations from the law of photoequivalence, depending on temperature, light intensity, wave length, and concentration.

Examples of photochemical reactions in the liquid phase

THE PHOTOCHLORINATION OF TETRACHLOROETHYLENE

The photochlorination of tetrachloroethylene has been studied by many investigators. This is an example of a photochemical reaction showing a high quantum yield. Leermakers and Dickinson (*J. Am. Chem. Soc.*, **54**, 4648, 1932) studied the reaction in carbon tetrachloride solution. Monochromatic light of wave length 4358Å from a mercury arc was used. The cell was of pyrex glass, cylindrical in shape, and was 2.0 centimeters in width by 3.05 centimeters in length. The intensity of the light was measured using thermopiles connected to high-sensitivity galvanometers. First the light intensity was measured using only solvent in the cell and again when the cell contained solution. By proper calibration of the galvanometer deflections as a function of chlorine concentration, the quantum efficiency could be determined.

A slight dark (thermal) reaction was found to occur, but since its rate was small compared to the photochemical rate, no correction was made upon the measured rate for the thermal influence. The temperature coefficient was found to be 1.16-fold in the specific rate per 10 degrees centigrade. The quantum efficiency according to these authors, Leermakers and Dickinson, varied from 300 to 2500. The main product of the reaction was C_2Cl_6, but discrepancies of 9 per cent, in the required amount of chlorine disappearing according to the reaction

$$Cl_2 + C_2Cl_4 \longrightarrow C_2Cl_6$$

were explained by assuming the possible formation of C_4Cl_8 (4.2 mole per cent) or C_4Cl_6 (2.9 mole per cent).

The following two mechanisms were proposed, either of which would lead to the correct mathematical formulation of the rate when the quantum yield is high.

Mechanism 1:

$$Cl_2 + h\nu \longrightarrow 2Cl \tag{1}$$
$$Cl + C_2Cl_4 \rightleftharpoons C_2Cl_5 \tag{2' and 2''}$$
$$C_2Cl_5 + Cl_2 \longrightarrow C_2Cl_6 + Cl \tag{3}$$
$$2C_2Cl_5 \longrightarrow 2C_2Cl_4 + Cl_2 \text{ (or } C_2Cl_6 + C_2Cl_4) \tag{4}$$
$$C_2Cl_5 + Cl \longrightarrow C_2Cl_4 + Cl_2 \text{ (or } C_2Cl_6) \tag{5}$$
$$2Cl \longrightarrow Cl_2 \tag{6}$$

Reactions (2′) and (3) constitute the chain which is finally broken by (4), (5), or (6).

Mechanism 2:

$$Cl_2 + h\nu \longrightarrow 2Cl \tag{1}$$
$$Cl + Cl_2 \longrightarrow Cl_3 \tag{2}$$
$$Cl_3 + C_2Cl_4 \longrightarrow C_2Cl_6 + Cl \tag{3}$$
$$2Cl \longrightarrow Cl_2 \tag{4}$$
$$Cl + Cl_3 \longrightarrow 2Cl_2 \tag{5}$$
$$2Cl_3 \longrightarrow 2Cl_2 + Cl_2 \tag{6}$$

In this mechanism reactions (2) and (3) propagate the chain which is broken by (4), (5), or (6).

Using mechanism 1 and noticing that when quantum yields are high

$$k_2'(Cl)(C_2Cl_4) = k_2''(C_2Cl_5) + k_3(Cl_2)(C_2Cl_5) \text{ nearly} \tag{10.39}$$

the rate expression can be written

$$-\frac{d(Cl_2)}{dt} = \frac{k_3}{\sqrt{k_4}} (I_{abs})^{\frac{1}{2}}(Cl_2) \left[1 + \frac{k_5[k_3(Cl_2)+k_2'']}{k_4 k_2'(C_2Cl_4)} + \frac{k_6[k_3(Cl_2)+k_2'']^2}{k_4 k_2'^2(C_2Cl_4)^2} \right]^{-\frac{1}{2}} \tag{10.40}$$

Satisfactory agreement with data was obtained by setting k_2'' and k_6 equal to zero, k_3/k_4 equal to 5.1, and $k_5 k_3/k_4 k_2'$ equal to 0.4. Thus Eq. (10.40) becomes

$$-\frac{d(Cl_2)}{dt} = 5.1(I_{abs})^{\frac{1}{2}}(Cl_2) \left[1 + 0.4 \frac{(Cl_2)}{(C_2Cl_4)} \right]^{-\frac{1}{2}} \tag{10.41}$$

Calculations showed that Eq. (10.41) corresponded to a mechanism made up of reactions (1), (2'), (3), (4), and (5) in mechanism 1. From mechanism 2 an equation of the form of Eq. (10.41) can be derived. This equation is likewise in agreement with experimental data.

The photochlorination of tetrachloroethylene is then an example of a reaction giving a high quantum efficiency and having a rate process explainable on the basis of a chain mechanism. The chain is propagated by means of free atoms and radicals. See Rollefson and Burton (*Photochemistry and the Mechanism of Chemical Reactions*, New York, Prentice-Hall, Inc., 1942) for a more general discussion.

AUTO-OXIDATION REACTIONS AND INHIBITION

Christiansen (*J. Phys. Chem.*, **28**, 145, 1924) developed a theory of *hot molecule* chains which may be summarized as follows. Reaction product molecules immediately after being formed possess available energy exceeding, to a marked degree, the mean energy at the temperature considered. Not only do these molecules possess the critical energy necessary for reaction to occur, but, in case of exothermic reactions, the product molecules possess this excess energy in the form of kinetic energy or in the form of potential energy which can be easily transformed into kinetic energy.

The hot molecules can by collision activate other reactant molecules, which reactants, upon reaction, produce molecules which in their turn can act as activators and so on. Thus one elementary reaction may cause a whole series of such reactions.

Negative catalysts, according to Christiansen, break the chains set up as described above by taking away the energy possessed by the hot molecules or by reacting with them in some way.

Bäckström (*J. Am. Chem. Soc.*, **49**, 1460, 1927) studied the inhibitory effect of certain substances upon the auto-oxidation of benzaldehyde, enanthaldehyde, and solutions of sodium sulfite. He was particularly interested in whether the photochemical and thermal chains in the case of these auto-oxidations were analogous in their reaction mechanism. We shall be particularly interested in the sodium sulfite reaction.

Pure sodium sulfite solution when shaken in the dark with oxygen gives a rather high rate which increases until practically all the sulfite has been oxidized, when a sudden drop occurs. Thus the study of the light reaction is rather difficult, since correction for the *dark rate* is rather arbitrary and makes the final result uncertain. As an illustration Bäckström gives the data for a run in which 10 cubic centimeters of solution contained 6 millimoles of sodium sulfite and 0.05 millimole of sulfuric acid. The rate of oxidation was very sensitive to the hydrogen ion concentration, and the sulfuric acid buffered the solution by converting a definite proportion of sulfite ion into bisulfite ion. The first burette reading was taken one minute after shaking was started. Bäckström's results are given in Table II.

TABLE II   Oxidation of sodium sulfite in solution

Illumination				$254 \text{ m}\mu$				$265 \text{ m}\mu$			
Time, min.	1	2	3	4	5	6	7	8	9	10	11
Rate	2.55	2.60	2.65	3.55	2.95	3.0	2.95	3.65	3.38	3.37	3.45
Average		2.60		2.79			2.97	3.17		3.37	
Molecules/$h\nu$				47,000				32,000			

Only the lines of wave lengths 254 and 265 mμ are appreciably absorbed by the solution. The absorption of line 254 should be practically complete, but there is not complete absorption of line 265.

That there is a photochemical after-effect is evident, since the dark reaction measured after a period of illumination is greater than would be expected from the rate of increase observed before illumination.

When inhibitors are present, the reaction is more regular, the velocity decreasing slowly as the sulfite in solution is being used. Thus for 10 cubic centimeters of solution made up as above except that there is also present 0.02 millimole of mannite, the rates before, during, and after illumination with line 254 mμ were: 1.36, 2.18, and 1.34 cubic centimeters per minute. The light reaction was from this data 0.83 cubic centimeter per minute, and at 305 watts, this gave a quantum yield of 53,000 molecules per quantum.

Bäckström found that light and dark reactions for sodium sulfite solutions showed a practically complete parallelism in their behavior toward one class of inhibitors, namely, the alcohols. In Table III the results obtained using alcohols as inhibitors are listed. The solution in each case contained 0.6 mole of sodium sulfite and 0.01 equivalent of sulfuric acid per liter of solution, in addition to the inhibitor.

TABLE III **Inhibitory action of mannite and alcohols**

Inhibitor	Conc. mole/liter	Dark rate obs.	Dark rate calcd.	Light rate in 254 mμ obs.	Light rate in 254 mμ calcd.
Mannite	0.04	0.200	0.197	0.136	0.136
Mannite	.02	.333	.346	.24	.24
Mannite	.01	.56	.56	.37	.39
Mannite	.005	.83	.81	.56	.56
Mannite	.003	1.085	.99	.68	.68
Mannite	.002	1.35	1.11	.83	.76
Methyl alcohol	.02	0.53	.53	.37	.37
Methyl alcohol	.01	.82	.78	.49	.54
Ethyl alcohol	.02	.28	.28	.205	.195
Ethyl alcohol	.01	.46	.47	.32	.33
Benzyl alcohol	.001	.145	.137	.094	.095
Benzyl alcohol	.00025	.43	.43	.27	.34

The results given in Table III can be summarized in the two formulas

$$v_d = \frac{0.009084}{kc + 0.00622} \tag{10.42}$$

and

$$v_e = 0.692 v_d \tag{10.43}$$

where v_d is the dark rate, v_e the light rate using line 254, c the concentration of inhibitor in moles per liter, and k a constant which is a measure of the relative efficiency of the inhibitor. The two formulas predict that two parallel straight lines should result when kcv is plotted against v. Such a plot was made by Bäckström and the expected results were obtained.

The formulas express the facts that, up to the limits of their applicability, i.e., up to around 0.8 cubic centimeter per minute, there is a constant ratio between light and dark reaction, and that both light and dark rates are inversely proportional to the sum of two quantities, one of which is a constant and the other proportional to the concentration of the inhibitor. From the standpoint of the chain-reaction theory these results indicate that the ability of the inhibitor to break the reaction chains is proportional to its concentration and independent of the nature of the primary activation; that is, the activation may be either thermal or photochemical. Further, the breaking of the chains is due also to some other constant cause similarly independent of the nature of the primary activation.

For the general case Eq. (10.42) and (10.43) may be written

$$v_d = \frac{k_1}{kc + k_2} \tag{10.44}$$

and

$$v_e = k_3 v_d = \frac{k_3 k_1}{kc + k_2} \tag{10.45}$$

where v_d, v_e, and c are defined as above, and k_1, k_2, k_3 are constants. The magnitude of k depends on the nature of the inhibitor (alcohol in this case) and is indicative of its relative inhibitory power. The role of the inhibitor, both in the thermal and in the photochemical oxidation, consists in the breaking of reaction chains.

The form of Eq. (10.44) and (10.45), as well as the complete analogy between light and dark reactions which they point out, shows that the presence of the alcohols has no effect upon the number of chains started per unit time; rather the alcohols act solely by breaking the reaction chains.

Bäckström (*Trans. Faraday Soc.*, **24**, 601, 1928) concludes that the mechanism by which the chains are broken by the inhibitor is probably an induced reaction between the inhibitor and one of the reactants. In support of this theory he mentions Chapman's (*J. Chem. Soc.*, **123**, 3079, 1923) conclusion that inhibition of the hydrogen-chlorine combination by oxygen is due to an induced or *photosensitized* reaction of oxygen with hydrogen, giving water. Bäckström also points out the results of Bigelow (*Z. physik. Chem.*, **26**, 493, 1898) who found that in the oxidation of sulfite solutions, primary, secondary, and iso-butyl alcohols acted as inhibitors, but tertiary alcohols had no effect. Thus there seemed to be in this case a direct relation between inhibitory power and oxidizability; and it seemed logical to believe that the alcohols are actually oxidized in the process of breaking the reaction chains.

Bäckström did not postulate any special mechanism of chain propagation, but described the reaction chain "as a series of processes whereby the oxidation of one sulfite ion induces the oxidation of another, and so on." He assumes that in the presence of the alcohol, the process leads sometimes to an induced oxidation of an alcohol molecule, and that this reaction is incapable of promoting additional oxidations or, at any rate, is less efficient than the corresponding reaction involving a sulfite ion.

Assuming that in the dark reaction the induced oxidation of the inhibitor is powerless to induce further oxidations, and thus always breaks the reaction chain, then every chain broken by the alcohol should result in the formation of one molecule of the oxidation product, for example, acetone when the inhibitor is isopropyl alcohol. Bäckström proceeded to check these assumptions in the following manner. If, in the dark reaction, the number of chains started and broken per minute is n, then the number of chains broken in that time by the alcohol will be given by the equation

$$\text{Number of chains broken by alcohol per minute} = n\,\frac{k_1 c}{kc + k_2} \quad (10.46)$$

and this number of acetone molecules will be formed per minute. Now the velocity, v, of sulfite oxidation is given by Eq. (10.44), and therefore the amount of acetone formed in one minute can be expressed by the formula

$$\text{Number of acetone molecules formed per minute} = \frac{n(k_1 c)}{kc + k_2} = ncv \quad (10.47)$$

where k_1 in Eq. (10.46) and (10.47) is the same k_1 that occurs in Eq. (10.44). From Eq. (10.47) the amount of acetone formed is proportional to cv, the product of inhibitor concentration and reaction velocity. From this proportionality the cv product should, at small inhibitor concentrations, increase with increasing values of c, and the rate of acetone formation should increase in proportion. However, when the inhibitor concentration is large, and $k_2 \ll kc$, from Eq. (10.47) the number of alcohol molecules oxidized and, hence, the number of acetone molecules formed is virtually constant and independent of the concentration of the alcohol. Increasing the alcohol concentration will cause the chains to be broken sooner, and lower the rate of sulfite oxidation, but the number of chains broken remains the same, and consequently the amount of alcohol oxidized in a given time should be constant, independent of its concentration.

Bäckström made plots of cv as ordinates against $\log c$ as abscissas. The concentration was taken in moles per liter and the reaction velocity in moles per liter per hour. The product cv was at low concentrations proportional to $\log c$ and then, beyond a certain increase of concentration, the product became constant and independent of $\log c$. This behavior would be expected from Eq. (10.44). A similar curve was obtained when the amounts of benzaldehyde formed per hour were plotted in the same manner against cv. The data in the former graph were made to fit Eq. (10.44) by making $k_1 = 0.00029$, $k = 1$ and $k_2 = 0.0012$. The data in the latter graph were made to fit the same expression multiplied by a constant factor.

From the theory one can see that within the concentration limits where all the chains are broken by alcohol, the number of alcohol molecules oxidized per unit time should be the same irrespective of the alcohol used. The only difference will be that the amounts of the different alcohols which have to be added to enter these limits will vary inversely as their specific inhibitory powers represented by k. The data in Table IV illustrates this point. In column 2 is recorded, for the three alcohols studied, the range of concentrations within

TABLE IV   From Bäckström (*Trans. Faraday Soc.*, **24**, 601, 1928)

Alcohol	Concentration range moles/liter	$cv \times 10^4$	Inhibitory power k (from cv)	Oxidation product formed	Rate of induced oxidation moles/ liter/hr.
Isopropyl	0.05–1.5	34	3.0	Acetone	0.000046
Sec.-butyl	0.15–1.8	103	1	Methyl-ethyl ketone	0.000049
Benzyl	0.0073–0.167	2.8	37	Benzaldehyde	0.000048

which cv, and also the rate of induced oxidation, were found to be constants within limits of error. In column 3 are given the average cv values within that range, in column 4 the corresponding values of k, and in the last column the average amounts of products formed, in moles per liter per hour.

When two alcohols are present in the same solution simultaneously, they should be oxidized in proportion to their concentrations and relative inhibitory powers. For an equimolar mixture of benzyl and isopropyl alcohols, the total number of moles oxidized per hour was found to be 0.000044. The two alcohols shared this total in the ratio of 13 moles of isopropyl alcohol to 1 mole of benzyl alcohol. The corresponding cv ratio of the two alcohols from Table I is 34 : 2.8 or 12 : 1. Thus the expectations of theory is verified.

To test this theory with respect to the photochemical reaction, a series of experiments with isopropyl alcohol was carried out. The light source was a mercury arc which was used with a chlorine-bromine filter. As with the thermal reaction so with the photochemical one, both cv and the rate of acetone formation was independent of the concentration over the range 0.05–1.5 moles per liter. As anticipated, both reaction rates were increased in the same proportion by illumination. Thus cv was increased from 0.0034 to 0.051, i.e., in a ratio of 1 to 15.0; the rate of acetone formation from 0.000046 to 0.00066, or 1 to 14.3. Therefore in a solution of given composition the lengths of the chains are the same whether the chains are initiated by thermal or photochemical means.

The chain lengths of the photochemical reaction may also be determined from quantum efficiency measurements on this type of reaction. Thus if every quantum of light absorbed by the solution starts a reaction chain, i.e., if no light-activated molecule is again *deactivated* before reacting with oxygen, then the quantum yield would be a measure of the chain length. Measurements made by Bäckström in monochromatic light of wave length 254 mμ and of known absolute intensity could be represented by a formula which, when applied to a solution containing 0.1 mole of benzyl alcohol per liter, gave a quantum yield of 64 molecules per hour. The data in Table IV for this concentration of alcohol give a chain length of $\dfrac{0.00028}{0.1 \times 0.000048} = 58$ molecules. This concentration of alcohol is well within the range where all the chains are broken by the molecules of the inhibitor. The agreement is without doubt significant. Thus the induced or photo-sensitized oxidation of the alcohol obeys Einstein's law of photochemical equivalence.

The results given above are rather direct proof that thermal chain reactions exist. The data further indicate that at least one mechanism by which reaction chains may be broken consists of an induced or photosensitized reaction of the inhibitor with one of the reactants.

Fuller and Crist (*J. Am. Chem. Soc.*, **63**, 1644, 1941) criticize the work of Bäckström and others on the rate of oxidation of sulfite ion by oxygen. Fuller and Crist found that the kinetics of the oxidation followed the first-order law from $0.015M$ sodium sulfite to the limit of precision of the measurements, namely, $0.001M$. These authors point out that Bäckström found deviations from the first-order law, but that his work was done at $0.6M$ sulfite solutions. Moreover, it was found that the first-order constant obtained by extrapolating Bäckström's data to zero concentration of inhibitor was 0.000343 instead of 0.013 as reported by them. These latter investigators suggested that the low value of the constant obtained from Bäckström's data could have been due to the presence of negative catalysts from such sources as the rubber connections used by Bäckström. Fuller and Crist further indicate that it is not clear from Bäckström's paper that the observed reaction rate was not influenced by the solution rate of oxygen.

Equations for the rate of sulfite oxidation in the presence of the negative catalyst (inhibitor) mannitol, of the positive catalyst cupric ion, and of the hydrogen ion were given by Fuller and Crist. Their findings may be summarized as follows. The inhibitory effect of mannitol was found to be uniform over a 10^5-fold change of mannitol concentration. The rate is directly dependent upon the cupric ion concentration when this is greater than $10^{-9}M$, and the catalytic constant is 2.5×10^6 liters per mole per second at $25°$ C. Bäckström (*J. Am. Chem. Soc.*, **49**, 1460, 1927) believed that the double effect of potassium cyanide as an inhibitor of the sulfite reaction could be related to the fact that the primary activations that cause the dark rate can be, partly at least, due to the presence of traces of copper salts. Fuller and Crist, however, in the analysis of the effect of cupric ion found evidence that there is a primary process independent of heavy metal ions. These investigators also found the reaction rate independent of the pH between 8.8 and 8.2. The rate decreased in a complicated manner between 5.9 and 3.2. This was explained by assuming that the rate is dependent on the sulfite ion concentration and the square root of the hydrogen ion concentration, but is independent of the acid sulfite ion concentration.

Fuller and Crist state that the unstable intermediates which are responsible for the development of chains may arise from the step-wise reduction of oxygen or oxidation of sulfite. The reduction process may give rise to HO_2 and H_2O_2 (or OH). The oxidation of sulfite may produce SO_3^-, $S_2O_6^=$, and $SO_5^=$. These authors further say that with the aid of these intermediates it is possible to formulate reaction mechanisms which will account for the rates either in acid or slightly alkaline solution. They add, however, that a mechanism that will hold for both types of solution has not yet been found.

GEOMETRICAL INVERSION IN LIGHT

Vaidya (*Proc. Roy. Soc.* (London), **A129,** 299, 1930) determined the quantum efficiencies for the inversion of several geometric isomers. The source of light was a mercury light with suitable filters. The average wave length used in all calculations was 3130Å. Energy measurements were made with a thermopile-galvanometer setup. Water solutions were used and their absorption spectra were determined. The courses of the reactions in all cases were followed by conductivity measurements. The pairs of isomers studied were

(1)   H—C—COOH →   H—C—COOH
         ‖   ‖
         H—C—COOH ← COOH—C—H
         Maleic acid   Fumaric acid

(2)   CH₃—C—COOH →   CH₃—C—COOH
         ‖   ‖
         HC—COOH ← COOH—C—H
         Citraconic acid   Mesaconic acid

(3) C₆H₄(OH)–C–H   → C₆H₄OH–C–H   C₆H₄–C–H
         ‖   ‖   → O   ‖
         H–C–COOH ← COOH–C–H   CO–C–H
     o-Coumaric acid (trans)   o-Coumaric acid (cis) unstable   Coumarin

(4)   C₆H₅—C—H   →   C₆H₅—C—H
         ‖   ‖
         H—C—COOH ← COOH—C—H
         Cinnamic acid   Isocinnamic acid

Quantum efficiencies found are given in Table V.

TABLE V

Acid	Concentration	(Quantum Efficiency)
Maleic acid	0.01M	0.048
	0.005M	0.052
Fumaric acid	0.01M	0.117
	0.005M	0.083
Citraconic	0.01M	0.18
	0.005M	0.22
Coumaric	0.005M	0.031
	0.002M	0.023
Cinnamic	0.003M	0.61
	0.002M	0.53
Isocinnamic	0.003M	0.21
	0.002M	0.15

Warburg (*Sitzungsber. Preuss. Akad. Wiss.*, **50**, 960, 1919) showed that the equilibrium position between two photoactive isomers could be calculated from a knowledge of their quantum efficiencies and absorption coefficients. In the case of isocinnamic and cinnamic acids, Vaidya arrives at the expression for the equilibrium in the manner set forth below. As the difference between the absorption coefficients of cinnamic and isocinnamic acids for the wave length 3130Å is small, the following relation holds:

$$\frac{dm_2}{dt} = I_0 A \left(\phi_1 - \frac{m_2}{m_1} (\phi_1 + \phi_2) \right) \qquad (10.48)$$

where m_2 is the concentration of the changing system at time t, I_0 the intensity of the incident light, A the absorption of the system, ϕ_1 the quantum efficiency of the reverse change, and ϕ_2 that of the direct change. At equilibrium $\frac{dm}{dt}$ is zero and therefore,

$$\frac{m_2}{m_0} = \phi_1/(\phi_1 + \phi_2) \qquad (10.49)$$

Taking m_0 the original concentration of cinnamic acid as unity, m_2 the concentration of isocinnamic acid at equilibrium, ϕ_1 the quantum efficiency of cinnamic acid, and ϕ_2 that of isocinnamic acid, Vaidya obtained for 0.003M solution $m_2 = 0.747$ or 74.7 per cent and for

$0.002M$ solution $m_2 = 0.776$ or 77.6 per cent. After ten hours exposure the values obtained experimentally were 72 and 75 per cent respectively.

Warburg explained the low quantum efficiencies of maleic and fumaric acids by supposing that one quantum disrupted the molecule into two parts, but that these parts reunited to produce the original molecule in greater proportion than its isomer. Vaidya points out that if this is the explanation of the low quantum yield in these cases, it can likewise be accepted as the reason for the low quantum yield in the case of o-coumaric acid. However, the relatively high quantum yield of cinnamic acid would have to be explained by some other mechanism, although this acid is quite similar to o-coumaric acid.

The substances studied here fall into two classes. Maleic, fumaric, and citraconic acids show general absorption, while coumaric, cinnamic, and isocinnamic acids show selective absorption. Except for o-coumaric acid, the substances showing general absorption have a low quantum efficiency, and those showing selective absorption have a higher quantum efficiency which would probably approach unity at lower wave lengths within one of the photochemically active bands. For substances showing more than one absorption band it is suggested that it might be necessary to distinguish between the photochemically active and inactive bands. Further it is believed that the inactive bands are on the long wave side of the spectrum. In an active band the quantum efficiency would tend to increase toward a maximum with decreasing wave length after the photochemical threshold is crossed. Thus Warburg (*Z. Electrochem.*, **54,** 28, 1920) found for potassium nitrate solutions a quantum efficiency of 0.02 at a wavelength of 3130Å and a quantum efficiency of 0.25 at 2070Å. As for the band for o-coumaric acid, the first band at 3150Å is inactive and the one at 2680Å would probably be active, although Vaidya did not test this since the mercury arc was unsuited for the wavelength 2680Å. Judging from the relatively high activity of cinnamic acid within its absorption band, it seems likely that the same band slightly shifted in the similar o-coumaric acid, would probably raise the quantum efficiency.

Glasstone (*Textbook of Physical Chemistry*, New York, D. Van Nostrand Company, Inc., 1940) discusses the interconversion of fumaric and maleic acids in aqueous solution when illuminated with ultraviolet light of wavelength from 2070 to 2820Å. A possible mechanism is that one of the electrons forming the double bond between the carbon atoms is excited by light of this wavelength. Then upon collision the double bond breaks to form a single bond for a short period of time. The mechanism can be represented in the manner given below:

$$
\begin{array}{c}
-\text{C}- \\
\parallel \\
-\text{C}-
\end{array}
+ h\nu \longrightarrow
\begin{array}{c}
-\overset{*}{\text{C}}- \\
\parallel \\
-\text{C}-
\end{array}
\longrightarrow
\begin{array}{c}
| \\
-\text{C}- \\
| \\
-\text{C}- \\
|
\end{array}
$$

Free rotation is possible in the single bonded state and there is consequently some interconversion of stereoisomers.

We have thus discussed photochemical processes of different types. The first case taken up was that of a reaction with high quantum efficiency in which the mechanism was that of chain propagated by free atoms and radicals. The second case illustrated was that of a reaction involving thermal and light-activated chains. The chain lengths are the same whether the chains are initiated by thermal or by photochemical means. The energy chains are propagated through activated hot molecules. The third example was that of a photochemical reaction with a low quantum efficiency. In some cases the quantum efficiency was much less than unity. This low quantum efficiency, according to the Franck-Robinowitch principle, was due to recombination of initial products before new products can be formed. A fourth type of photochemical process is the photosensitized reaction.

PHOTOSENSITIZATION

In this type of photochemical reaction, the molecules which absorb the light in many instances merely act as energy carriers, and do not otherwise enter into the chemical process. Such processes are quite common in the gaseous state, for example, the mercury-photosensitized reactions of ethylene at high temperatures studied by LeRoy and Steacie (*J. Chem. Phys.*, **10**, 676, 1942). The steps in this reaction are given as

$$\text{Hg}(^3P_1) + \text{C}_2\text{H}_4 \longrightarrow \text{C}_2\text{H}_4^* + \text{Hg}(^1S_0) \tag{1}$$

$$\text{C}_2\text{H}_4^* + \text{C}_2\text{H}_4 \longrightarrow 2\text{C}_2\text{H}_4 \tag{2}$$

$$\text{C}_2\text{H}_4^* \longrightarrow \text{C}_2\text{H}_2 + \text{H}_2 \tag{3}$$

Also to explain the high quantum yields the steps

$$\text{Hg}(^3P_1) + \text{C}_2\text{H}_4 \longrightarrow \text{C}_2\text{H}_3 + \text{H} + \text{Hg}\,(^1S_0) \tag{4}$$

$$\text{C}_2\text{H}_3 + \text{C}_2\text{H}_4 \longrightarrow \text{C}_4\text{H}_7 \tag{5}$$

$$\text{C}_4\text{H}_7 + \text{C}_2\text{H}_4 \longrightarrow \text{C}_6\text{H}_{11}, \text{ etc.} \tag{6}$$

are given as well as the ones

$$H + C_2H_4 \longrightarrow C_2H_5 \tag{7}$$
$$C_2H_5 + C_2H_4 \longrightarrow C_4H_9, \text{ etc.} \tag{8}$$

and to account for the formation of propylene at high temperatures a final process

$$C_4H_9 \longrightarrow C_3H_6 + CH_3 \tag{9}$$

is also written.

West and Paul (*Trans. Faraday Soc.*, **28**, 688, 1932) studied the decomposition of the alkyl halides in hexane and benzene solution. The quantum efficiency of the process in the two solvents was practically the same, even though the benzene absorbed in the photoactive region while the hexane did not. They explained this by saying that it was a case of optical sensitization and that the energy absorbed by a benzene molecule was transferred to an alkyl halide molecule, and in this way the whole of the energy absorbed by the system becomes available in effecting the decomposition of the halide. A case similar to this was the transformation of *o*-nitro-benzaldehyde into *o*-nitroso-benzoic acid in acetone solution, for which the yield is the same in a part of the spectrum in which acetone absorbs most of the light as in a region where practically all of the absorption is due to the aldehyde. Weigert and Prunker (*Z. physik. Chem., Bodenstein Festband*, 1931), who studied this latter reaction, made the generalization that in the presence of several absorbing substances there is no photoequivalent of Beer's law, but as regards the photochemical change, the whole of the energy absorbed by the system is available.

Electron transfer spectra and their photochemical effects

This subject has been dealt with by Rabinowitch (*Rev. Modern Phys.*, **14**, 112, 1942) and must needs be mentioned in any except the most elementary presentation of photochemistry. A common characteristic of electron transfer spectra is the transfer of an electron from one atom to another. That the probability of such a transfer be fairly great the two atoms must be bound together by relatively strong forces. However, the bonding must not interfere with the assignment of the electrons to particular atoms, that is, the bond must be of an ionic or ion-dipole character, rather than a true atomic (electron-pair) bond.

Absorption bonds of this nature are those of gaseous ionic molecules, ionic crystals, and simple and complex ions in solution.

The spectra of all complex ions investigated in the far ultraviolet give bands which from their intensity and position can be interpreted as *electron transfer bands*. The extinction coefficients in the maxima of these bands approach the intensity of the absorption bands of organic

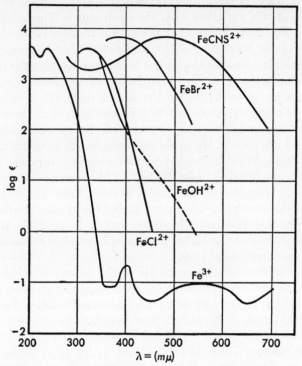

Figure 2   Absorption curves of Fe^{3+} and $Fe^{3+}X^-$ complexes in aqueous solution.

dyes and are of the order of 10^4. The *electron excitation bands* of colored ions in the visible and near ultraviolet give molar extinction coefficients much less than 10^4. That for the intensely colored MnO_4^- ion is about 2000 and that of the $CrO_4^=$ ion is of the order of 4000. The colored cations show even weaker absorption bands, for example Ni^{++} has a maximum molar extinction coefficient of 1. The electron transfer bands are generally much more intense than the electron excitation bands and are situated much farther toward shorter waves, generally slightly above or below 2000Å. In complexes each associate has its characteristic absorption curve. Furthermore, the absorption curves for a given cation are a function of the associated anion and vice versa. In Fig. 2 is given the curves from Rabinowitch (*loc. cit.*) for the absorption curves of $Fe^{+++}X^-$ complexes in aqueous solution, and in Fig. 3 are the absorption curves for the Fe^{+++} ion and of various associates of this ion taken from the same source. The bands represented in Fig. 2 are interpreted as electron transfer bands since the positions of the $FeOH^{++}$, $FeCl^{++}$, and $FeBr^{++}$ bands correspond to the order of electron affinities. It has been suggested that the bands of the associated ions are absorption bands of the metal ion shifted toward longer wavelengths by the electric field of the associated anion. Rabinowitch points out if this were true that there should be a relationship between the strength of the association and the position of the band. He gives the energies of association as increasing from $FeCl^{++}$ (-8.5 kilogram calories) through $FeBr^{++}$ (-6.1 kilogram calories) to $FeOH^{++}$ ($+1.2$ kilogram calories), whereas the *red shift* is greatest in the case of $FeBr^{++}$. From Fig. 3 it can be seen that the absorption curves run higher the greater the degree of association, and Rabinowitch states that it is probable that the extinction curves of the higher associates have higher maxima than those of the binary complexes.

If these intense absorption bands of the anion-cation complexes are taken as electron transfer bands, they should be photochemically active, and the primary process must be the reduction of the cation and the oxidation of the anion. Now the photochemical effect may become observable or not depending on whether the electron returns from the oxidized anion to the reduced cation by a *primary back reaction*, or whether it has a chance of avoiding recombination. In the case that separation does take place with a fair quantum yield, the process may still be reversed by a *secondary* back reaction such as

$$FeCl^{++} \underset{}{\overset{h\nu}{\rightleftharpoons}} Fe^{++}Cl \text{(Photo-oxidation of } Cl^- \text{ and primary back reaction)}$$
$$Fe^{++}Cl \longrightarrow Fe^{++} + Cl \text{ (Separation of primary products)}$$
$$Cl + Fe^{++} \longrightarrow Fe^{+++} + Cl^- \text{ (Secondary back reaction)}$$

While it is recognized that ferric ions play the part of the photosensitive component in the photochemical oxidation of organic acids by ferric salts, there has been no report of photochemical changes in simpler solutions such as that of pure ferric halide or of pure lead halide. Rabinowitch suggests that perhaps no one has looked for them closely enough.

Thus it would seem that only a small part of the chemical changes which occur in solution under the influence of light are detectable

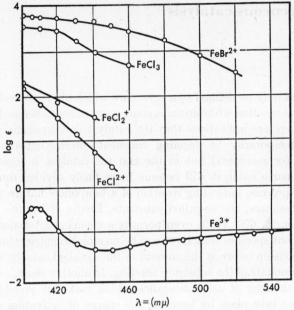

Figure 3 Absorption curves of Fe^{3+} ion and of various associates of this ion.

analytically. The others are either too slow or too easily reversible to be detected by ordinary analytical means. If the intense cation and anion bands are electron transfer bands, then solutions of all common acids, bases, and salts, when illuminated with ultraviolet light contain unstable oxidation and reduction products, free atoms, and radicals which when opportunity presents itself can be converted into stable products by secondary reactions. This according to Rabinowitch would explain among other puzzling things the strong photogalvanic potentials observed in solutions of photostable acids, bases, and salts.

CHAPTER XI

Homogeneous catalysis

A catalyst may be defined as a substance which alters the velocity of a chemical reaction without undergoing a permanent chemical change itself. There are indications that the catalyst does undergo chemical change temporarily by forming transient intermediates with the reactant (or reactants) but in the end the catalyst is regenerated. Thus a coarse catalyst will become more finely divided during the chemical process, indicating reaction of a temporary nature with the other substances, the so-called substrate. Bredig (*Ulmann's Enzykl. tech. Chem.*, **6**, 670, 1909) even permits a chemical alteration of the catalyst, but specifies that there can be no stoichiometric whole number relationship between the amount of the so-called catalyst changed and the amounts of the substrate reacting. In another sense, a catalyst may be thought of as a substance which makes it possible for a reaction to take place by lowering the energy of activation or, from the standpoint of absolute reaction rates, the free energy of activation requirements of the process. The energy of activation of a process depends on how the process takes place. Thus the energy requirements for molecule A to react with molecule B to form product AB according to the reaction

$$A + B \longrightarrow AB$$

may be high, but the energy necessary for catalyst C to react with molecule A to form intermediate AC, and then for intermediate AC to react with molecule B to form AB and regenerate catalyst C according to the steps

$$A + C \longrightarrow AC$$
$$AC + B \longrightarrow AB + C$$

may be low enough to cause production of AB at a marked rate according to the second mechanism, when the reaction would be imperceptibly slow by the first mechanism. From these considerations have

234

arisen two divergent views of the function of a catalyst, which even today have not been conclusively reconciled. Ostwald maintained that a catalyst could not initiate a reaction, but merely changed the rate of the existing processes. Lowery, however, argued that there are certain processes which will take place only in the presence of a catalyst. It could be that these reactions in the absence of a catalyst are too slow to be perceptible even over long periods of time and that the catalyst merely speeds up the reaction to where its rate is observable.

The process of changing the rate of a chemical reaction by use of a catalyst is called catalysis. If the rate of a reaction is increased by a catalyst, the process is called *positive catalysis;* if the rate of a reaction is decreased by the catalyst, we have *negative catalysis.* In catalysis the equilibrium point in a reversible reaction is not altered; the time necessary for equilibrium to be established is altered. Thus a catalyst must affect the rates of the forward and reverse reactions proportionally since the equilibrium constant is not altered and is given by the expression

$$K = \frac{k_1'}{k_2'} \tag{11.1}$$

where K is the equilibrium constant of the reversible reaction, k_1' is the specific reaction rate constant of the forward reaction, and k_2' is the specific reaction rate constant of the reverse reaction.

A catalytic process is called *homogeneous* if the same phase contains both the catalyst and the substrate. In *heterogeneous* catalysis, the catalytic process occurs at the phase interface, i.e., the catalyst and substrate occur in different phases. *Microheterogeneous* catalysis involves dispersed systems in which there is no well-defined phase difference between catalyst and substrate (see Schwab, Taylor, and Spence, *Catalysis*, New York, D. Van Nostrand Co., 1937).

In the sections which follow we shall be chiefly interested in catalytic processes which involve at least one liquid phase.

Homogeneous catalysis in solution

In this section we shall deal only with acid-base catalysis, since this is the most important example of homogeneous catalysis in solution.

General acid catalysis

Early experimental work of Ostwald (*Z. prakt. Chem.*, **29**, 401, 1884; *J. physik. Chem.*, **1**, 78, 1887) and of Arrhenius (*Z. physik. Chem.*, **28**,

319, 1899) indicated a rate of reaction which was proportional to hydrogen ion concentration for acid-catalyzed reactions, and a rate of reaction which was proportional to hydroxyl ion concentration for base catalyzed reactions. Goldschmidt and Sunde (*Ber.*, **39,** 711, 1906) found that in alcoholic solutions, the velocity of esterification increased more rapidly than hydrogen ion concentration with increasing concentration of acid. Braune (*Z. physik. Chem.*, **85,** 170, 1913), Bredig (*Z. Electrochem.*, **18,** 535, 1912), and Hantzsch (*Ber.*, **58,** 612, 1925) likewise confirmed that there was a catalyzing power of undissociated acid molecules. Snethlage (*Z. physik. Chem.*, **85,** 211, 1913) showed that in the picric acid catalysis of diazoacetic acid ester the decreasing constants with increasing addition of salt all fell on the same curve. After reaching a minimum, the constants did not change further with addition of salt (or base). Snethlage gave the equation for the curve as

$$k' = (\alpha k'_H + (1 - \alpha)k'_M)C \qquad (11.2)$$

where k' is the over-all velocity constant, k'_H is the velocity constant due to oxonium ion catalysis, k'_M is the velocity constant due to undissociated acid molecule, C is the concentration of the acid, and α is the degree of ionization of the acid.

The catalysis by undissociated acid molecules as well as by the oxonium ion is termed the *dual theory* of catalysis.

Brönsted and Wynne-Jones (*Trans. Faraday Soc.*, **25,** 59, 1929) investigated acid catalysis of hydrolytic reactions. The reactions may be typified by the hydrolysis of ethylorthoacetate, which may be written

$$CH_3C(OC_2H_5)_3 + H_2O \longrightarrow 2C_2H_5OH + CH_3COOC_2H_5$$

The investigators found that the hydrolysis of ethyl orthoacetate, orthopropionate, and orthocarbonate showed catalysis by the molecules of water, *m*- and *p*-nitrophenols, and cacodylic and acetic acids in addition to the oxonium ion. The over-all constant for the hydrolysis was written

$$k' = k'_0 + k'_H m_H + k'_A m_A \qquad (11.3)$$

where k'_0 represents the catalysis by water, k'_H that by the oxonium ion, and k'_A that by the acid molecule. The m terms refer to the concentrations of the indicated species.

A catalysis by all acids and not merely by oxonium ion alone is called a general acid catalysis. The equation for the total rate may be written

$$k' = \sum_i k_i'(A_i) \tag{11.4}$$

where k' is the over-all catalytic constant, k_i' is the catalytic constant of the ith type of substance, and (A_i) is the concentration of that substance.

King and Bolinger (*J. Am. Chem. Soc.*, **58**, 1553, 1936) found that the decomposition of the diazoacetate ion in aqueous solution was a reaction which was phenomenally sensitive to general acid catalysis and that the molar catalytic constant for hydrion, 3.57×10^8 at 25° C, is the highest recorded for any reaction. Stempel and Schaffel (*J. Am. Chem. Soc.*, **66**, 1158, 1944) made a comparative study of the reactions between hydroxylamine, phenylhydrazine, and semicarbazide with *d*-carvone. The data showed these reactions to be general acid catalyzed. Many other instances of general acid catalysis are recorded in the literature.

To show that a reaction is subject to general acid catalysis, the method of Brönsted and Guggenheim (*J. Am. Chem. Soc.*, **49**, 2554, 1927) is generally used. In this method the oxonium ion concentration is held constant in each of several solutions containing different amounts of acid HA. The procedure is to add to each solution enough of the anion A⁻ of the acid to make the concentration of A⁻ to that of HA the same in all solutions.

General base catalysis

A catalysis by all bases and not merely by hydroxide ion alone is called a general base catalysis. The equation for the over-all rate constant k' is

$$k' = \sum_i k_i'(B_i) \tag{11.5}$$

where k_i is the catalytic rate constant for the base of species i and (B_i) is the concentration of this species of base.

Brönsted and Guggenheim (*loc. cit.*) and Westheimer (*J. Org. Chem.*, **2**, 431, 1937) found that the mutarotation of glucose was catalyzed by bases generally. Brönsted and Pedersen (*Z. physik. Chem.*, **108**, 185, 1924) and others showed that the decomposition of nitramide also responded to general base catalysis. In acetate buffers the total rate constant k' is given by the equation

$$k' = 0.63 \times 10^{-5} + k_c'(C_2H_3O_2^-) \tag{11.6}$$

where the catalytic constant due to water as a base is $k_0' = 0.63 \times 10^{-5}$ and k_c' is the catalytic constant of the base $C_2H_3O_2^-$. Again the literature is replete with reactions which are general base catalyzed.

Both general acid and general base catalysis

Catalysis by both all acids and all bases is termed both general acid and general base catalysis. The over-all specific rate constant k' for such processes is given by the equation

$$k' = \sum_i k_{A_i}'(A_i) + \sum_i k_{B_i}'(B_i) \tag{11.7}$$

In this equation the meanings of the terms are clear from what has already been said.

Bell and Baughan (*J. Chem. Soc.*, **1937**, 1947) found that the depolymerization of dimeric dihydroxyacetone was catalyzed generally by both acids and bases. In buffer solution containing an uncharged acid A and the corresponding base B (i.e., the anion of the acid) the general expression for the reaction velocity is

$$k' = k_0' + k_{H_3O^+}'(H_3O^+) + k_{OH^-}'(OH^-) + k_A'(A) + k_B'(B) \tag{11.8}$$

where k_0' is the velocity of the water catalyzed reaction and k_x' is the catalytic constant of the species x. Equation (11.8) can be written in the form

$$k' = k'' + \alpha(B) \tag{11.9}$$

where

$$k'' = k_0' + k_{H_3O^+}'(H_3O^+) + k_{OH^-}'(OH^-) \tag{11.10}$$

and

$$\alpha = k_B' + k_A'(A)/(B) \tag{11.11}$$

There were no conditions under which it was possible to neglect the last two terms in k'', and in order to determine the separate catalytic constants it was necessary to carry out a series of experiments in which (H_3O^+) and (OH^-) were constant. This was done by varying (A) and (B) but keeping the ratio of (A)/(B) constant, and also keeping the total salt concentration constant at $0.1N$ by adding sodium chloride when necessary. Under these conditions k'' and α are constant for a given series and can be obtained from a linear plot of k' against (B). Finally by carrying out two or more such series with different values of (A)/(B), the separate values of k_A' and k_B' can be obtained. The results for some of the buffer solutions studied by Bell and Baughan are listed in Table I. The catalytic constant for water was obtained by dividing the spontaneous rate k_0' by 55.5.

TABLE I

Trimethyl acetic acid; $k_B' = 4.2 \times 10^{-1}$

$$A/B = 1.034, \ (H_3O^+) = 1.52 \times 10^{-5}, \ 10^4 k'' = 456$$

C(CH₃)₃COO⁻		0.0501	0.0398	0.0300	0.0225	0.0100
$10^4 k'$	obs.	644	639	582	540	499
	calc.	666	623	582	551	498

$$A/B = 1.795, \ (H_3O^+) = 2.64 \times 10^{-5}, \ 10^4 k'' = 276$$

C(CH₃)₃COO⁻		0.0305	0.0229	0.0151	0.00726
$10^4 k'$	obs.	401	372	338	308
	calc.	404	372	340	307

Mandelic acid; $k_A' = 1.04 \times 10^{-2}$, $k_B' = 2.00 \times 10^{-2}$

$$A/B = 0.129, \ (H_3O^+) = 7.78 \times 10^{-5}, \ 10^4 k'' = 106.2$$

CHPh(OH)COO⁻		0.100	0.0750	0.0500	0.0250
$10^4 k'$	obs.	130.3	122.0	120.2	110.6
	calc.	127.5	122.2	116.9	111.6

$$A/B = 0.613, \ (H_3O^+) = 3.70 \times 10^{-4}, \ 10^4 k'' = 46.7$$

CHPh(OH)COO⁻		0.0996	0.0747	0.0498	0.0249
$10^4 k'$	obs.	73.4	66.3	61.4	52.5
	calc.	73.0	66.4	59.8	53.3

$$A/B = 1.30, \ (H_3O^+) = 7.82 \times 10^{-4}, \ 10^4 k'' = 46.1$$

CHPh(OH)COO⁻		0.0980	0.0735	0.0490	0.0245
$10^4 k'$	obs.	81.2	70.6	62.0	55.6
	calc.	78.9	70.7	62.5	54.6

Brönsted and Guggenheim (*loc. cit.*) studied the general catalysis by both acids and bases of the mutarotation of glucose. Dawson and coworkers (*J. Chem. Soc.*, **1927**, 458; **1928**, 543; **1931**, 2658; **1930**, 2180) found that the reactions of ketones with iodine were generally catalyzed by both acids and bases. In the mutarotation reaction and in the reaction of acetone with iodine, the acid catalysis by water molecules is negligible compared with the basic catalysis. In the depolymerization reaction, however, both types of catalysis contribute to the *spontaneous* rate, i.e., water acts both as an acid and as a basic catalyst because k'_A and k'_B calculated from the Brönsted equations (see the section on the Brönsted equation) are of the same order of magnitude, and also because the observed value of $k'_0/55.5$ is considerably greater than either k'_A or k'_B.

Specific ion catalysis

Brönsted and Wynne-Jones (*loc. cit.*) observed that in the hydrolysis of acetal and of ethyl orthoformate, catalysis by acids other than the hydrogen ion is undetectable. This circumstance makes the reaction suitable for the determination of hydrogen ion concentrations and the study of salt effects. In the hydrolysis of ethyl orthoformate in cacadylic acid buffers, it is clear from Table II that not only is there no effect due to the undissociated acid, but also that the substitution of chloride ions for cacodylate ions does not affect the activity coefficients of the buffer constituents to a measurable extent.

TABLE II **Hydrolysis of ethyl orthoformate in cacodylic acid-cacodylate buffers, at 20° C.**

Ionic strength	Conc. of NaCl	Conc. of Na cacodylate	Conc. of cacodylic acid	A/B	$k' \times 10^3$
0.05	0.0242	0.0258	0.0242	0.938	13.3
.05	.0371	.0129	.0121	.938	13.3
.05	.0435	.00645	.00605	.938	13.4
.05	.0194	.0306	.0194	.0634	8.7
.05	.0347	.0153	.0097	.0634	8.8
.05	.0423	.00765	.00485	.0634	8.7

Ray and Dutt (*J. Indian Chem. Soc.*, **20**, 81, 1943) found that the racemization velocity of the pure optical enantiomers *l*- and *d*-cobaltic trisbiguanidine chloride was not affected by anions except the hydroxyl ion, which strongly accelerates the reaction.

Hammett (*Physical Organic Chemistry*, First Ed., New York and London, McGraw-Hill Book Company, Inc., 1940) gives the criterion of distinction between a specific oxonium-ion catalysis and a general acid catalysis as the behavior of the rate when the concentrations of both components of a buffer solution are increased in the same proportion and at constant ionic strength. If the rate remains the same, the catalysis is of the specific oxonium type; if the rate increases, the catalysis is of the general acid type.

Mechanisms of acid-base catalysis

Lowry's mechanism

Brönsted (*Rec. trav. Chem.*, **42**, 718, 1923) and Lowry (*Chem. and Ind.*, **42**, 43, 1923) independently define an acid as a substance which can split off a proton or unsolvated hydrogen ion, and a base as a substance which can accept a proton and become an acid. Lewis (*J. Franklin Inst.*, **226**, 293, 1938) extended these concepts and defined an acid as a substance which can accept an electron pair from a base to form a coordinate bond, and a base as a substance which can donate an electron pair to form a conjugate bond.

Lowry (*J. Chem. Soc.*, **127**, 1371, 1925) has proposed the theory that reactions which are produced by both acid and base are really produced by combined action of the two. Lowry and Richards (*J. Chem. Soc.*, **127**, 1385, 1925) distinguish between inactive solvents such as chloroform, which have no catalytic properties; ampholytic solvents such as water, which can act as a complete solvent, i.e., are both acidic and basic in their catalytic power; and solvents such as pyridine, which are not catalysts when pure but develop catalytic properties in the presence of an auxiliary catalyst. The mixed catalysts formed in this way are more efficient than the complete catalyst.

Lowry (*Chem. Rev.*, **4**, 231, 1927) proposed for the initial stage in the conversion of the oxidic into the aldehydic form of reducing sugars such as glucose, a mechanism formulated as depending on the combination of sugar either with a base plus water (which is here a proton donor or an acid) or with an acid plus water (which is here a proton acceptor or a base). The scheme is as follows:

The theory was proposed because many tautomeric changes which are base catalyzed do not occur in a solvent that is freed from impurities which might function as acids, but do occur when acid impurities are present. Thus Lowry and Richards (*loc. cit.*) found that the tautomeric mutarotation of tetramethyl glucose was very slow in chloroform to which either the base pyridine or acid cresol had been added. However, the reaction became quite rapid when both the base and acid were added. Being amphoteric, water can function as an acid or as a base or as both an acid and a base. Roberts and Urey (*J. Am. Chem. Soc.*, **61**, 2584, 1939) have confirmed that Lowry's mechanism yields the critical complex required by the kinetics.

Brönsted and Guggenheim (*loc. cit.*), using two prototropic forms of sugar as HS and SH respectively, give the mechanism for the mutarotation transformation under the combined influence of a base B and an acid HA as

$$B + HS + HA \rightleftharpoons BH^+ + SH + A^-$$

In this case the complete catalyst may include either the molecules B and HA or the ions A^- and BH^+ which act as base and acid respectively. In water solutions the reaction will generally be

$$B + HS + HOH \rightleftharpoons BH^+ + SH + OH^-$$

or

$$OH_2 + HS + HOH \rightleftharpoons OH_3^+ + SH + OH^-$$

where water plays the part of an acid when the catalyst is a base, or of a base when the catalyst is an acid.

Pedersen (*J. Phys. Chem.*, **38**, 581, 1934) discussed Lowry's explanation applied to prototropic changes and concluded that it could not be accepted in cases of acid and basic catalysis in prototropic systems which have been studied. Pedersen (*Trans. Faraday Soc.*, **34**, 237, 1938) pointed out that Hsü, Ingold, and Wilson (*J. Chem. Soc.*, **1935**, 1778) find from their study of the methylene azomethine system that the termolecular mechanism of Lowry's scheme applied to certain mobile prototropic systems where the anion is so difficult to form that it never attains kinetic independence. Pedersen explained that the rareness of collision of three molecules with proper orientation required by Lowry's mechanism, is compensated for in that the mechanism requires a smaller energy of activation than the consecutive bimolecular reactions of other proposed theories.

Lewis' electron pair exchange picture of acid-base catalysis

Luder (*Chem. Rev.*, **27**, 547, 1940) called the electron theory of valence the most powerful tool now available to the chemist. This theory was originated by G. N. Lewis (*J. Am. Chem. Soc.*, **38**, 762, 1916), who has applied it systematically to the explanation of the nature of acids and bases (*J. Franklin Inst.*, **226**, 293, 1938); (*J. Am. Chem. Soc.*, **61**, 1886, 1939; **61**, 1894, 1939). Germann (*J. Am. Chem. Soc.*, **47**,

2461, 1925; **47,** 2275, 1925), Cady and Elsey (*J. Chem. Edu.,* **5,** 1425, 1928), Wickert (*Z. physik. Chem. A,* **178,** 361, 1937) and Smith (*Chem. Rev.,* **23,** 165, 1938) have extended the solvent system theory of acids and bases to include aprotonic systems. Cady and Elsey (*loc. cit.*) define an acid as a substance which forms by its direct ionization only cations identical with the positive ions formed by the ionization of the solvent molecules. A base by their definition is a substance whose molecules yield by direct ionization only anions identical with those formed by the ionization of the solvent molecules.

An example of the interpretation of catalytic action by the electronic theory of acids and bases is the base catalyzed reaction between alcohols and benzoyl chloride studied by Hückel (*Ann.,* **540,** 274, 1939). Pyridine as a solvent promotes rapid action, and conductance measurements indicate ionization. Benzoyl chloride, a secondary acid, and pyridine react to produce ions in the following manner:

$$\text{Ph–C(:\ddot{O}:)(:\ddot{Cl}:) + :N(C_5H_5)} \longrightarrow \left[\text{Ph–C(:\ddot{O}:)–N(C_5H_5)}\right]^+ \ Cl^-$$

$$\left[\text{Ph–C(:\ddot{O}:)–N(C_5H_5)}\right]^+ \ Cl^- + R:\ddot{O}:H \longrightarrow \left[\text{Ph–C(:\ddot{O}:)(:\ddot{O}:R)–N(C_5H_5)H}\right]^+ \ Cl^-$$

$$\longrightarrow \text{Ph–C(:\ddot{O}:)(:\ddot{O}:R)} + \left[C_5H_5N:H\right]^+ \ Cl^-$$

Smith (*J. Chem. Soc.*, **1943,** 521) expressed the Lewis definition of acids and bases by the scheme

$$B) +)A \rightleftharpoons BA$$

where) after a letter represents a free electron pair and) before a letter represents the corresponding deficiency, i.e., B is a base with a free electron pair which may enter the shell of another atom or group and A is an acid which can receive such an electron pair. The hydrolysis of the halogen acetates, which Smith found to be subject to general basic catalysis, is then explained on the basis of the Lewis theory as follows. The ion $CH_2XCO_2^-$ may be regarded as composed of the base $\overline{X}$ and the acid $^+CH_2CO_2^-$. The $\overline{X}$ base may be any halogen ion. The strong base $\overline{B}$ displaces the weak base $\overline{X}$ from its acid. The base $\overline{B}$ may be any of the anions used to displace $\overline{X}$. This then becomes a normal acid-base reaction. Thus the reaction

$$CH_2XCO_2^- + \overline{B}) \longrightarrow CH_2BCO_2^- + \overline{X})$$

and the reaction

$$H_3O^+ + \overline{B}) \rightleftharpoons HB + H_2O)$$

are essentially of the same type, i.e., acid-base reactions. This treatment is in harmony with the Lewis electron pair exchange concept of acid base reactions.

Mechanisms involving carbonium ions and carbanions

A carbonium ion is a group of atoms possessing a carbon atom which is associated with only six electrons. Hammett (*Physical Organic Chemistry*, First Ed., New York and London, McGraw-Hill Book Co., Inc., 1940) gave the common feature of all carbonium reactions to be the linking of the carbonium ion to a nucleophilic reagent, that is, a reagent that possesses an unshared electron pair. Hammett states that the most satisfactory explanation of the complex set of reactions, involving hydration, the formation of sulfuric esters, condensations, polymerization, and rearrangement, which accompany the solution of an olefin in strong sulfuric acid, is in terms of a carbonium ion intermediate.

Whitmore (*J. Am. Chem. Soc.*, **54,** 3274, 1932) pointed out that organic molecules which give a poor yield of *metathetical* products, or products resulting from the elimination of an inorganic molecule, or which yield rearranged products, contain a portion which can be written electronically in one of two ways, namely:

(1) $: \overset{..}{\text{A}} : \overset{..}{\text{B}} : \overset{..}{\text{X}} :$ (2) $\overset{..}{\text{A}} : : \overset{..}{\text{B}} : \overset{..}{\text{D}} : \overset{..}{\text{X}} :$

in which X is generally oxygen, halogen, or other strongly electronegative atom, and A, B, and D are atoms like carbon and nitrogen which are neither strongly electropositive nor strongly electronegative. System (1) is involved in such *two-atom* rearrangements as the pinacolic, the retropinacolic, the Hoffman, the Beckmann and others. System (2) is observed in many types of allylic or triad rearrangements.

In any reaction which results in the removal of X from a molecule containing system one, then *whatever is the mechanism of the process*, X retains a complete octet of electrons and leaves B with an open sextet of electrons. Thus

$$: \overset{..}{\text{A}} : \overset{..}{\text{B}} : \overset{..}{\text{X}} : \longrightarrow : \overset{..}{\text{A}} : \text{B} + : \overset{..}{\text{X}} :$$

One of the three different changes may then occur:

(1) The positive organic fragment may have a long enough life to allow it to combine with a negative ion.

$$: \overset{..}{\text{A}} : \text{B} + : \overset{..}{\text{Y}} : \longrightarrow : \overset{..}{\text{A}} : \overset{..}{\text{B}} : \overset{..}{\text{Y}} :$$

This is similar to the simple metathetical reactions of organic chemistry, which some organic reactions follow exclusively.

(2) For cases where B has a greater attraction for electrons than A, a change in the fragment will leave A with an open sextet of electrons. This shift in the electron pair will include the atom or group with which it is associated. The equation for the shift is

$$: \overset{..}{\text{A}} : \overset{..}{\text{B}} \longrightarrow \text{A} : \overset{..}{\text{B}} :$$

The fragment may then combine with the ion X or a new negative ion Y.

$$: \overset{..}{\text{Y}} : + \text{A} : \overset{..}{\text{B}} \longrightarrow : \overset{..}{\text{Y}} : \overset{..}{\text{A}} : \overset{..}{\text{B}} :$$

thus resulting in a rearranged product.

(3) If the atom A has a hydrogen atom attached to it, the fragment may become stabilized by loss of a proton.

$$\overset{\text{H}}{: \overset{..}{\text{A}} : \text{B}} \longrightarrow \text{H}^+ + : \overset{..}{\text{A}} : : \overset{..}{\text{B}} :$$

Thus an olefin or other unsaturated molecule is formed.

Whitmore pointed out that in change (2), if there is a hydrogen attached to atom B in the rearranged positive fragment, then the system may lose a proton. These electron shifts within the molecule and the stabilization by loss of protons are monomolecular processes which are sensibly as rapid as the bimolecular reaction of the positive fragments with ions. In this way considerable amounts of abnormal products are formed.

This mechanism of positive ion fragments containing an atom with an *open sextet* of electrons was used by Whitmore (*Ind. Eng. Chem.*, **26,** 94, 1934) to explain the polymerization of olefins. He applied it to polymerization of isobutylene, a process of present industrial significance. Furthermore, Whitmore pointed out that the process is catalyzed by any substance which gives hydrogen ions which by adding to the olefins present can start the cycle of changes again.

Brown and Widiger (*J. Am. Chem. Soc.*, **62,** 115, 1940), studying the acid catalyzed dimerization of anethol, concluded that it was difficult to find any support in their results for the Whitmore mechanism of polymerization.

Lowry (*Chem. and Ind.*, **43,** 1128, 1924) suggested that the Walden inversion depends on the momentary formation of a carbonium cation during an interchange of anions or negatively charged radicals, and similar views were held with respect to the Beckmann rearrangement. (See Waters, *Physical Aspects of Organic Chemistry*, London, George Ruthledge and Sons Ltd.) Brynmor Jones (*Chem. Rev.*, **35,** 355, 1944), discussing the Beckmann rearrangement of benzophenone oxime by hydrogen chloride, and the kinetics and mechanism of the transformation of ketoximes, concluded that there was no evidence that the spontaneous transformation of such compounds involves any actual dissociation into free ions, although the effect of polar molecules on the velocity of rearrangement suggests that some dissociation occurs as a preliminary to rearrangement. The retention of optical activity during the conversion of optically active ketoximes shows, however, that the migrating hydrocarbon group is never kinetically free. The change is best regarded as intramolecular in nature.

It may be pointed out that Whitmore's general theory included any atom not too strongly electropositive nor too strongly electronegative, such as carbon and nitrogen, which could exist with an *open sextet* of electrons in a molecular fragment.

Carbanions, i.e., molecular fragments possessing carbon atoms with an unshared pair of electrons out of a full complement of eight electrons, likewise enter into many reactions. Among other reactions Hammett (*Physical Organic Chemistry*, First Ed., New York and London, McGraw-Hill Book Company, Inc., 1940) mentions that carbonium ions attach themselves to carbanions acting as bases, thus creating a new carbon-carbon linkage. Many chain lengthening procedures depend upon this reaction. Conant and Wheland (*J. Am. Chem. Soc.*, **54**, 1212, 1932) and McEwen (*J. Am. Chem. Soc.*, **58**, 1124, 1936) use carbanions to demonstrate the acidity of many weakly acidic substances and to measure approximately their acid strengths.

Equations of rates for acid or base catalyzed reactions

BRÖNSTED EQUATION

Snethlage (*Z. Electrochem.*, **18**, 539, 1912; *Z. physik. Chem.*, **85**, 211, 1913) noted the correlation between rates of acid catalyzed reactions and the strengths of the catalyzing acids after it had become clear that acid catalysis could be separated into a catalysis by hydrogen ion and one by undissociated acid.

Taylor (*Medd. K. Vetenskapsakad. Nobelinst.*, **2**, No. 37, 1) also studied the relative rates of catalysis by undissociated acid molecules and by hydrogen ions. He expressed the relationship quantitatively by the equation (*Z. Electrochem.*, **20**, 201, 1914)

$$k'_m/k'_H = C_H/C_m^{\frac{1}{2}} \tag{11.12}$$

where k'_m and k''_H are the catalytic rate constants for undissociated acid molecules and for hydrogen ions respectively, and C_m and C_H are the respective concentrations of these two catalysts.

Taylor's equation has been largely superseded by the more adaptable equation of Brönsted, to a consideration of which this section will be largely devoted.

The rate constant of an acid catalyzed reaction is given by Brönsted (*Trans. Faraday Soc.*, **24**, 630, 1928; *Chem. Rev.*, **5**, 231, 1928) for an acid catalyst possessing one ionizable hydrogen atom as

$$k'_{a_0} = G_1 K_{a_0}^x \tag{11.13}$$

where G_1 and x are constants determined by the reaction and K_{a_0} is the acid dissociation constant, which for a typical acid-base reaction such as

$$AH + H_2O \rightleftharpoons A^- + H_3O^+$$

can be defined as

$$K_{a_0} = \frac{k' \, diss.}{k' \, ass.} \tag{11.14}$$

if the reaction from left to right be (arbitrarily) called a dissociation and from right to left an association, and if $k' \, diss.$ and $k' \, ass.$ represent the respective velocities of the dissociation and association processes.

For basic catalysis by a base having one point at which a proton can attack itself the relationship may be written

$$k'_{b_0} = G_2 K_{b_0}^{1-x} \tag{11.15}$$

where

$$K_{b_0} = \frac{1}{K_{a_0}}$$

Correcting the theory as expressed in Eq. (11.13) and (11.15) for the probability factor that arises from the possibility of more than one acid or basic center (if we let p represent the number of acid centers and q the number of basic centers) for the acid catalyzed rate we have

$$k'_a = G_1 K_a^x q^x p^{1-x} \tag{11.16}$$

and for the base catalyzed rate

$$k'_b = G_2 K_b^{1-x} q^x p^{1-x} \tag{11.17}$$

Brönsted and Guggenheim's (J. Am. Chem. Soc., **49**, 2554, 1927) plots of log k'_a and log k'_b versus log K_a for the mutarotation of glucose in the presence of various acids and bases are given in Fig. 1. Here the influence of electric types to be expected theoretically and also statistical effects have been omitted. From the graph it is evident that water acts both as an acidic and as a basic catalyst. Except for the base having a double positive charge, the points corresponding to basic catalysis lie approximately on a straight line. The curve for acid catalysis is not so well established as the one for basic catalysis, but the increasing catalytic effect with increasing acid strength is obvious. The relationship between the catalytic effect of an acid or a base and its strength is striking, when it is remembered that the plot covers a range of 10^{18} in K_a and 10^8 in K_b.

Many confirmations of these equations have been made. In Peluger's plot (J. Am. Chem. Soc., **60**, 1513, 1938) of the catalytic constants for the base catalyzed glucose mutarotation against those for the nitramide reaction, the data on a variety of catalysts are given by a single straight line. The same data expressed by the Brönsted law (Eq. 11.16 and 11.17) would require several lines.

HAMMETT'S EQUATION

Hammett's equation (*J. Am. Chem. Soc.*, **59**, 96, 1937) takes into account the effect of a substituent upon the rate or equilibrium constant of a general reaction for a member of a class of aromatic com-

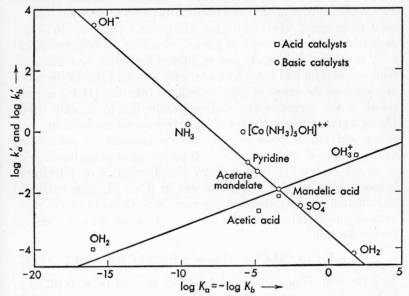

Figure 1 Dependence of acid and basic catalysis on the strength of acid and base.

pounds. A general reaction is one that a compound and its derivatives will commonly undergo. The equation for the rate or equilibrium constant for a general reaction for a member of a class of aromatic compounds according to Hammett is

$$\log k' = \log k^{0'} + \sigma\rho \tag{11.18}$$

Here $k^{0'}$ is the rate or equilibrium constant of the general reaction for an unsubstituted member of the class; σ is a substituent constant, depending upon the substituent, and ρ is a reaction constant, dependent upon the reaction, the medium, and the temperature.

Now the only data available give the $\sigma\rho$ product; therefore it is necessary to assign an arbitrary value to some σ or ρ. Hammett chooses $\rho = 1$ for the ionization equilibrium of substituted benzoic acids. Thus the difference between the logarithm of the ionization constant of substituted benzoic acid and the logarithm of the ionization constant of benzoic acid gives the value of σ for that substituent. Taking these σ values, ρ values for other reactions can be obtained, and from these in turn other σ values can be calculated for substituents whose effects upon the ionization of benzoic acid have never been determined. He found that thirty-eight reactions involving derivatives of benzoic acid, of phenol, of aniline, of benzenesulfonic acid, of phenylboric acid, and of phenylphosphine, and including both equilibrium and rate constants, gave a mean value of the probable error of the values of $\log k'$ calculated from Eq. (11.18) as compared to the corresponding observed quantities to be only 0.067. Figure 2 gives Hammett's plot of $\log k'$ versus σ for the following ionization and kinetic processes: (1) Acidity constants of substituted anilinium ions in water at 25° C; (2) ionization of phenylboric acids in 25 per cent ethyl alcohol at 25° C; (3) reaction of substituted benzoyl chlorides with methyl alcohol at 0° C; (4) base catalyzed bromination of substituted acetophenones in acetic acid-water medium with sodium acetate as catalyst at 35° C. Thus for the rate constant for the reaction

$$p\text{-BrC}_6\text{H}_5\text{CH}_2\text{Cl} + \text{KI} \longrightarrow p\text{-BrC}_6\text{H}_5\text{CH}_2\text{I} + \text{KCl}$$

we have from Hammett's data $\log k^{0'}$ of Eq. (11.18) is 0.167, ρ is 0.785, and σ is 0.232. The $k^{0'}$ is the rate constant for the reaction of unsubstituted benzyl chloride with potassium iodide

$$\text{C}_6\text{H}_5\text{CH}_2\text{Cl} + \text{KI} \longrightarrow \text{C}_6\text{H}_5\text{CH}_2\text{I} + \text{KCl}$$

ρ is a constant characteristic of the general reaction of substituted phenylchlorides with potassium iodide

$$\text{XC}_6\text{H}_5\text{CH}_2\text{Cl} + \text{KI} \longrightarrow \text{XC}_6\text{H}_5\text{CH}_2\text{I} + \text{KCl}$$

and σ is a constant for para substitution of chlorine.

Hammett gives an extensive list of σ values (substituent constants). The ρ values must be evaluated for each general reaction. Hammett makes a list of ρ values for several general reactions. Among other checks on the theory might be mentioned the work of Hartmann,

Hoogsteen, and Moede (*J. Am. Chem. Soc.*, **66**, 1714, 1944). These authors determined the hydrion-catalyzed esterification of twenty-two substituted benzoic acids with cyclohexanol. They took into account the reaction between the catalyst and the solvent. The

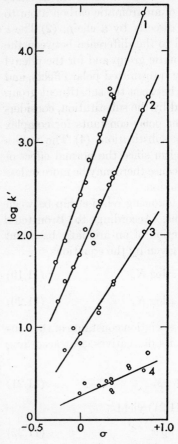

Figure 2 Relationship between log k' and σ for various reactions.

Curve 1. Acidity constants of substituted anilinium ions in water at 25° C.

Curve 2. Ionization of substituted phenylboric acids in 25% ethyl alcohol at 25° C.

Curve 3. Reaction of substituted benzoyl chlorides with methyl alcohol at 0° C.

Curve 4. Base catalyzed bromination of substituted acetophenones in acetic acid-water medium with sodium acetate as catalyst at 35° C.

experimental values of esterification rate constants for meta and para substituents are found to be in close agreement with those calculated using Hammett's equation. The values of σ were those reported by Hammett, and the value of ρ was obtained by the method of least squares. The average difference between $-\log k'$ calculated and $-\log k'$ observed by these authors was 0.082 or about 2 per cent.

Branch and Calvin (*The Theory of Organic Chemistry*, New York, Prentice-Hall, Inc., 1941, by permission of the publishers) emphasize that Hammett's equation is an approximate empirical one applicable only within certain limits. These authors offer the following criticisms: (1) The equation is a good approximation when the substituent effect is one of change in the electric charge of an aromatic carbon atom to which the reacting group is attached directly by a chain. (2) The σ value for this case is then proportional to the difference between the polar constants for the substituted aromatic group and for the phenyl group. (3) When steric factors, directly transmitted polar effects, and important resonances other than those between the substituent group and the aromatic resonances are caused by the substitution, considerable error is introduced by using either polar constants for complex groups or values determined only by substitution. (4) The values assigned to groups are subject to criticism since the normal effect of the substituent is difficult to obtain, because there may be more or less perturbation in any chosen general reaction.

Branch and Calvin worked out the following relationship between Brönsted's and Hammett's equations. According to Brönsted's theory, the rate constants for the reaction of an aromatic base and one of its meta or para derivatives are given by the equations

$$\log k_u' = \log G - x \log K_u \tag{11.19}$$

and

$$\log k_\sigma' = \log G - x \log K_\sigma \tag{11.20}$$

In these equations K_u and K_σ are the dissociation constants of the conjugate acids of the aromatic base and its derivatives. But according to Hammett's equation

$$\log K_\sigma = \log K_u + \sigma\rho' \tag{11.21}$$

combining Eq. (11.19), (11.20), and (11.21) yields

$$\log k_\sigma' = \log k_u' - \sigma\rho'x \tag{11.22}$$

Here x is determined by the substrate and ρ' is determined by the aromatic acids, hence $\rho'x$ is determined by a general reaction of a class of aromatic acids, that is, $\rho'x$ is ρ for this general reaction. Knowing ρ and ρ', x can be calculated. Thus ρ' for aniline is 2.73, and ρ for the reaction of substituted anilines with dinitrochloronaphthalene in ethyl alcohol medium is 3.69; therefore x is 1.3.

The correlation of reaction rates with acidity function

Hammett and Deyrup (*J. Am. Chem. Soc.*, **54**, 2721, 1932) correlated rates and acidity functions up to 100 per cent sulfuric acid. The equation they used was

$$\log k' = -H_0 + \text{constant} \qquad (11.23)$$

Here k' is the velocity constant, and H_0 is the acidity function. They point out that an exact parallelism between the reaction velocity and the acidity can be expected only if the velocity is proportional to the concentration of the ion formed by one hydrogen ion to one molecule of neutral substrate, if the ratio of the concentration of this ion to the total concentration of substrate is small, and if there is no further ionization by addition of another hydrogen ion. Since the equation held in sulfuric acid-water mixtures, for the decomposition of malic acid, the condensation of *o*-benzoylbenzoic acid, and the Beckmann transformation of acetophenone oxime, the necessary conditions are fulfilled for these reactions. In measuring the acidity function, Hammett and Deyrup used the *step-method* of the relative basicities of indicators. They assumed that the relative strength of two bases of the same charge type was independent of the medium in which they were compared. A simple basic indicator is defined as a non-ionized or neutral substance capable of adding one hydrogen ion per molecule without any complicating further reactions and in such a way that a color change is determined by the extent of the reaction. Further the strength of such an indicator or any other monoacid base is defined by the function

$$PK' = -\log \frac{A_{H^+}A_B}{A_{BH^+}} = -\log \frac{C_{H^+}C_B}{C_{BH^+}} - \log \frac{f_{H^+}f_B}{f_{BH^+}} \qquad (11.24)$$

where A is the activity, C is the concentration, and f is the activity coefficient, and refer activities in all solvents to the same reference standard, a dilute aqueous solution. In such a solution therefore,

$$\log \frac{f_{H^+}f_B}{f_{BH^+}} = 0 \qquad (11.25)$$

and

$$PK' = -\log \frac{C_{H^+}C_B}{C_{BH^+}} \qquad (11.26)$$

If now we determine the ionization ratios of two such bases B and C in any given solution whatsoever, then

$$PK'_B - PK'_C = -\log \frac{C_B C_{CH^+}}{C_{BH^+} C_C} - \log \frac{f_B f_{CH^+}}{f_{BH^+} f_C} \qquad (11.27)$$

If the indicators are bases, the first term on the right is measurable colorimetrically, and according to the assumption stated earlier the activity coefficient term is zero and the activity coefficient ratio f_B/f_{BH^+} in a given solution is the same for all bases. Therefore, the relative strengths of the two bases are given by the equation

$$PK'_B - PK'_C = -\log \frac{C_B C_{CH^+}}{C_{BH^+} C_C} \qquad (11.28)$$

Thus in a series of simple basic indicators covering any range of acidities whatever, a step-wise application of this procedure, using any convenient solutions, gives the base strength relative to water of the whole series.

Hammett and Deyrup define the acidity function H_0 by the equation

$$H_0 = \log \frac{C_B}{C_{BH^+}} + PK'_B \qquad (11.29)$$

TABLE III   **Showing the constancy of $(\log k' + H_0)$ for the decomposition of o-benzoylbenzoic acid in sulfuric acid and oleum of various concentrations at 75° and 85° C**

% H_2SO_4	% Free SO_3	H_0 at 25° C	Log k' at 75° C	Log k' at 85° C	Log $k' + H_0$ at 75° C	Log $k' + H_0$ at 85° C
86		−7.34	−4.06		−11.40	
89		−7.74	−3.53		−11.27	
91		−8.01	−3.23		−11.24	
93		−8.20	−2.89		−11.09	
96		−8.67	−2.32		−10.99	
98		−8.95	−2.11	−1.64	−11.06	−11.59
100	0	−10.70	−1.93	−1.47	−12.63	−12.17
100.4	1.8	−10.71	−1.91	−1.43	−12.61	−12.14
101.8	8.0	−10.73	−1.89	−1.42	−12.62	−12.15
103.2	14.0	−10.94	−1.87	−1.42	−12.81	−12.36
104.5	20.0	−11.04	−1.84	−1.38	−12.88	−12.42
105.4	24.0	−11.16		−1.36		−12.52
105.9	−26.2	−11.22	−1.77	−1.34	−12.99	−12.56
106.5	28.8	−11.45		−1.32		−12.77

Substituting for PK'_B the value given by Eq. (11.24) into Eq. (11.29) gives an equivalent definition of H_0, namely

$$H_0 = \log \frac{C_B}{C_{BH^+}} - \log \frac{C_B}{C_{BH^+}} - \log C_{H^+} - \log \frac{f_{H^+}f_B}{f_{BH^+}} = -\log a_{H^+} \frac{f_B}{f_{BH^+}} \tag{11.30}$$

In dilute aqueous solutions where f_B and f_{BH^+} both become unity

$$H_0 = -\log a_{H^+} = pH \tag{11.31}$$

Deane (*J. Am. Chem. Soc.*, **67**, 329, 1945) found that in fuming sulfuric acid, the *o*-benzoylbenzoic acid decomposition according to the equations (Deane and Huffman, *Ind. Eng. Chem.*, **35**, 684, 1943)

corroborates the correlation method of Hammett and Deyrup. In Table III are given data for the constancy of the $(\log k' + H_0)$ term from Eq. (11.23). It can be seen that up to 28.8 per cent free SO_3, the predictions of Eq. (11.23) are fulfilled fairly well.

Deane used the data of Lewis and Bigeleisen (*J. Am. Chem. Soc.*, **65**, 1144, 1943) for the acidity function H_0 in fuming sulfuric acid, for making these correlations in sulfuric acid containing free SO_3.

Electrostatics of acid-base catalysis

THE SECONDARY KINETIC SALT EFFECT

In the case of a change in concentration by added salt of catalytically active ions, the phenomenon is known as the *secondary salt effect* in catalysis. This effect is quite pronounced when the catalytic ions are produced by the ionization of a weak electrolyte, but is insignificant when a strong acid or base is the catalyst.

Let us illustrate the secondary kinetic salt effect by showing how the oxonium ion concentration in a water solution of a weak acid is a function of the concentration of a neutral salt. For a weak acid, HA, in water solution the dissociation constant can be written

$$K_a = \frac{a_{H_3O^+} a_{A^-}}{a_{HA}} = \frac{C_{H_3O^+} C_{A^-}}{C_{HA}} \cdot \frac{f_{H_3O^+} f_{A^-}}{f_{HA}} \tag{11.32}$$

and solving for $C_{H_3O^+}$ we obtain

$$C_{H_3O^+} = K_a \frac{C_{HA}}{C_{A^-}} \frac{f_{HA}}{f_{H_3O^+} f_{HA}} \tag{11.33}$$

When C_{HA}/C_{A^-} is held constant

$$C_{H_3O^+} = K_a \frac{f_{HA}}{f_{H_3O^+} f_{A^-}} \tag{11.34}$$

Hence $C_{H_3O^+}$ will vary with ionic strength since $f_{HA}/f_{H_3O^+} f_{A^-}$ is dependent upon ionic strength. The catalytic influence of the oxonium ion is thus a function of the concentration of a salt. This is the secondary kinetic salt effect.

Assuming f_{HA} to be unity, we have from Eq. (2.39) and (4.5) for dilute solutions, where the denominator of Eq. (2.39) is approximately unity:

$$\ln k' = \ln k'_0 + (z^2_{H_3O^+} + z^2_{A^-}) A \sqrt{\mu} \tag{11.35}$$

if the primary salt effect remains constant. Here A is the Debye-Hückel constant, which for water at 25° C is 0.5091, and μ is the ionic strength.

Brönsted and King (*J. Am. Chem. Soc.*, **47**, 2523, 1925) consider the secondary kinetic salt effect in the case of hydroxyl-ion catalysis. The data they used were on the decomposition of nitroso-triacetone-amine in both piperidine-piperidinium buffer and phosphate buffer.

The piperidine-piperidinium buffer gives the equilibrium

$$C_5H_{11}N + H_2O \rightleftharpoons C_5H_{12}N^+ + OH^-$$

and the equilibrium constant in dilute solutions is given by

$$K_a = \frac{C_{C_5H_{12}N^+}C_{OH^-}}{C_{C_5H_{11}N}} \cdot \frac{f_{C_5H_{12}N^+}f_{OH^-}}{f_{C_5H_{11}N}} \qquad (11.36)$$

Therefore taking $f_{C_5H_{11}N}$ as unity and $f_{C_5H_{12}N^+} = f_{OH^-} = f$, then

$$C_{OH^-} = K_a \frac{C_{C_5H_{11}N}}{C_{C_5H_{12}N^+}} \frac{1}{f^2} \qquad (11.37)$$

Increase of salt concentration increases the $\frac{1}{f^2}$ term in Eq. (11.37) and hence the hydroxyl-ion concentration. In Table IV are given the data

TABLE IV Decomposition of nitroso-triacetone-amine at 15° C in piperidine solutions. Stoichiometric concentrations: $C_{pip} = 0.15M$, $C_{HCl} = 0.01M$

C_{NaCl}	$C_{NaCl} + C_{ptp.H^+}$	C_{OH^-}	k'
0.0	0.0205	.0105	0.001985
.02	.0411	.0111	.00207
.05	.0709	.0119	.00217
.08	.1025	.0125	.00223
.15	.1736	.0136	.00232
.20	.2244	.144	.00234

of Brönsted and King for the piperidine-piperidinium buffer. For equal concentrations of piperidine and piperidinium ion in Eq. (11.37)

$$C_{OH^-} = K_a \frac{1}{f_2} \qquad (11.38)$$

and

$$\ln k' = \ln k_0' + 2A\sqrt{\mu} \qquad (11.39)$$

since $z^+ = z^- = 1$.

In Table IV the concentrations of the hydroxyl ion, C_{OH^-}, were calculated from the observed effect of salt concentrations upon the rate.

Considering the phosphate buffers, which give the following equilibrium

$$PO_4^{---} + H_2O \rightleftharpoons HPO_4^{--} + OH^-$$

application of the mass law yields the following equilibrium expression:

$$K_a = \frac{C_{HPO_4^{--}}C_{OH^-}}{C_{PO_4^{---}}} \frac{f_{HPO_4^{--}}f_{OH^-}}{f_{PO_4^{---}}} \qquad (11.40)$$

or

$$C_{OH^-} = K_a \frac{C_{PO_4^{---}}}{C_{HPO_4^{--}}} \frac{f_{PO_4^{---}}}{f_{HPO_4^{--}} \cdot f_{OH^-}} \tag{11.41}$$

As the activity coefficient factor decreases with increasing concentration of salt, C_{OH^-} will decrease likewise and a negative secondary kinetic salt effect would be expected. Thus for $C_{PO_4^{---}} = C_{HPO_4^{--}}$ and a constant primary salt effect

$$\ln k' = \ln k'_0 + (z^2_{HPO_4^{--}} + z^2_{OH^-} - z^2_{PO_4^{---}})A\sqrt{\mu}$$
$$= \ln k'_0 - 4A\sqrt{\mu} \tag{11.42}$$

Table V contains the data of Brönsted and King for the decomposition of nitroso-triacetone-amine in phosphate buffer. It can be seen that

TABLE V Decomposition of nitroso-triacetone-amine at 15° C in phosphate solutions. Stoichiometric concentrations: $C_{PO_4^{---}} = 0.01M$, $C_{HPO_4^{--}} = 0.00333M$

C_{NaCl}	$C_{total\ salt}$	C_{OH^-}	k'
0.0	0.0367	0.00455	0.000854
.02	.0567	.00418	.000774
.05	.0867	.00397	.000718
.10	.1367	.00356	.000621
.15	.1867	.00331	.000556
.20	.2367	.00303	.000497

k' decreases with increasing salt concentration as required by theory. The C_{OH^-} values were again obtained from the effect of salt concentration upon the rate. The equilibrium constant based on concentrations K_C for the two buffers is related to the equilibrium constants based on activities K_a by the expressions:

$$K_C = K_a \frac{f_{C_5H_{11}N}}{f_{C_5H_{12}N^+} \cdot f_{OH^-}} = \frac{K_a}{f_1^2} \tag{11.43}$$

and

$$K_C = \bar{K}_a \frac{f_{PO_4^{---}}}{f_{HPO_4^{--}} \cdot f_{OH^-}} = \frac{K_a f_3}{f_1 f_2} \tag{11.44}$$

where f_1, f_2, and f_3 refer to activity coefficients of univalent, bivalent, and trivalent ions respectively. The best survey of the salt effect is obtained from the change in K_C caused by added salt and computed from velocity measurements. Brönsted and King found for the piperidine and phosphate equilibria that the change in K_C with salt concentration agreed approximately with the change in the two activity factors obtained from solubility and other data.

For a reaction of the type

$$X + Y \rightleftharpoons XY \longrightarrow \text{products}$$

where XY is an intermediate complex, added salt may change the actual concentration of X or Y as discussed under the secondary salt effect. In this case there is a shift in the equilibrium involving X or Y. However, the added salt may alter the factor $\frac{f_X f_Y}{f_{XY}}$ in the equation

$$k' = k_0' \frac{f_X f_Y}{f_{XY}} \tag{11.45}$$

This is the *primary salt effect.*

For processes involving the reaction of a neutral molecule catalyzed by oxonium ion or by hydroxyl ion, the equation

$$X + Y^{\pm} \rightleftharpoons XY^{\pm} \longrightarrow \text{products}$$

can be written. The rate for dilute solutions should be independent of ionic strength, if it is assumed that the limiting law of Debye and Hückel measures the effect of the neutral salt upon the activity coefficients. This is true since $z_A z_B$ is zero. For concentrations where the extended equation

$$-\ln f = A z^2 \sqrt{\mu} + \beta \mu \tag{11.46}$$

must be used to measure the ionic strength dependence of the activity coefficient of an ion constituent, and expressing the dependence upon the ionic strength of the activity coefficient of a neutral molecule by the equation

$$\ln f = \beta \mu \tag{11.47}$$

the logarithm of the kinetic activity factor for a reaction between a neutral molecule and a univalent ion can be written

$$\ln \frac{f_X f_{Y\pm}}{f_{XY\pm}} = \mu(\beta_X + \beta_{Y\pm} - \beta_{XY\pm}) = \mu\beta \tag{11.48}$$

In this equation

$$\beta = \beta_X + \beta_{Y\pm} - \beta_{XY\pm} \tag{11.49}$$

Therefore,

$$k' = k_0' e^{-\mu\beta} \tag{11.50}$$

and for β small

$$k' = k_0'(1 + \mu\beta) \tag{11.51}$$

From the predictions of this equation it has been generally accepted that the primary salt effect should result in a linear variation of the observed velocity constant with the ionic strength, since k_0' and β are constants for a given process. Brönsted (*Trans. Faraday Soc.*, **24**, 630, 1928) found that the inversion of sucrose, the hydrolysis of esters, and other reactions give the linear dependence of the specific velocity constants upon the ionic strength predicted by Eq. (11.51).

If the formation of the complex is the governing step in the proposed mechanism, the reactions of molecules with catalytic ions can be classified as the ion dipole type and the theory of Amis and Jaffé, Eq. (8.35), which is

$$\ln k' = \ln k_{\varkappa=0}' + \frac{\epsilon z_B \cos \theta}{DkTr_0^2} (\mu_0^* - \mu^* e^{-\varkappa r_0}[1 + \varkappa r_0]) \quad (11.52)$$

can be applied. In Chapter VIII the application of this equation to the influence of ionic strength upon the rate of sucrose inversion catalyzed by hydrochloric acid, and upon the rate of the perchloric acid catalyzed hydrolysis of ethylene acetal is given. The mechanism of the sugar inversion might be used to illustrate the requirements of the theory as to the nature of the reaction process. Thus if S stands for sucrose, the reaction for the inversion can be written

$$S + H_3O^+ \rightleftharpoons SH_3O^+ \text{ (slow)}$$
$$SH_3O^+ + H_2O \longrightarrow \text{Invert sugars} + H_3O^+ \text{ (fast)}$$

In Chapter VIII it was pointed out that Amis, Jaffé, and Overman (*J. Am. Chem. Soc.*, **66**, 1823, 1944) applied this theory to the hydroxyl ion catalyzed decomposition of diacetone alcohol. The overall mechanism of the reaction is

$$
\underset{\substack{|\\ \text{OH}}}{\overset{\substack{\text{CH}_3\\ |}}{\text{CH}_3\text{—C—CH}_2\text{—}}}\underset{\substack{\|\\ \text{O}}}{\text{C—CH}_3} + \text{OH}^- \longrightarrow 2\text{CH}_3\text{—}\underset{\substack{\|\\ \text{O}}}{\text{C}}\text{—CH}_3 + \text{OH}^-
$$

and the mechanism required by this theory is, if D is used to represent diacetone alcohol and A to represent acetone,

$$D + OH^- \rightleftharpoons DOH^- \text{ (slow)}$$
$$DOH^- \longrightarrow 2A + OH^- \text{ (fast)}$$

The data for this reaction are given in Figs. 3, 4, and 5 of Chapter VIII.

Laidler and Eyring's theory, Eq. (8.52), also applies to the salt effect upon this reaction. It was pointed out there that the equation, which is,

$$\ln k' = \ln k'_0 + \frac{\epsilon^2 z_A^2 N}{2RT}\left(\frac{1}{D} - 1\right)\left(\frac{1}{r_{Y\pm}} - \frac{1}{r_{XY\pm}}\right) - \frac{N}{RT}\frac{\mu_X^{2'}}{r_X^3}\frac{D_0 - 1}{2D_0 + 1}$$
$$+ \left(b_{Y\pm} + b_{XY\pm} + \frac{\epsilon^2 \delta N}{DrRT}\right)\mu + \frac{N(\phi_{Y\pm} + \phi_X - \phi_{XY\pm})}{RT}$$

$$(11.53)$$

predicts a linear dependence of $\ln k'$ upon μ when the dielectric constant of the medium is held constant and concentrations are appreciable. Such a relationship was found by Brönsted and Wynne-Jones (*Trans. Faraday Soc.*, **25**, 59, 1929) for the hydrogen ion catalyzed hydrolysis of acetals.

The significant difference between Eq. (11.51) and (11.52) is that Eq. (11.52) makes it possible to evaluate approximately the factor which multiplies the ionic strength in terms of the physical properties of the reactants and solvent, and clearly demonstrates that this factor is not a constant. Equations (11.52) and (11.53) differ in their predictions as is shown in Table III of Chapter VIII. In the author's opinion, Eq. (11.52) can in general, and especially when put in the non-dimensional form, be more easily applied to data than can Eq. (11.53).

For molecule-catalyzed reactions of molecules, no satisfactory equation for the salt effect has been worked out. This effect would probably be small, but perhaps significant.

For ion-catalyzed reactions of ions Eq. (4.28) applies, and numerous examples have been given, as curves 1 and 4 in Fig. 1 of Chapter IV.

While the reaction represented by curve 1 is neither an acid nor a basic catalysis in the ordinary sense of the word, the mercuric ion being the catalyst, yet the reaction illustrated by curve 4 is an acid- and a base-catalyzed reaction. The process is the decomposition of hydrogen peroxide in a bromine-bromide solution. The reaction has been extensively studied by Livingston and co-workers (*J. Am. Chem. Soc.*, **45**, 1251, 1923; **45**, 2048, 1923; **48**, 53, 1926).

The over-all equations for the process are given as

$$H_2O_2 + 2Br^- + 2H^+ \longrightarrow Br_2 + 2H_2O$$
$$H_2O_2 + Br_2 \longrightarrow O_2 + 2Br^- + 2H^+$$

so that the acid catalyst H^+ and the basic catalyst Br^- are used up and regenerated, and the sum of the two equations is the decomposition of hydrogen peroxide

$$2H_2O_2 \longrightarrow 2H_2O + O_2$$

When the reaction has reached a steady state the rate is first-order with respect to hydrogen peroxide.

The velocity equation is written

$$-d(H_2O_2)/dt = k_a'C_{H_2O_2}a_{H^+}a_{Br^-} = k_a'C_{H_2O_2}C_{H^+}C_{Br^-}f_{HBr}^2 \quad (11.54)$$

where k_a' is the *activity rate constant* and f_{HBr} is the activity coefficient of HBr. k_a' is related to the *concentration rate constant* k_C' by the equation

$$k_C' = k_a'f_{HBr}^2 \quad (11.55)$$

The mechanism proposed for the reaction is

$$H_2O_2 + H^+ + Br^- \longrightarrow HBrO + H_2O$$

and

$$H_2O_2 + HBrO \longrightarrow O_2 + H_2O + H^+ + Br^-$$

From the standpoint of the electrostatics of the reaction as given by curve 1, the rate-governing step, assuming the above mechanism, must be

$$H_2O_2 + H^+ + Br^- \longrightarrow H_2O_2HBr$$

since the slope of the plot is -1 which is that required for $z_A z_B = -1$ when Eq. (4.28) is employed.

THE EFFECT OF THE SOLVENT IN SO FAR AS THE DIELECTRIC CONSTANT IS CONCERNED

Harned and Samaras (*J. Am. Chem. Soc.*, **54,** 1, 1932) studied the velocity of hydrolysis of ethyl orthoformate in various mixed solvents of which one component was water. They proposed the equation

$$\log k_0' - \log k' = \frac{a}{b}(D_0 - D) \quad (11.56)$$

to correlate the change in reaction velocity and change in dielectric constant for different media. In this equation k_0' is the velocity in aqueous solution, and k' is the velocity in mixed solvents. D_0 is the dielectric constant of pure water and D that of the mixed solvent. The average value of a/b for all the mixed solvents studied was about 0.032, and the various values were in fair agreement ranging from

0.030 to 0.036. Converting to natural base logarithms, Eq. (11.56) becomes

$$\ln k_0' - \ln k' = 0.07(D_0 - D) \tag{11.57}$$

These authors further assume that the effect of the solvent upon the rate of orthoacetic ester hydrolysis is a secondary effect proportional to the concentration of hydrogen ions, and show that, based upon this assumption

$$\ln k_0' - \ln k' = \frac{\epsilon^2}{D_0^2 a_i k T} (D_0 - D) \tag{11.58}$$

where ϵ is the electronic charge, a_i is the ionic radius, T is the absolute temperature, k is the Boltzmann gas constant, and the other terms are as defined above. Using 4.77×10^{10} electrostatic units for ϵ, 78.8 for D_0, 1.37×10^{-16} ergs for k, and 1.5Å for a_i, gave

$$\ln k_0' - \ln k' = 0.06(D_0 - D) \tag{11.59}$$

which compares favorably with Eq. (11.57) obtained experimentally.

The primary medium effect on the reaction between methyl iodide and sodium thiosulfate and on the transformation of chloroamino benzenes are in agreement with theory. However, Harned and Samaras found that the hydrogen-ion catalysis of ethyl acetate and the hydroxide-ion catalysis of the decomposition of diacetone alcohol could not be computed by the above theory.

If the governing step in the process is the reaction of a catalytic ion and a molecule or the reaction between a catalytic molecule and an ion, the reaction is of the ion-dipolar molecule type, and Eq. (11.52) and (11.53) are applicable. In Chapter VIII these equations were applied to the dielectric constant effect upon many acid-base catalyzed reactions.

For a rate-governing step involving two ions Eq. (4.28) applies. This equation has received much attention in the literature and its application is discussed at length in Chapter IV.

In the case of a rate-governing step between two dipolar molecules, Laidler and Eyring's theory, Eq. (8.55) which is

$$\ln k' = \ln k_0' - \frac{N}{RT} \frac{D-1}{2D+1} \left(\frac{\mu_A^2}{a_A^3} + \frac{\mu_B^2}{a_B^3} - \frac{\mu_{M*}^2}{a_{M*}^3} \right) + \frac{N(\phi_A + \phi_B - \phi_{M*})}{RT} \tag{11.60}$$

can be used to correlate rate constant changes with dielectric constant changes of the medium. As was mentioned in Chapter VIII, the plot of $\ln k'$ against $\dfrac{D-1}{2D+1}$ should approximate a straight line provided nonelectrostatic terms in Eq. (11.60) are small enough to be neglected.

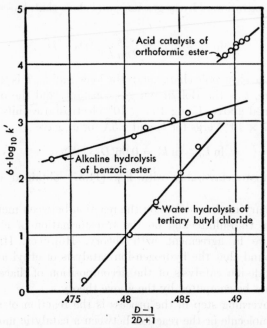

Figure 3 The logarithm of the specific rate plotted against $(D-1)/(2D+1)$ for the acid hydrolysis of ethyl orthoformate $(H_2O + HC(OEt)_3)$, the alkaline hydrolysis of ethyl benzoate $(H_2O + PhCOOEt)$, and the water hydrolysis of tertiary butyl chloride $(H_2O + (CH_3)_3CCl)$.

In Fig. 3 is given the plot by Laidler and Eyring for $\log k'$ versus $\dfrac{D-1}{2D+1}$ for various reactions, some acid and some base catalyzed. It can be seen that data conform with theory well in these instances.

The *alkaline* hydrolysis of tertiary butyl chloride studied by Hughes (*J. Chem. Soc.*, **1935**, 255) and given in the graph, might be used to illustrate the necessary mechanism for the application of Eq. (11.60). The over-all reaction is given by the author as

$$OH^- + (CH_3)_3CCl \longrightarrow (CH_3)_3COH + Cl^-$$

but if Eq. (11.60) is to apply, this is evidently not the governing step in the reaction. This step is perhaps

$$(CH_3)_3CCl + H_2O \longrightarrow (CH_3)_3CClH_2O$$

and subsequently

$$(CH_3)_3CCl \cdot H_2O + OH^- \longrightarrow (CH_3)_3COH + H_2O + Cl^-$$

If this mechanism is accepted, the reaction can be considered as a water catalyzed reaction of the chloride with hydroxyl ion.

CHAPTER XII

Adsorption, heterogeneous catalysis, and heterogeneous reactions

The Van der Waals adsorption and activated adsorption

The Van der Waals adsorption is thought to involve physical forces, and is generally associated with but small heat changes, for example, one to five kilogram calories per mole of adsorbate taken up by the surface. Activated adsorption, or chemisorption, takes place with the formation of bonds which are similar to ordinary chemical bonds, and the heat changes in chemisorption are of like magnitude to the heat changes in chemical reactions, namely, from 10 to 75 kilogram calories per mole of adsorbate adsorbed. Taylor (*J. Am. Chem. Soc.*, **53**, 578, 1931) points out that the rate of adsorption may be extremely slow when heats of activation are large, and concludes that in general it is the adsorptions with the higher heats of activation which are important in catalytic change.

Langmuir (*J. Am. Chem. Soc.*, **38**, 2221, 1916; *ibid.*, **39**, 1848, 1917; *ibid.*, **40**, 1361, 1918) proved that true adsorbed films are only one molecule thick. He also showed that the range of surface forces, which are chemical in nature and which are responsible for chemisorption, are of the order of 10^{-8} centimeter. Thicker films than monolayers may be found, when forces acting between the first and second layers of adsorbed molecules are greater than those holding the first layer to the surface, or when, in the case of a nearly saturated vapor, the rate of evaporation from the second layer of molecules is comparable with rate of condensation.

Langmuir (*loc. cit.*) developed a quantitative theory of adsorption some parts of which we give below:

266

Simple adsorption

This type of adsorption prevails for a plane surface, having only one kind of elementary space, and in which each space can hold only one type of molecule.

The rate of collision of gas molecules with a surface is given by the equation

$$m = \sqrt{\frac{M}{2\pi RT}}\, p \tag{12.1}$$

where m is the number of grams of gas striking the surface per square centimeter per second, M is the molecular weight, T the absolute temperature, p the pressure in bars (1 bar = 0.98692 atmosphere), and R the gas constant is 83.2×10^6 ergs per degree. Let

$$n = \frac{m}{M} \tag{12.2}$$

then

$$n = \frac{p}{\sqrt{2\pi MRT}} = 43.75 \times 10^{-6}\, \frac{p}{\sqrt{MT}} \tag{12.3}$$

Also let α be the fraction of the molecules striking a surface which condense, and are therefore held by the surface forces until the molecules evaporate again. In general α is very close to unity, and thus the rate at which a gas condenses on a bare surface will be given by

$$r_a = \alpha n \tag{12.4}$$

Now if N_0 is the number of elementary spaces per square centimeter, then, according to the assumptions made above, the number of gas molecules absorbed cannot exceed N_0, except by adsorption of additional layers of molecules. Now the forces acting between the surface and the first layer of molecules are usually much greater than the forces acting between two layers of gas molecules. Hence the rate of evaporation from the second layer will be much faster than from the first, and the number of molecules in the second layer will, therefore, be negligible. A molecule striking a portion of the surface already covered in effect is reflected and the rate of condensation r_a of a gas on the surface is

$$r_a = \alpha\theta n \tag{12.5}$$

where θ is the fraction of the surface which is bare. Similarly the rate of evaporation r_e of the molecules from the surface is

$$r_e = \nu_1\theta_1 \tag{12.6}$$

where ν_1 = rate at which the gas would evaporate if the surface were completely covered, and θ_1 is the fraction covered by the adsorbed molecules. When the gas and surface are in equilibrium these two rates are equal, and therefore,

$$\alpha \theta n = \nu_1 \theta_1 \qquad (12.7)$$

also

$$\theta + \theta_1 = 1 \qquad (12.8)$$

and hence

$$\theta_1 = \frac{\alpha n}{\nu_1 + \alpha n} \qquad (12.9)$$

Setting

$$\sigma_1 = \frac{\alpha}{\nu_1} \qquad (12.10)$$

Equation (12.9) becomes

$$\theta_1 = \frac{\sigma_1 n}{1 + \sigma_1 n} \qquad (12.11)$$

If η is the number of gram molecules adsorbed per unit area of surface, then

$$\frac{N}{N_0} \eta = \frac{\sigma_1 n}{1 + \sigma_1 n} \qquad (12.12)$$

where N is the Avogadro number.

Equation (12.12) gives the relation between the pressure of a gas, which by Eq. (12.3) is proportional to n, and η, the amount adsorbed on a plane. Now n and η can be determined experimentally, and using Eq. (12.12), N_0 and σ_1 can be calculated.

More than one kind of elementary space

Let the different kinds of elementary spaces represent the fractions β_1, β_2, β_3, etc., of the surface. Then

$$\beta_1 + \beta_2 + \beta_3 + \cdots = 1 \qquad (12.13)$$

Each of these fractions may be considered as an independent surface and an equation of the type of Eq. (12.11) will hold. The total amount adsorbed η will thus be given by

$$\frac{N}{N_0} \eta = \beta_1 \theta_1 + \beta_2 \theta_2 + \beta_3 \theta_3 + \cdots \qquad (12.14)$$

where θ_1, θ_2, θ_3, etc., represent the fractions of the various surfaces occupied by the adsorbed molecules.

This equation can also be written

$$\frac{N}{N_0} \eta = \frac{\beta_1 \sigma_1 n}{1 + \sigma_1 n} + \frac{\beta_2 \sigma_2 n}{1 + \sigma_2 n} \qquad (12.15)$$

Each elementary space can hold more than one adsorbed molecule

Let each elementary space hold n' molecules, and let $\nu_{n'}$ be the rate of evaporation from a space containing n' molecules; also let $\alpha_{n'}$ be the reflection coefficient corresponding to spaces containing $(n' - 1)$ molecules. In addition θ will represent the fraction of the spaces which contain no adsorbed molecules, and $\theta_{n'}$ the fraction of spaces containing n molecules. Then

$$\theta + \theta_1 + \theta_2 + \theta_3 + \cdots + \theta_{n'} = 1 \tag{12.16}$$

The total quantity of adsorbed gas η is given by

$$\frac{N}{N_0}\eta = \theta_1 + 2\theta_2 + 3\theta_3 + \cdots + n'\theta_{n'} \tag{12.17}$$

At equilibrium we have

$$\alpha_1\theta n = \nu_1\theta_1$$
$$\alpha_2\theta_1 n = \nu_2\theta_2 \tag{12.18}$$
$$\alpha_3\theta_2 n = \nu_3\theta_3$$

and placing

$$\frac{\alpha_n}{\nu_{n'}} = \sigma_{n'} \tag{12.19}$$

we obtain

$$\theta = \theta_1/\sigma_1 n$$
$$\theta_2 = \sigma_2 n\theta_1$$
$$\theta_3 = \sigma_2\sigma_3 n^2\theta_1 \tag{12.20}$$
$$\theta_4 = \sigma_2\sigma_3\sigma_4 n^3\theta_1$$

Substituting these in Eq. (12.16) and (12.17) and eliminating θ_1 gives

$$\frac{N}{N_0}\eta = \frac{\sigma_1 n + 2\sigma_1\sigma_2 n^2 + 3\sigma_1\sigma_2\sigma_3 n^3 + \cdots}{1 + \sigma_1 n + \sigma_1\sigma_2 n^2 + \sigma_1\sigma_2\sigma_3 n^3 + \cdots} \tag{12.21}$$

An equation of this general form will probably hold in other cases where adjacent molecules influence each other's rate of evaporation.

Atomic adsorption

The forces which hold adsorbed substances act primarily on the individual atoms rather than on the molecules. When these forces are sufficiently strong, it may happen that the atoms leaving the surface pair off in a manner different from the original molecules.

Starting with a bare surface, from time to time two molecules will happen to be adsorbed in adjacent spaces. For diatomic molecules, one atom of one molecule and one of the other may then evaporate as a new molecule, leaving two isolated atoms which cannot evaporate and thus must remain on the surface. At the stationary state there will thus be a haphazard distribution of atoms over the surface.

Let θ_1 be the fraction of the surface covered by adsorbed atoms and θ the fraction which is bare. For a diatomic molecule to condense on a surface two adjacent elementary spaces must be vacant. The chance that one will be vacant is θ, and the chance that both will be vacant is θ^2. The rate of condensation r_a is then

$$r_a = \alpha\theta^2 n \tag{12.22}$$

Evaporation can take place when atoms are adjacent. The chance that an atom occupies a given space is θ_1, and the chance that atoms occupy adjacent spaces is θ_1^2. The rate of evaporation r_e is then

$$r_e = \nu_1\theta_1^2 \tag{12.23}$$

where ν_1 is the rate of evaporation from a completely covered surface. At equilibrium the two rates are equal and, therefore,

$$\alpha\theta^2 n = \nu_1\theta_1^2 \tag{12.24}$$

The number of gram molecules of the diatomic gas adsorbed per unit area is given by

$$\frac{2N}{N_0}\eta = \theta_1 \tag{12.25}$$

also

$$\theta + \theta_1 = 1 \tag{12.26}$$

and combining Eq. (12.24), (12.25), and (12.26), we obtain for the case when θ is approximately unity, i.e., when the total amount of adsorption is only sufficient to cover a small fraction of the surface, the expression

$$\frac{2N}{N_0}\eta = \sqrt{\sigma n} \tag{12.27}$$

Eq. (12.12) can be written from empirical data

$$q = \frac{abp}{1 + ap} \tag{12.28}$$

where p is the pressure in bars and q is the amount of gas (in cubic millimeters at 20° C and 760 millimeters pressure) adsorbed.

Equation (12.28) can be further written

$$p/q = \frac{1}{ab} + \frac{p}{b} \tag{12.29}$$

To test this equation p/q may be plotted against p and, if the results agree with the equation, a straight line of slope $1/b$ having an intercept $1/ab$ on the Y-axis should result. Many data have been shown to conform to the requirements of Eq. (12.12) and (12.29).

Other adsorption equations

The Freundlich equation (*Kapillarchemie*, Leipzig, 1909) is

$$q = ap^{1/b} \qquad (12.30)$$

where q is the quantity of adsorbed gas, p is the pressure, and a and b are constants. Langmuir (*loc. cit.*) points out that this equation is only poorly in agreement with experiment for large ranges of pressure.

In the case of adsorption from solution the equation is

$$q = ac^{1/b} \qquad (12.31)$$

where c is the equilibrium concentration of the adsorbed substance in solution.

Langmuir further points out that no single equation, other than purely thermodynamic ones should be expected to cover all cases of adsorption. The Gibbs adsorption equation is derived from thermodynamic considerations as follows:

When a system is in equilibrium it is possible to extend the surface between two phases by doing work upon the system. The amount of work to increase the surface by unit amount is called the surface tension. Since the work is done upon the system the free energy of the system increases by an amount equal to the work done. Therefore

$$dF = \gamma \, d\sigma \qquad (12.32)$$

where F is the free energy, γ is the surface tension, and σ is the area of the surface.

Surface tension may be varied by changing the composition of either phase. If n_s the number of moles of solute present in an entire system only is varied, then the total free energy F of the system is a function of σ and n_s (temperature, pressure, and other constituents are constant) and

$$\left[\frac{\partial}{\partial n_s} \left(\frac{\partial F}{\partial \sigma} \right)_{n_s} \right]_\sigma = \left[\frac{\partial}{\partial \sigma} \left(\frac{\partial F}{\partial n_s} \right)_\sigma \right]_{n_s} \qquad (12.33)$$

Now

$$\left(\frac{\partial F}{\partial n_s} \right)_{T, P, \sigma, \cdots} = \mu_s \qquad (12.34)$$

where μ_s is the partial molal free energy, or chemical potential of the solute in the solution, and from Eq. (12.32), (12.33), and (12.34)

$$\left(\frac{\partial \gamma}{\partial n_s}\right)_\sigma = \left(\frac{\partial \mu_s}{\partial \sigma}\right)_{n_s} \tag{12.35}$$

Furthermore

$$\left(\frac{\partial \mu_s}{\partial \sigma}\right)_{n_s} = -\left(\frac{\partial \mu_s}{\partial n_s}\right)_\sigma \left(\frac{\partial n_s}{\partial \sigma}\right)_{\mu_s} \tag{12.36}$$

and

$$\mu_s = \mu_s^0 + RT \ln a_s \tag{12.37}$$

where μ_s^0 is the partial molal free energy of the solute, which depends upon an arbitrarily chosen standard state of the solute and upon the temperature, but is independent of the composition of the solution. Therefore,

$$d\mu_s = RT \, d \ln a_s \tag{12.38}$$

From Eq. (12.35), (12.36), (12.37), and (12.38) we obtain

$$\frac{1}{RT}\left(\frac{\partial \gamma}{\partial \ln a_s}\right)_\sigma = -\left(\frac{\partial n_s}{\partial \sigma}\right)_{\mu_s} \tag{12.39}$$

and defining

$$\left(\frac{\partial n_s}{\partial \sigma}\right)_{\mu_s} = T_s \tag{12.40}$$

we have

$$\frac{1}{RT}\left(\frac{\partial \gamma}{\partial \ln a_s}\right)_\sigma = -T_s \tag{12.41}$$

and for an ideal dilute solution

$$\frac{1}{RT}\left(\frac{\partial \gamma}{\partial \ln C_s}\right)_\sigma = \frac{C_s}{RT}\left(\frac{\partial \gamma}{\partial C_s}\right)_\sigma = -T_s \tag{12.42}$$

McBain and Swain (*Proc. Roy. Soc.*, **154A**, 608, 1936) found that the measurements obtained for positive adsorption of phenol and of hydrocinnamic acid, and for the negative adsorption of sodium chloride on motionless or static surfaces at an air-water interface agree with the predictions of the Gibbs adsorption theorem, which from Eq. (12.42) can be stated as follows: *Those substances which lower the surface tension of a solvent in which they are dissolved have a greater concentration in the surface layer than in the body of the solution, whilst those substances which raise the surface tension have a smaller concentration in the surface than in the body of the solution.*

In Fig. 1 are shown the results for the adsorption of phenol, represented by circles. The data were for adsorption in a static air-water interface. The two broken horizontal lines are to show the values for close-packed anhydrous monomolecular films, both for molecules in a vertical position and for molecules in a horizontal position. One curved solid line is for adsorption with moving bubbles and the other

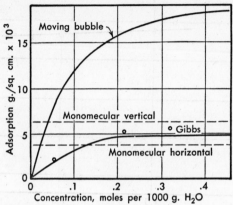

Figure 1 The adsorption of phenol in the static air-water interface together with the values found with moving bubbles and those predicted for close-packed monomolecular layers of vertical and of horizontal molecules and those calculated from the exact form of the Gibbs equation. The circles represent observed values.

solid curve is calculated from the theoretical equation of Gibbs. The adsorption of phenol measured by the moving bubble method is much greater than the adsorption predicted by the Gibbs equation. It is evident that the data for the static measurements most nearly correspond to the Gibbs equation. In Fig. 2 are reproduced the data for the negative adsorption of sodium chloride in the static air-water interface. The sloping line is calculated from the Gibbs equation, and the circles, triangles, and squares are adsorption values for sodium chloride found from data at the air-water interface; x is the value found for moving bubbles. From the figure it can be concluded that the data fulfill the prediction of the Gibbs equation that sodium chloride will exhibit a negative adsorption, or surface deficiency, proportional to the concentration. This is equivalent to a positive adsorption of solvent water to the extent of approximately a monomolecular layer, definitely more than this in dilute solution, and less in concentrated solution.

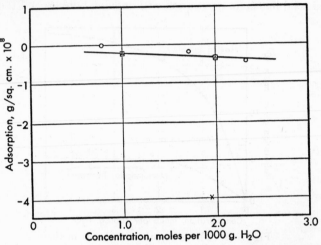

Figure 2   The negative adsorption of sodium chloride in the static air-water interface together with the value found for moving bubbles and the values calculated by the exact form of the Gibbs equation. x is the value found for moving bubbles. o, Δ, □ are values observed in the air-water interface, and the non-horizontal curve is calculated from the exact form of the Gibbs equation.

Active centers

Taylor (*Proc. Roy. Soc.*, **108A,** 105, 1925) set forth the theory that only a small fraction of the surface of a solid catalyst is catalytically active. In a catalytic solid the degree of constraint or saturation imposed by the orderly arrangement of atoms within the solid becomes progressively less and less as we proceed outward from the granule proper towards the most exposed atoms. The atoms in the edge of a granule have one less degree of saturation than those in the surface proper; atoms at a corner have two less degrees of saturation than those in the surface and one less than those at an edge. Thus a greater degree of unsaturation exists at the edges and corners, and would also exist at fissures, cracks, protuberances, or other imperfections; these localities constitute active centers where unbalanced forces similar to valence forces will cause an enhanced adsorption. Langmuir (*Trans. Faraday Soc.*, **17,** 621, 1922) had derived a theory of the kinetics of reactions at catalytic surfaces based on the assumption that the velocity of such reactions depended upon the fraction of catalytic surface covered by adsorbed substances. Langmuir explained the rate of combination of sulfur dioxide with oxygen at a platinum surface on the basis of his theory. However, Taylor stated that other experimental evidence warranted the modification of Langmuir's theory to include the concept of active centers. Heterogeneous reactions have greater velocities than corresponding homogeneous ones because of diminution of the energy of activation. Since the adsorption forces are similar to valence bonds, the atoms in molecules are to some extent separated by adsorption, and the energy of activation required for reaction is consequently lowered. Burk (*J. Phys. Chem.*, **32,** 1601, 1928) assumes that a molecule is adsorbed at two or more points in order that the surface may lower the energy of activation. This theory of multiple adsorption would explain the different modes of decomposition of a substance due to catalytic action. These specific activations for a reaction which can proceed in more than one way are conceivably due to different modes of attachment of the atoms to the catalysts, whereby strains are set up at different bonds, and as a result different types of reactions take place.

Steps involved in heterogeneous catalysis

In the catalysis of a reaction by the adsorption of the reactants by a solid five steps are involved. These steps are:

(1) Diffusion of the reactants to the surface of the solid
(2) Activated adsorption of the reactants at the catalytic interface
(3) Reaction between adsorbed reactants
(4) Activated desorption of products at the catalytic interface
(5) Diffusion of the products away from the catalytic interface

Of these five steps one may be slowest and rate-controlling. It is doubtful that steps (1) or (5) would be rate-determining in solid catalyzed gaseous reactions since the rate would then depend on the square root of the temperature, and in reality the dependence of such reactions on the temperature is exponential. In liquid reactions catalyzed by solid surfaces, diffusion might be the controlling step, since diffusion rates in liquids are relatively slow. Steps (2) or (4) may often be rate-determining since the energy of activation of adsorption or desorption may be higher than the energy of activation for the reaction proper. Taylor and Jungers (*J. Am. Chem. Soc.*, **57**, 660, 1935) conclude that in the synthesis of ammonia on an iron catalyst the process

$$N_{2\ gas} \rightleftharpoons 2N_{adsorbed}$$

is the rate-determining step.

We now turn to solid catalysts and reaction rates where the procedure of Hougen and Watson (*Ind. Eng. Chem.*, **35**, 529, 1943) will be followed practically as given in the article.

ACTIVATED ADSORPTION

It will be assumed that all the active centers behave similarly and that the energy of activated adsorption is the same for all spots, or an average value of this energy will be assumed to represent the entire surface.

Let L' be the active centers per unit area on which adsorption can take place, a_{Ai} be the activity of a component A in the fluid at the interface, C_l' be the concentration of vacant active centers per unit area of surface, C_A' be the concentration of A molecules adsorbed per unit area, and A' be the catalytic area per unit mass. Then

$$L = A'L'/N_0 = \text{maximum molal adsorption capacity per gram of catalyst with one molecule per active center.} \tag{12.43}$$

$$C_A = A'C_A'/N_0 = \text{moles of adsorbed A per unit mass of catalyst.} \tag{12.43a}$$

$$C_l = A'C_l'/N_0 = \text{molal adsorption sites unoccupied per unit mass of catalyst.} \tag{12.43b}$$

Expressing the rate of adsorption r in moles per unit time per unit mass of catalyst:

$$r = k_A' a_{Ai} C_l \tag{12.44}$$

The rate of desorption is given by

$$r = k_A'' C_A \tag{12.45}$$

and at equilibrium between the processes of adsorption and desorption

$$k' a_{Ai} C_l = k_A'' C_A \tag{12.46}$$

or

$$\frac{C_A}{a_{Ai} C_l} = \frac{k_A'}{k_A''} = K_A \tag{12.47}$$

In the above equations k'_A and k''_A are adsorption and desorption velocity constants, respectively, of component A.

For components A, B, R, S, and I adsorbed on active centers of the same type, rate and equilibrium equations similar to Eq. (12.44), (12.45), and (12.47) may be written. Then

$$C_l = L - (C_A + C_B + C_R + C_S + C_I + \cdots) \tag{12.48}$$

At equilibrium each of the adsorbate concentration terms may be substituted for by a term similar to that obtained by solving Eq. (12.47) for C_A:

$$C_l = L - C_l(a_{Ai}K_A + a_{Bi}K_B + a_{Ri}K_R + a_{Si}K_S + a_{Ii}K_I + \cdots)$$
$$= \frac{L}{1 + a_{Ai}K_A + a_{Bi}K_B + a_{Ri}K_R + a_{Si}K_S + a_{Ii}K_I + \cdots} \tag{12.49}$$

By combining Eq. (12.47) and (12.49)

$$C_A = \frac{a_{Ai}K_A L}{1 + a_{Ai}K_A + a_{Bi}K_B + a_{Ri}K_R + a_{Si}K_S + a_{Ii}K_I + \cdots} \tag{12.50}$$

In these equations C_X is the surface concentration of component X in moles per unit mass of catalyst, a_{Xi} is the activity of component X at the interface, K_X is the adsorption equilibrium constant of component X, and when X is I, the component is an inert in the reaction mass. These inerts may serve as poisons by taking up the active centers on the catalyst. Similar expressions may be written for the equilibrium surface concentrations of the other components of the mixture.

Surface reactions

Surface reactions may be assumed to take place either between an adsorbed molecule and a molecule in the fluid phase or between molecules on adjacently situated active centers. If two adsorbed molecules A and B react, the rate of reaction is proportional to the number of A and B molecules per unit area of surface. Also, if in a monomolecular reaction, adsorbed molecule A is reacting with a vacant active center to form an intermediate complex which subsequently decomposes into two adsorbed product molecules, the rate of the reaction will be proportional to the number of A molecules per unit area adsorbed adjacent to vacant active centers.

It is assumed that there is a regular geometrical distribution of active centers, so that each particular center has S' other centers spaced equidistant from it. Let θ_l be the fraction of the total centers which is vacant and θ_B be the fraction of the total centers which is occupied by B molecules. Then $S'\theta_l$ is the number of vacant centers adjacent to an average adsorbed A molecule and $S'\theta_B$ is the number of adsorbed B molecules adjacent to each adsorbed A molecule. The surface concentration of A molecules and vacant active centers adjacent to each other is then given by $\frac{1}{2}S'C'_A\theta_l$ and the surface concentration of A molecules and B molecules adsorbed adjacent to each other is given by $\frac{1}{2}S'C'_A\theta_B$. The factor $\frac{1}{2}$ arises from counting each pair of adjacent molecules and centers twice, in the summation represented by the product of the concentration and fractional adsorption terms.

But

$$\theta_l = C'_l/L' \tag{12.51}$$

and

$$\theta_B = C'_B/L' \tag{12.52}$$

Therefore

$$C'_{Al} = \frac{S'}{2L'} C'_A C'_l \tag{12.53}$$

and

$$C'_{AB} = \frac{S'}{2L'} C_A C'_B \tag{12.54}$$

where C_{Al} is the surface concentration of pairs of adsorbed A molecules and vacant centers adjacent to each other, and C'_{AB} is the surface concentration of pairs of adsorbed A and B molecules in adjacent positions.

For a monomolecular reaction involving an adsorbed A molecule and an adjacent active center, the rate is given by the equation

$$r = k'C_{Al} = k' \frac{S'}{2L} C_A C_l \tag{12.55}$$

and for a surface reaction between A and B molecules the rate becomes

$$r = k'C_{AB} = \frac{k'S'}{2L} C_A C_B \tag{12.56}$$

Over-all surface rate equations

From the above theory a general equation may be written for the following surface reaction

$$A + B \rightleftharpoons R$$

In the general case there will be inert components I in the fluid phase. The net rate of the reaction in the forward direction will be the difference between the rates of the forward and reverse reactions, represented by Eq. (12.56) and (12.55), respectively. We thus obtain

$$r = \frac{S'}{2L} (k'C_A C_B - k''C_R C_l) \tag{12.57}$$

Here k' and k'' are the forward and reverse reaction velocity constants, respectively. The surface concentration may be obtained in terms of the activities in the fluid at the interface from Eq. (12.44) and (12.45). Thus the over-all rate of reaction is equal to the net rate of adsorption of component A, which is the difference in the rates of adsorption and desorption, i.e.,

$$r = k'_A a_{Ai} C_l - k''_A C_A = k''_A (K_A a_{Ai} C_l - C_A) \tag{12.58}$$

and

$$C_A = K_A a_{Ai} C_l - r/k''_A \tag{12.59}$$

In this manner similar expressions may be written for other reactant and product adsorptions, and these substituted in Eq. (12.57) give

$$r = \frac{S}{2L} [k'(K_A a_{Ai} C_l - r/k''_A)(K_B a_{Bi} C_l - r/k''_B) - k''(K_R a_{Ri} C_l + r/k''_R)] \tag{12.60}$$

The concentration of vacant centers can be expressed in terms of fluid-phase activities at the interface.

$$C_l = L - (C_A + C_B + C_R + C_I + \cdots) = L - C_l(K_A a_{Ai} + K_B a_{Bi} + K_R a_{Ri} + K_I a_{Ii} + \cdots) + r\left(\frac{1}{k''_A} + \frac{1}{k''_B} - \frac{1}{k''_R}\right)$$

$$= \frac{L + r\left(\dfrac{1}{k''_A} + \dfrac{1}{k''_B} - \dfrac{1}{k''_R}\right)}{(1 + K_A a_{Ai} + K_B a_{Bi} + K_R a_{Ri} + K_I a_{Ii} + \cdots)} \tag{12.61}$$

Combining Eq. (12.60) and (12.61), one would obtain a complete expression for the rate of reaction in terms only of activities of the fluid at the interface, and the constants of the system. If the constants were known the resultant equation could be solved by graphical means to obtain the rate under specified conditions. The equation, however, is cumbersome, and may be simplified and made more practical by assuming a slow rate-governing step with the other steps so fast that equilibrium may be assumed. The slow step may be the surface reaction, the adsorption of any reactant or the desorption of any product.

Simplified equations for monomolecular surface reactions

For surface reactions monomolecular in both directions, e.g., isomerization reactions, two mechanisms are possible: (1) an adsorbed molecule acquires sufficient energy to react and form a product molecule (all the time held on a single active center); (2) an adsorbed molecule acquires sufficient energy to form a complex with an adjacent active center, and the complex then decomposes to form an adsorbed product molecule. For *the first mechanism* the rate of reaction is proportional to the concentration of adsorbed reactant molecules, and the equation for the rate of the reaction

$$A \rightleftharpoons R$$

is

$$r = k'C_A \tag{12.62}$$

and from Eq. (12.49), (12.50), (12.55), and (12.62) we have

$$r = \frac{k'L}{1 + K_A a_{Ai} + K_R a_{Ri} + K_I a_{Ii} + \cdots} \left(K_A a_{Ai} - \frac{K_R a_{Ri}}{K'} \right) \tag{12.63}$$

where

$$K' = \text{surface equilibrium constant} = \frac{k'}{k''} \tag{12.64}$$

At equilibrium the net rate becomes zero and

$$\frac{a_{Ri}}{a_{Ai}} = \frac{K_A}{K_R} K' = K \tag{12.65}$$

Substituting Eq. (12.65) into (12.63) there results:

$$r = \frac{kLK_A}{1 + K_A a_{Ai} + K_R a_{Ri} + K_I a_{Ii} + \cdots} \left(a_{Ai} - \frac{a_{Ri}}{K} \right) \tag{12.66}$$

For mechanism (2):

$$r = \frac{kS'LK_A}{2(1 + K_A a_{Ai} + K_R a_{Ri} + K_I a_{Ii} + \cdots)^2} \left(a_{Ai} - \frac{a_{Ri}}{K} \right) \tag{12.67}$$

The squared term in the denominator of Eq. (12.67) particularly distinguishes it from Eq. (12.66). For $a_{Ri} = 0$, the initial rate according to Eq. (12.66) is continually increased with increasing activity of the reactant in the fluid phase. However, according to Eq. (12.67), the rate may increase with increasing activity of A at low activities, reach a maximum and then decrease. Such effects have been actually observed when the pressure was varied on monomolecular catalytic reactions.

ADSORPTION OF REACTANT CONTROLLING

It is assumed in this case that the surface reaction and the other adsorption steps are in equilibrium. The rate equation is

$$r = k'_A a_{Ai} C_l - k''_A C_A \tag{12.68}$$

In this equation all surface concentrations may be expressed in terms of the equilibrium in Eq. (12.47) with the exception of C_A, which must be obtained from the condition of equilibrium in the surface reaction. Thus

$$C_A = \frac{C_R K_A}{K K_R} = \frac{K_A C_l a_{Ri}}{K} \tag{12.69}$$

and

$$\begin{aligned}
C_l &= L - (C_A + C_B + C_l + \cdots) \\
&= L - \left(\frac{K_A a_{Ri}}{K} + K_R a_{Ri} + K_I a_{Ii} + \cdots\right) \\
&= \frac{L}{1 + \dfrac{K_A a_{Ri}}{K} + K_R a_{Ri} + K_I a_{Ii} + \cdots}
\end{aligned} \tag{12.70}$$

From Eq. (12.68), (12.69), and (12.70) one obtains for the rate the equation

$$r = \frac{k'_A L}{1 + \dfrac{K_A a_{Ri}}{K} + K_R a_{Ri} + K_I a_{Ii} + \cdots} \left(a_{Ai} - \frac{a_{Ri}}{K}\right) \tag{12.71}$$

which is independent of the nature of the mechanism of the surface reaction.

Comparing Eq. (12.66), (12.67), and (12.71) as to form, it can be observed that when the adsorption of the reactant is controlling, that is, for $a_{Ri} = 0$, the initial rate is directly proportional to the activity of the reactant; if the surface reaction is controlling, the initial rate will increase to a less extent with increased activity of reactant than a direct proportionality between these two quantities would require.

Further if the over-all equilibrium constant is small, the net rate of the reverse reaction of Eq. (12.71) is independent of the activity of A. This would be true of reactions in which the rate is controlled by the rate of desorption of the product.

Bimolecular-monomolecular reaction

For a reaction bimolecular in one direction and unimolecular in the other, the chemical equation for the process can be written

$$A + B \rightleftharpoons R$$

For the case where the reaction is between adjacently adsorbed molecules, the monomolecular reverse reaction follows Eq. (12.55). By the same methods used in the preceding section the rate equations given below are developed.

SURFACE REACTION CONTROLLING

$$r = \frac{k'SLK_AK_B}{2(1 + K_Aa_{Ai} + K_Ba_{Bi} + K_Ra_{Ri} + K_Ia_{Ii} + \cdots)^2}\left(a_{Ai}a_{Bi} - \frac{a_{Ri}}{K}\right)$$

(12.72)

ADSORPTION OF A CONTROLLING

$$r = \frac{k'_AL}{1 + K_Ba_{Bi} + \dfrac{K_Aa_{Ri}}{Ka_{Bi}} + K_Ra_{Ri} + K_Ia_{Ii} + \cdots}\left(a_{Ai} - \frac{a_{Ri}}{Ka_{Bi}}\right)$$

(12.73)

ADSORPTION OF R CONTROLLING

$$r = \frac{k'_RLK}{1 + K_Aa_{Ai} + K_Ba_{Bi} + KK_Ra_{Ai}a_{Bi} + K_Ia_{Ii} + \cdots}\left(a_{Ai}a_{Bi} - \frac{a_{Ri}}{K}\right)$$

(12.74)

Equation (12.72) predicts an increase in the initial reaction rate when a_{Bi} is increased, whereas Eq. (12.73) predicts a decrease in the rate for a_{Ri} equal to zero when a_{Bi} is increased. Thus in bimolecular reactions in which the adsorption of a reactant is the controlling step, the initial rate is reduced by increased activity of the other reactant.

The over-all equilibrium constant appears in both the numerator and denominator of the multiplying fraction in Eq. (12.74). When K is large and conditions are favorable for the forward reaction, the rate may approach k'_RL/K_R, and thus be independent of both reactants and product.

For reaction between an adsorbed A molecule and an unadsorbed B molecule in the fluid phase, the rate is proportional to the product of the surface concentration of A and the interfacial fluid activity of B. The resulting equations are similar to Eq. (12.72), (12.73), and (12.74), except that the adsorption equilibrium constant of B does not appear, and if the surface reaction is controlling, there is no $S/2$ term and the denominator group is to the first power.

Reactions bimolecular in both directions

The chemical equation

$$A + B \rightleftharpoons R + S$$

is representative of such reactions. If it is assumed that the surface reaction takes place between adjacently adsorbed molecules, the following rate equations may be derived using methods similar to those described above:

SURFACE REACTION CONTROLLING

$$r = \frac{k'SLK_AK_B}{2(1+K_Aa_{Ai}+K_Ba_{Bi}+K_Ra_{Ri}+K_Sa_{Si}+K_Ia_{Ii}+\cdots)^2}\left(a_{Ai}a_{Bi}-\frac{a_{Ri}a_{Si}}{K}\right)$$

(12.75)

ADSORPTION OF A CONTROLLING

$$r = \frac{k'_AL}{1+\dfrac{K_Aa_{Ri}a_{Si}}{Ka_{Bi}}+K_Ba_{Bi}+K_Ra_{Ri}+K_Sa_{Si}+K_Ia_{Ii}\cdots}\left(a_{Ai}-\frac{a_{Ri}a_{Si}}{Ka_{Bi}}\right)$$

(12.76)

ADSORPTION OF R CONTROLLING

$$r = \frac{k'_RLK}{1+a_{Ai}K_A+a_{Bi}K_B+\dfrac{a_{Ai}a_{Bi}K_RK}{a_{Si}}+a_{Si}K_S+a_{Ii}K_I+\cdots}\left(\frac{a_{Ai}a_{Bi}}{a_{Si}}-\frac{a_{Ri}}{K}\right)$$

(12.77)

These three equations for reactions bimolecular in both directions compare among themselves as do the three equations for bimolecular-monomolecular reactions. When the rate is controlled by the adsorption of a reagent, the initial rate is decreased by the increase in activity of the other reagent. When adsorption of a product is the controlling step in the rate, the initial rate is independent of the activities of reactants for large over-all equilibrium constants and negligible reverse reaction.

Reactions involving more than two molecules

In the adsorption theory of catalysis there is the possibility of the simultaneous interaction of several molecules, and it is not necessary to assume the simultaneous collision of all the molecules, which would be highly improbable. The rates of such reactions would be proportional to the concentration of groups of the required number of molecules adsorbed on adjacent active centers.

Such reactions would be slow except for the case of a single particle of species A reacting with several particles, all of the same species B. In this case high rates would result with a catalyst which strongly adsorbs the B particle, so that the most of the surface is covered by adsorbed B particles, and thus a large proportion of A particles which are adsorbed are surrounded by the required number of B particles on adjacent centers.

Adsorption with dissociation

It is suggested that when a molecule is dissociated during adsorption, it is commonly first adsorbed on a dual adsorption site consisting of two adjacent active centers. When the molecule decomposes the atoms jump to two vacant active centers. Representing a molecule by A_2 and the dual adsorption site by l_2 we have

$$A_2 + l_2 \rightleftharpoons A_2l_2$$
$$A_2l_2 + 2l \rightleftharpoons 2Al + l_2$$

It is thought that the first step is rate-controlling and that equilibrium is maintained in the second. Then expressing r in moles of A_2,

$$r = k'_{A_2}a_{A_2}C_{l_2} - k''_{A_2}C_{A_2l_2} \tag{12.78}$$

And since the second step maintains equilibrium

$$C_{A_2l_2} = \frac{C^2_{Al}C_{l_2}}{K'_A C^2_l} \tag{12.79}$$

The concentration of dual adsorption sites can be expressed by an equation similar to Eq. (12.53) and (12.54), thus,

$$C_{l_2} = \frac{S}{2L} C^2_l \tag{12.80}$$

Combining Eq. (12.78), (12.79), and (12.80), we obtain

$$r = \frac{S}{2L}\left(k'_{A_2}a_{A_2}C^2_l - k''_{A_2}\frac{C^2_{Al}}{K'_A} \right) \tag{12.81}$$

at equilibrium,

$$\frac{C^2_{Al}}{a_{A_2}C^2_l} = \frac{k'_{A_2}K'_A}{k''_{A_2}} = K_{A_2} \tag{12.82}$$

$$C_A = C_{Al} = C_l\sqrt{a_{A_2}K_{A_2}} \tag{12.83}$$

If A_2 is adsorbed with dissociation from a mixture containing components B, R, and I, an equation similar to Eq. (12.50) may be developed for adsorption equilibrium conditions:

$$C_A = \frac{\sqrt{a_{A_2}K_{A_2}}L}{1 + \sqrt{a_{A_2}K_{A_2}} + a_BK_B + a_RK_R + a_IK_I + \cdots} \tag{12.84}$$

From the form of Eq. (12.84) it is apparent that Eq. (12.66), (12.67), (12.72), and (12.75) in which all adsorption is in equilibrium, may be modified to apply where a component is dissociated and one-half molecule participates in the reaction merely by raising to the one-half power the activity and adsorption equilibrium constant of the component which is dissociated wherever either appears in the equation.

The effects of dissociation where adsorption rate is controlling can be illustrated by consideration of the effect on Eq. (12.76) of the dissociation of B first and then A. If A is not dissociated, the rate is expressed by Eq. (12.44) and (12.45):

$$r = k'\left(a_A C \cdot - \frac{C_A}{K_A}\right) \tag{12.85}$$

If B is dissociated and only $\frac{1}{2}$B molecule enters into the reaction an expression for C_A is derived from the equilibrium of the surface reaction:

$$C_A = \frac{C_R C_S}{C_{\frac{1}{2}B} K'} = \frac{C_l K_R a_{Ri} K_S a_{Si}}{\sqrt{K_B a_{Bi}} \, K'} = \frac{C_l K_A a_{Ri} a_{Si}}{\sqrt{a_{Bi}} \, K} \tag{12.86}$$

$$C_l = \frac{L}{1 + \frac{K_A a_{Ri} a_{Si}}{K a_{Bi}} + K_B a_{Bi} + K_R a_{Ri} + K_S a_{Si} + K_I a_{Ii} + \cdots} \tag{12.87}$$

and substituting Eq. (12.86) and (12.87) into Eq. (12.85), we obtain

$$r = \frac{k_A' L}{1 + \frac{K_A a_{Ri} a_{Si}}{\sqrt{a_{Bi}} K} + \sqrt{K_B a_{Bi}} + K_R a_{Ri} + K_S a_{Si} + K_I a_{Ii} + \cdots}\left(a_{Ai} - \frac{a_{Ri} a_{Si}}{\sqrt{a_{Bi}} K}\right) \tag{12.88}$$

From a comparison of Eq. (12.76) and (12.88), it can be seen that if the substance whose rate of adsorption is the slowest rate-determining step is not dissociated, the rate equations are modified in order to apply to the case where a component is dissociated and only one-half enters the reaction by raising the activity and adsorption equilibrium constant of the dissociated component to one-half power wherever they appear in the equation.

If component A of Eq. (12.76) is dissociated and only $\frac{1}{2}$A molecule enters the reaction, one must resort to the application of Eq. (12.81).

From the equilibrium of the surface reaction,

$$C_{\frac{1}{2}A} = \frac{C_R C_S}{C_B K'} = \frac{C_l \sqrt{K_A} a_{Ri} a_{Si}}{K a_{Bi}} \tag{12.89}$$

$$C_l = \frac{L}{1 + \frac{K_A a_{Ri} a_{Si}}{K a_{Bi}} + K_B a_{Bi} + K_R a_{Ri} + K_S a_{Si} + K_I a_{Ii} + \cdots} \tag{12.90}$$

From the substitution of Eq. (12.89) and (12.90) into Eq. (12.81), one obtains

$$r = \frac{SL k_A'}{2\left(1 + \frac{a_{Ri} a_{Si} \sqrt{K_A}}{a_{Bi} K} + K_B a_{Bi} + K_R a_{Ri} + K_S a_{Si} + K_I a_{Ii} + \cdots\right)^2} \left(a_A - \left(\frac{a_{Ri} a_{Si}}{K a_{Bi}}\right)^2\right) \tag{12.91}$$

Equation (12.91) is quite different from Eq. (12.81), and it is also dependent on the mechanism chosen for the adsorption and dissociation of A.

Effect of temperature

Each of the equilibrium constants occurring in the rate equations expressed as a function of temperature is given by the following equation applicable to both chemical and adsorption equilibria:

$$K = e^{-\frac{\Delta F^0}{RT}} = e^{-\left(\frac{\Delta H^0}{RT} - \frac{\Delta S^0}{R}\right)} \tag{12.92}$$

Now ΔF^0 varies markedly with temperature as a rule; however, it is often quite satisfactory to assume ΔH^0 and ΔS^0 to be independent at average values.

But from Eq. (7.55), resubstituting ΔH^* for ΔE^* and inserting the asterisks to indicate the activated state, we have

$$k' = \frac{kT}{h} K^* = \frac{kT}{h} e^{-\left(\frac{\Delta H^*}{RT} - \frac{\Delta S^*}{R}\right)} \tag{12.93}$$

where k' is the reaction velocity constant in moles per unit time per unit mass of catalyst, ΔH^* and ΔS^* are, respectively, the molal standard heat and entropy of activation for the formation of the activated complex, and K^* is the equilibrium constant based on partition functions for the activated complex in equilibrium with reactants. This equation is applicable to both activated adsorptions and surface reactions. Since all the rate equations have the reaction velocity constant multiplied by either L or $\dfrac{SL}{2}$, it is convenient to group the constants together:

$$k'L \text{ or } \frac{k'SL}{2} = C''Te^{-\left(\frac{\Delta H^*}{RT} - \frac{\Delta S^*}{R}\right)} \qquad (12.94)$$

where C' is a function of the nature and extent of the catalytic surface.

The catalytic rate equations can be extended to all temperatures by substituting for all equilibrium and velocity constants their values expressed respectively by Eq. (12.92) and (12.94). For ease of manipulation it is preferable to consider separately the temperature variation of the individual constants with the aid of simplifying assumptions which will be discussed later.

Limitations of the surface rate equations

The rate equations given above are ideal forms and involve many assumptions which are not exact. Some of these assumptions are:

(1) All active centers on the catalytic centers behave similarly. There is evidence that such is not the case; for example, the energy of activation gradually increases in some cases as the active centers are progressively occupied. Likewise surface activity is determined by spatial arrangement of active centers, which may not be the same over the complete surface.

(2) Each component is adsorbed independently of interaction between the adsorbed molecules of like or unlike species, and again such in general is not the case. Interaction between adsorbed molecules tends to reduce the loss in heat content ordinarily accompanying activated adsorption.

(3) The activities of reactants and products in the fluid phase at the catalytic interface are constant throughout the catalytic mass. However, for porous catalysts and where finite rates are produced, concentration gradients exist within a catalyst particle because of the diffusion and flow of reactants into the inner pores, and the diffusion and flow of products out to the main fluid stream at the particle surface. The reaction rate per unit surface may vary widely from a maximum at the exterior to a minimum at the center of the particle. The *effectiveness factor* E_A of the particle is the ratio of the actual reaction rate per unit mass of catalyst to the rate which would result if no concentration gradients existed within the particles, and it is suggested that an empirical method of taking into account variations

in effectiveness factor be based on the curve developed by Thiele (*Ind. Eng. Chem.*, **31**, 916, 1939) for spherical particles catalyzing a first-order reversible reaction. The effectiveness factor is given as a function of a modulus $D_p'\sqrt{k'}/4r_pD_v$ in Fig. 3. In this modulus, D_p'

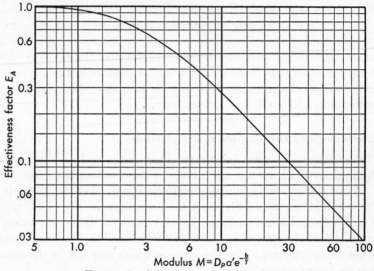

Figure 3   Catalytic effectiveness factors.

is defined as the diameter of a sphere having the same surface area per unit volume as the particle. Thus

$$D_p' = 6/A_p\rho_p \qquad (12.95)$$

Here A_p is the area of the catalyst particle and ρ_p is its density. Equation (12.95) is true, since the diameter of a sphere is six divided by the area, and the density factor ρ_p arises from the fact that the greater the density of the particle of a given substance, the less porous it is and the less the sphere required to have the same surface area per unit volume. The reaction velocity constant k' of the modulus is the proportionality factor relating reaction rate and the difference between the reactant concentration and the equilibrium value in a reversible reaction. D_v is the coefficient of diffusion and r_p is the average hydraulic radius of catalyst pores.

Application of Fig. 3 to other than first-order reactions involves the assumption of a linear relation between reactant concentration and reaction rate. This is a fair approximation in many cases, and it is believed that Fig. 3 is a useful approximation for general application, particularly if the constants of the modulus are empirically determined at the conditions in the range of operating interest.

For a given catalyst and reaction system, the square root terms of Thiele's modulus may be assumed a function only of temperature, represented by the usual exponential function, and may be written as $D'_p a' e^{-b/T}$, and

$$E_A = f(m) = f(D'_p a' e^{-b/T}) \qquad (12.96)$$

with the function represented by Fig. 3. Here a' and b are empirical constants.

All the preceding equations should include the effectiveness factor E_A as a multiplier on the right-hand side, when the catalyst used is porous enough for the external area of the particle to be negligible compared to the internal area.

(4) The rate equations are all expressed in terms of activities in the fluid phase at the catalytic interface, which, by inclusion of the effectiveness factor in the equations, are assumed to be the same as the activities in the fluid phase at the gross exterior surface of the catalyst particle. These interfacial activities are less or greater than the activities in the main stream of fluid surrounding the particles by the amounts of the activity gradients necessary to maintain diffusion. Thus if a_A is the activity in the main fluid stream and a_{Ai} the activity of A at the interface, then

$$a_{Ai} = a_A - \Delta a_A \qquad (12.97)$$

and similarly for product S diffusing away from the surface

$$A_{Si} = a_S + \Delta a_S \qquad (12.98)$$

The activity differences Δa_A and Δa_S are functions of diffusion and flow characteristic of the system which may be calculated with satisfactory accuracy for many gaseous systems and may be empirically evaluated by similar methods for other systems.

Hougen and Watson express the contacting characteristics of a system in terms of the height of a transfer unit ($H.T.U.$). Chilton and Coluburn ($Ind. Eng. Chem.$, **27**, 255, 1935) conceived the idea of transfer unit. It is defined as the length or height of contacting zone required to produce a unit concentration change in the main body of the fluid stream in the direction of flow as the results of a diffusional driving force producing the transfer of unit concentration difference. For a given packing material the $H.T.U.$ is a function of the modified Reynolds number D_pG/η and the Schmidt number $\eta/\rho D_v$, where η is the viscosity, D_p is the effective average diameter of the catalyst particles, G is the mass velocity per unit total cross section, ρ is the density of the fluid, and D_v is the coefficient of diffusion. Thus the drop in partial pressure of the gaseous component A as a result of mass transfer was represented by Hougen and Watson by the following equations:

For equimolal counterdiffusion of the two components in a binary system,

$$\Delta p_A = \left(\frac{r}{A_p}\right)\frac{M_m\pi}{G}\,a(H.T.U.) \tag{12.99}$$

and for diffusion in a binary system resulting in removal of component A, the other component remaining,

$$\Delta p_A = \left(\frac{r}{A_p}\right)\frac{M_m p_{gf}}{G}\,a(H.T.U.) \tag{12.100}$$

where p_{gf} = log mean of $(\pi - p_A)$ and $(\pi - p_{Ai})$. In these equations p_A is the partial pressure of A in the main fluid stream, p_{Ai} is the partial pressure of component A at the particle interface, r is the reaction rate in moles per unit mass of catalyst per unit time, A_p is the gross external area of catalyst particles per unit mass of catalyst, M_m is the molecular weight, π is the total pressure, G is the mass velocity per unit cross section, and $a(H.T.U.)$ is a dimensionless group which may be evaluated from Fig. 4, which is a plot of $a(H.T.U.)$ as a function of the Reynolds and Schmidt numbers.

Hougen and Watson suggest that concentration differences resulting from diffusion in complex reacting systems be evaluated by use of Eq. (12.99) where there is no volume change resulting from the reaction. The terms in the Schmidt group may be determined by considering each component as diffusing in a binary system composed of itself and of all the other components of the mixture in the average proportions in which they occur in the diffusional film. Diffusion may then be calculated from Gilland's formula (*Ind. Eng. Chem.*, **26,** 681, 1934). The partial pressure differences of all the components involved should be zero.

If the volume changes during the reaction, a mass flow effect in the direction of volume decrease is superimposed on the diffusional effects that would be calculated from Eq. (12.99). The result is a decrease in the concentration difference necessary to maintain diffusion in the direction of volume decrease, and an increase in the concentration differences necessary to cause diffusion in the opposite direction.

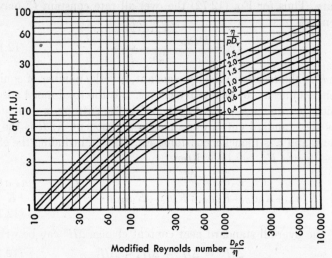

Figure 4 Diffusional mass transfer in gases flowing through granular solids.

By comparison of Eq. (12.99) and (12.100), Hougen and Watson arrived at an approximate multiplying factor f_D,

$$f_D = \left(\frac{p_{af}}{\pi}\right)^{-\Delta n} \qquad (12.101)$$

where Δn is the change in number of moles per mole of reaction. This factor is used to correct the results obtained from Eq. (12.99) where a change of volume accompanies the reaction. Concentration differences of reactants are multiplied by f_D, while those of products are divided by f_D. The corrections expressed by Eq. (12.101) are generally not large. For low conversion rates and high mass velocities, the concentration differences may in many cases be entirely neglected.

Evaluation of rate equation constants

In the rate equations each of the equilibrium and velocity constants is a function of the temperature expressed by Eq. (12.92) or (12.93).

When Eq. (12.93) is substituted in a rate equation it is advisable for the sake of simplicity to incorporate all the multiplying constants into an over-all rate constant. The entropy changes may also be included in the constant if they are considered independent of temperature. Thus for Eq. (12.72) the over-all rate constant C' may be written

$$C' = \frac{k'SLe^{\frac{\Delta S^* + \Delta S_A^0 + \Delta S_B^0}{R}}}{2h} \qquad (12.102)$$

where k' is the reaction velocity constant, S is the number of equidistant sites adjacent to each active center, L is the total molal adsorption sites per unit mass of catalyst, ΔS^* is the entropy of activation, ΔS_X^0 is the standard entropy change for component X, R is the gas constant, and h is Planck's constant. Eq. (12.72), including the effectiveness factor E_A, can be written:

$$r = \frac{E_A C' T e^{-\frac{\Delta H^{0'}}{RT}}}{(1 + K_A a_{Ai} + K_B a_{Bi} + K_R a_{Ri} + K_S a_{Si} + K_I a_{Ii} + \cdots)} \left(a_{Ai} a_{Bi} - \frac{a_{Ri} a_{Si}}{K} \right)$$
$$(12.103)$$

where the over-all standard heat content change $\Delta H^{0'}$ can be written

$$\Delta H^{0'} = \Delta H^* + \Delta H_A^0 + \Delta H_B^0 \qquad (12.104)$$

Here ΔH^* is the standard heat content of activation and ΔH_X^0 is the standard heat content change of component X. In Eq. (12.103), a_{Xi} is the activity at the interface of component X, K_X is the adsorption equilibrium constant of component X, and K is the over-all fluid-phase reaction equilibrium constant. K can ordinarily be evaluated from thermodynamic data.

The constants in complex equations, such as Eq. (12.103), are best determined by use of a differential reactor containing a bed of catalyst so shallow that relatively small changes in composition are obtained. The design of the reactor also should be such as to produce the smallest composition changes which permit accurate evaluation of rate of reaction using available analytical means. The temperature of the differential bed should be as uniform as possible, which means a small diameter reactor with good heat transfer provisions in the walls of the container.

The average activity of each component of a reaction mixture in a differential reactor may be taken as the arithmetic average of the inlet and outlet values for small changes, or better yet, obtained from the logarithmic mean of the differences between the activities at the inlet and outlet for the reactants. The mean activity of a product R may be taken as its activity a_{Re} when the reaction is at equilibrium, minus the log mean value of $(a_{Re} - a_R)$ at the terminal conditions, where a_R is the activity of R in the main fluid phase. Then by calculating the diffusional activity differences from Eq. (12.99) and (12.101), the interfacial activities are obtained, corresponding to the measured average rate.

EFFECTIVENESS FACTOR

To evaluate this factor as a function of temperature, differential rate measurements are made with two widely different particle sizes at each of two different temperatures, holding the activities constant at each temperature. At each temperature the ratio of the rates equals the ratio of the effectiveness factors, thus,

$$\frac{r_1}{r_2} = \frac{E_{A_1}}{E_{A_2}} \tag{12.105}$$

corresponding to the particle sizes D_{p_1} and D_{p_2}. At each temperature these rate ratios are determined and the Thiele modulus read directly from Fig. 5, which is derived from Fig. 3. From the determinations of the modulus at two different temperatures, a' and b of Eq. (12.96) are obtained, thus giving E_A as a function of particle size and temperature. In Fig. 5, m_1 and m_2 are the moduli of the two sizes of particles.

ADSORPTION EQUILIBRIUM CONSTANTS

The adsorption equilibrium constants of the rate equations are best determined for a given reaction by making rate measurements over a wide range of concentrations. For complex systems, to minimize tedious algebraic solutions of simultaneous equations, the effective average value of adsorption equilibrium constant of each component is determined by a constant temperature series of three differential rate measurements in which the activity of the desired component is varied over a wide range, while the activities of all the other components are held constant. It is generally desirable to run each component at maximum, medium, and minimum values of activity in the range desired, while the activities of the other components are held constant.

Having determined all the adsorption equilibrium constants, each single rate measurement permits calculation of the group $C'e^{-\frac{\Delta H^{0'}}{RT}}$.

EFFECT OF TEMPERATURE

The dependence of each adsorption equilibrium constant upon temperature is given by Eq. (12.92). For a complete experimental evaluation of the standard heat content and entropy changes of adsorption under reaction conditions, it is necessary to evaluate at

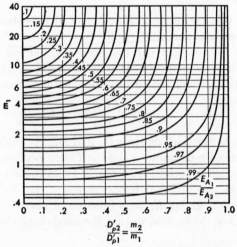

Figure 5 Determination of effectiveness factor modulus.

different temperatures the individual average adsorption equilibrium constants as described above. When such complete data are not available the standard entropy change of adsorption at one atmosphere may be assumed to be 23.0 entropy units lost. This is similar to Trouton's rule. Entropy changes may be obtained from activated adsorption equilibrium measurements for the individual components on the catalyst.

If standard entropy changes in adsorption are obtained in any of the above ways, a single determination of the equilibrium constant permits calculation of a standard heat content change, and a complete expression of the constant as a function of temperature. If these functions are evaluated for all components, C' and $\Delta H^{o'}$ may be calculated from any two rate measurements at different temperatures. The errors in the temperature coefficients of the equilibrium constants are absorbed in the calculation of $\Delta H^{o'}$ in this procedure, and may have little influence on the over-all accuracy of the equation.

Activated adsorption measurements

It is believed that much useful information concerning the correct mechanism and equation for the reaction may be obtained by measurements of activated adsorption rates and equilibrium constants of the individual components on the catalyst, even though the results cannot be substituted directly into the final rate equation because of interaction effects and variability of active centers. These adsorption measurements will serve to establish the relative values of the equilibrium constants, detect dissociation during adsorption, and allow the calculation of entropy change during adsorption.

Poisons

A poison may be defined as a component of a reaction mixture which retards the reaction by reducing the number of active centers available for the reactants. Such poisons may be either temporary or permanent.

It is observable from the rate equations that any inert component, I, which is adsorbed on the active centers promoting the reaction, is a poison. The effectiveness of the inert component as a poison depends on its concentration and its adsorption equilibrium constant. A poisoning effect which is temporary and quickly reaches a constant value is characteristic of an inert which shows a reversible adsorption of moderate equilibrium constant. Such poisoning effect can be eliminated by removal of the component from the reaction mixture. The effect of this type of inert is included in the rate equation.

Another type of poisoning is that resulting from the permanent, substantially irreversible adsorption of components present in small quantities in the reaction mixture. The effect of this type of poisoning is to reduce progressively the number of active centers per unit area, L', as the catalyst continues in service. A small amount of catalyst poison may thus have an effect out of proportion to its concentration. The loss of activity of a catalyst while in use may be due to this type of poisoning, to structural changes affecting the area and L, or to physically coating the active surface with solid or semisolid material either present in the reactants or formed by secondary reactions. Thus the coating of catalysts in high-temperature organic reactions with high molecular weight compounds approaching pure carbon in composition is an example of the poison reducing the effective concentration of active centers L.

Burk (*J. Phys. Chem.*, **30,** 1134, 1926) explains poisoning on the basis of multiple adsorption, since a surface could be completely blocked with respect to multiple adsorption by the adsorption of relatively few poison particles if they are permanently held and are randomly distributed over the surface.

Promoter action

A *promoter* is a substance added in small amounts to a given catalyst to increase the effectiveness of the catalyst in speeding up the desired reaction. Thus the decomposition of hydrogen peroxide by glass wool is promoted by copper sulfate and manganous sulfate (see Elissafoff, *Z. Electrochem.*, **21,** 352, 1915). Burk (*loc. cit.*) explains this promoter action by the theory of multiple adsorption. Thus H_2O_2 is supposed to be doubly adsorbed on glass wool which has a strong surface attraction for the oxygen atoms of H_2O_2 but only weak attraction for the hydrogen atoms, or vice versa. When copper or manganese salts are added they are adsorbed on the surface of the glass, and offer strong points of attraction for whichever atom of H_2O_2 is weakly adsorbed on the glass, thus offering in conjunction with the glass, effective pairs for the catalysis of the H_2O_2 decomposition. The marked effect of the promoter is shown by the following table.

TABLE I

Conc. of $CuSO_4$ millimols/liter	Amount of glass wool (grams)	Relative rate
0.0	0.5	0.06
1.54	0.5	0.67
3.10	0.5	0.68
1.54	0.0	0.10
Conc. of $MnSO_4$		
0.0	2.3	0.0085
0.2	2.3	0.0860
0.2	0.0	0.0052

At low temperatures dry aluminum halides are apparently inert to all paraffins. Addition of hydrogen halide or water to the aluminum halide makes of it an active isomerization catalyst. Leighton and Heldman (*J. Am. Chem. Soc.*, **65**, 2276, 1943), on the basis of kinetic experiments, postulated this isomerization catalyst to be $HAlBr_4$ in the case of hydrogen bromide-aluminum bromide mixtures. It is known that other substances besides hydrogen halides can function as promoters for aluminum halide catalysis (Egloff, Hulla, and Komarewski, *Isomerization of Pure Hydrocarbons*, New York, Reinhold Publishing Corporation, 1942). Heldman (*J. Am. Chem. Soc.*, **66**, 1786, 1944; **66**, 1789, 1944; **66**, 1791, 1944) has studied several of these promoters for catalysis by aluminum bromide of the isomerization of paraffin hydrocarbons.

The theory is that aluminum exhibits a coordination number greater than 4 during isomerization catalysis, i.e., that the AlX_4^- is still an acid. The mechanism is then described by Heldman (*loc. cit.*) as follows:

"First there is an oriented collision of the catalyst with the paraffin to produce a configuration with a hydrogen on the third or fourth carbon in the paraffin chain near a halogen of the catalyst and the methyl group from the end of the chain near the aluminum. These configurations are chosen because the primary reaction is always the interchange of a methyl group with a hydrogen atom two (sometimes three) carbon atoms removed and because these are the only configurations leading to sterically probable structures.

"AlX_4^- acts as an acid toward the end methyl group and as a base toward the hydrogen, forming a transient activated complex with the methyl and hydrogen loosely attached to the catalyst and the hydrocarbon residue restrained from moving from the vicinity by the residual attraction of the methyl and hydrogen or by the cage effect (if the isomerization is in the liquid phase).

"An electron pair then shifts from the middle to the new end carbon of the hydrocarbon fragment. Concomitantly the fragment rotates with respect to the catalyst, so that it is brought into a new position with the methyl group and hydrogen adjacent to the middle and end carbon, respectively. Reattachment yields the 2- or 3-methyl isomer as the product.

"At higher temperatures, where the rotation may become so violent as to remove the catalyst with the methyl and/or the hydrogen attached, from the hydrocarbon fragment, or with larger hydrocarbons, where the long tail may whip the reacting end out of the catalysts' reach during the transformation, the usual side reactions producing a variety of lower and higher boiling materials would occur, as observed."

The theory as given above is idealized and does not take into account complications arising from secondary or side reactions. Caution should be exercised in extending the equations to conditions far different from those at which the constants are evaluated, since serious errors might result from the assumption of constancy of such variable factors as heat content changes in activated adsorption.

Uyehara and Watson (*Ind. Eng. Chem.*, **53**, 541, 1943) apply the above principles to the data of Lewis and Ries on the oxidation of sulfur dioxide in a flow system over platinized asbestos catalyst. The data are well represented on the assumption that the rate-controlling step is a surface reaction between activated-adsorbed sulfur dioxide and atomic oxygen. The experimental data show somewhat less deviation from this general equation than from the empirical expression proposed by Lewis and Ries (*Ind. Eng. Chem.*, **19**, 830, 1927).

While this and many other heterogeneous catalysts involve gaseous reactants, yet many solid catalyzed reactions occur in liquid media. The decomposition of hydrogen peroxide cited above is an example of solid catalysis in liquid media. The equations of Hougen and Watson are general and will apply to liquid reactants if the constants are determined under the conditions specified. In liquid systems diffusion rates may be so slow as to become rate governing, but outside of this possibility the case of liquid reactants is well covered in the general theory.

Specific studies on adsorption, heterogeneous catalysis, and heterogeneous reactions

We shall digress now from the more theoretical considerations of adsorption, heterogeneous catalysis, and heterogeneous reactions, to study some particular cases appertaining to these fields. The topics that will be discussed are the nature and rate of adsorption of solutes by active carbon, the solution of metals in aqueous and in non-aqueous acid solutions, and the catalytic decomposition of sodium hypochlorite solutions.

Nature and rate of adsorption of solutes by active carbon

THE NATURE OF ACTIVE CARBON

In this section we will be particularly interested in the adsorption by carbon of solutes, especially dyes, from solution, although some general ideas of adsorption will be developed. Hassler and McMinn (*Ind. Eng. Chem.*, **37,** 645, 1945) discuss the nature of active carbon. We will first consider the contents of this paper, since the ideas contained therein are pertinent. Different industries have divergent needs for active carbon, and to meet these needs many types of active carbon are manufactured. These different active carbons show wide variations in specific adsorptive power. For comparison of the adsorptive power of different carbons, time of contact presents a difficult problem, since the rate of adsorption is not the same for all solutes or for all carbons. For all the carbons investigated, the rate of adsorption was very rapid during the first five or ten minutes and then fell off sharply. When the active carbons were ground for an additional time, the adsorptive power increased slightly at first but then decreased as grinding continued. That the extent of this change varied with the different carbons was attributed to differences of mechanical strengths of the various carbons, depending on the raw material and type of processing. In the case of an individual carbon there was not always the same relative change with grinding in all specific adsorptive powers, as would have been the case if there had been the partial destruction of a homogeneous surface. These variations in the effect of grinding on different specific adsorptive powers are evidence of a heterogeneous surface. That the active surface on carbon is heterogeneous is supported by the changes in adsorptive power brought about by the action of certain oxidizing chemicals. Carbon *B* was allowed to react several hours with 50 per cent by weight of potassium permanganate in an acidified solution, bisulfite was added to reduce any unchanged permanganate, and the inorganic constituents were removed by suitable washing. This treatment reduced the adsorptive power of carbon, a reduction which ranged between 15 per cent for methylene blue to 50 per cent for ponceau red. Apparently there is preferential oxidation of certain specific adsorptive powers.

From the standpoint of activation, lengthening the time of activation generally increased the over-all adsorptive power, but in some processes all specific adsorptive powers do not develop simultaneously or at the same rate. In the production of active carbon from cellulose waste, the adsorptive powers for phenol and molasses were developed independently of each other. This was shown by the adsorptive power for phenol developing rapidly and reaching a maximum value within a 30-minute activation period; and that for molasses developing more slowly but continuing up to 60 minutes activation.

Broadly an *active center* may be defined as the sum of the forces which hold an adsorbed molecule. Several species of active centers are present on a heterogeneous surface.

The influence of solvent upon adsorptive power of an active carbon shows that an individual substance may be adsorbed by different types or species of active center. The carbons studied by Hassler and McMinn adsorbed less dye from solutions in alcohol than from water. This behavior could be due to many factors, among them the effect of the solvent upon the solubility, association, orientation, and ionization of solute, and the extent of such influence would vary from one dye to another. However, these factors would not alter the relative adsorptive power of different carbons for a specific substance. In the cases examined, changing the solvent altered the relative adsorptive power of certain carbons. Thus two carbons, distinguished by the letters A and H, were equivalent for adsorbing malachite green from an aqueous solution, but with alcohol as solvent, carbon H had less than half the efficiency of A. Thus the active centers which adsorbed malachite green on carbon A had different properties from the corresponding centers on carbon H.

The study of adsorption isotherms lend support to the concept that individual substances can be adsorbed on different species of centers. Figures 6 and 7 represent Freundlich isotherms. In these figures the vertical distance represents concentration on the carbon surface, and the horizontal distance represents concentration remaining in solution. The rate of change of the equilibrium relation between adsorption and solution concentration is given by the slope of the line. Sometimes different carbons are found to have different adsorptive capacities for a typical substance, for example, iodine. When such is the case, the difference between such carbons could arise from a greater number of active centers on the more powerful carbons (see Calingaert and Davis, *Ind. Eng. Chem.*, **17,** 1287, 1925). When the isotherms do not have the same slope such an interpretation is inadequate. The change in slope is evidence of different surface properties, and the active centers differ not only in number but also in kind. The nature of the active center depends on the method of preparation, but it is not a hard and fast rule that a different method of activation will result in a different isotherm slope. In Fig. 6 several of the commercial carbons have the same slope and others have different slopes.

An individual species of active center may have adsorptive power for more than one kind of substance. This is shown by many adsorbable compounds competing for the same active centers and thus

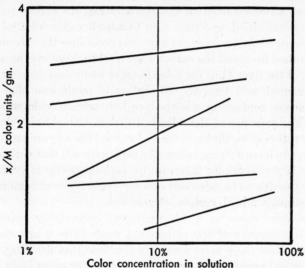

Figure 6 Isotherms of several commercial carbons. Here some isotherms have the same slope and others have different slopes.

displacing one another's adsorption. The factor of steric hinderance by the more strongly adsorbed molecules must be included when considering the power of one molecule to displace another. Thus the active centers may be so close together that there is not sufficient room for simultaneous adsorption of all the different kinds of molecules that could be held independently. Assuming that displacement of adsorption indicates that an individual species of center can attract different substances, then many of the differences between carbons could arise from various assortments of a relatively few species. Various proportions of a few species could provide many variations in adsorptive power.

If a substance is adsorbed simultaneously on several species of centers, the experimental data would yield an isotherm which is a composite of these individual primary centers. Experimentally the composite nature of the adsorption would be indicated by a change in isotherm slope accompanied by a partial loss of adsorptive power. An indirect study by Hassler and McMinn consisted of adsorbing one substance and then adsorbing on the carbon a second substance under such conditions that the first material was not displaced. Thus a dye was adsorbed from an aqueous solution; the carbon was separated, washed, dried, and then used to adsorb vapors of a solvent in which the dye is not soluble. In a reverse procedure the solvent vapor was adsorbed first, and the carbon then used to decolorize an aqueous solution of the dye. Thus the adsorption of methylene blue by carbon was measured, and then the adsorption of methylene blue by the same carbon containing adsorbed carbon tetrachloride was determined. The presence of the adsorbed carbon tetrachloride decreased the adsorption of methylene blue and caused the adsorption isotherm of the dye to have a steeper slope. An explanation is that carbon tetrachloride is preferentially taken up by certain species of centers and permits the dye to be adsorbed on only those types of centers which do not strongly adsorb carbon tetrachloride.

There were cases in which treatment appreciably reduced the adsorptive capacity of the carbon but made little if any change in the slope. Now there is no reason to conclude that grinding, the use of a chemical agent, or other treatment operates exclusively on only one species of primary center. There could be a partial though unequal destruction of many species. The reduction in the amount of adsorption is given by the sum of the individual effects, whereas a change in the isotherm slope is a function of a difference. Thus if an observed isotherm X is a composite of two primary isotherms Y and Z, then if Y and Z are reduced to the same proportionate extent, the composite isotherm X will move to a lower level but the slope will not change. There will be a change of slope only if Y is destroyed to a greater extent than Z or vice versa. Furthermore, the experimentally determined isotherms differ little in slope, and, if this is true of primary isotherms, one isotherm would have to be destroyed in considerable excess before a change in the observed slope would be clearly defined in experimental work.

Comparisons under exactly the same experimental conditions

must be carried out if isotherm slopes are used to differentiate between the species of active centers. Thus malachite green was adsorbed from various mixtures of alcohol and water. As can be seen from Fig. 7, any increase in the proportion of alcohol resulted in a decreased adsorption of dye and a change in isotherm slope. In this case the change in slope could be due to the change in solubility, degree of ionization, and association with change in composition of solvent. Thus the alteration of slope is not necessarily evidence of different types of centers.

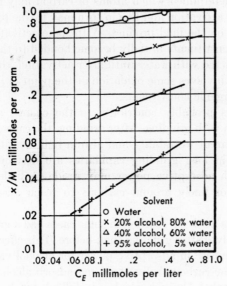

Figure 7 Adsorption isotherms for malachite green on carbon using water and mixture of water and alcohol as solvents.

Variations in the specific adsorptive power are brought about in the process of activation, the two stages of which are broadly: (1) carbonization of the raw carbonaceous material at relatively low temperatures (below 600° C), and (2) activation proper by mildly oxidizing the char with steam or carbon dioxide at 800° to 900° C, or with air at lower temperatures. The basic process may be modified by supplementary conditions, some of which are trade secrets and some of which are fully described in the literature. Certain adsorptive powers may be developed in a sequence of stages. In many cases various chemicals are added. Some, such as zinc chloride and calcium chloride, are added before carbonization; others, such as ortho-phosphoric acid and sodium hydroxide, are used to impregnate the char just before activation proper. The chemicals mentioned in the first group are dehydrators, but their full functions are little understood. Nevertheless they influence greatly the specific adsorptive powers finally developed. In the second group orthophosphoric acid raises the ignition point of a charcoal, and sodium hydroxide lowers it. Thus may be determined which atoms of carbon may be selectively oxidized during activation and this in turn may fix the pattern for the atomic spacing on the final product. With some activation processes the inorganic constituents initially become bonded to the carbon and cannot be extracted with water until after activation, thus indicating that activation involves some oxidation at the point of bond between carbon and inorganic constituents.

Many factors probably contribute to the change of adsorptive power of carbon with grinding. After grinding, the carbons showed an increase in apparent wettability and also in bulk density. The latter indicates that in long grinding capillaries are destroyed. In these capillaries much adsorptive power may reside. A little longer time was required for finely ground carbons to reach adsorption equilibrium.

For alcohol as a solvent, carbon in some cases had a greater adsorptive power for dyes after grinding than before. This effect seems to be related to a decrease in adsorptive power for alcohol vapor. It could be that the same carbons before grinding adsorb alcohol so strongly as to form a blanket, through which it is difficult for dye molecules to penetrate and find the room to occupy the active centers on which they would otherwise be adsorbed.

RULES APPERTAINING TO ADSORPTION

Gurwitsch (*J. Russ. Phys. Chem. Soc.*, **47,** 805, 1915; *Z. Physik. Chem.*, **87,** 323, 1914) found that the volumes of different liquids adsorbed at saturation were approximately constant for a given adsorbent. The rule is well illustrated by the results of Hallstrom (*Diss.*, Helsingfors, 1920) with a wide variety of solids and vapors. McBain (*Sorption of Gases by Solids*, London, 1932, p. 140) casts doubt on its general validity. Broad and Foster (*J. Chem. Soc.*, **1945,** 366) show that the best test of Gurwitsch's rule is to plot q the saturation value of adsorbed substance, say in milligrams per gram of adsorbent, against d the density of the adsorbate. A straight line which passes through the origin should result according to the equation

$$\frac{q}{M} = \frac{V_0 d}{M} - K \qquad (12.106)$$

where M is the molecular weight of adsorbate; V_0 is the total volume of pores, assumed to be conical, in the adsorbate; and K is a constant for a constant slope of conical pore. The necessity of assuming tapering or conical pores is due to the fact that the amounts of adsorbate adsorbed on the adsorbent (here silica gel) decreases as the diameter of the adsorbed molecule increases. As to Gurwitsch's rule, Broad and Foster point out that although Coolidge (*J. Am. Chem. Soc.*, **46,** 596, 1924) found in the adsorption of vapors by charcoal variations from 424 to 490 cubic millimeters per gram of charcoal, yet a large scale plot of q/M against d/M according to Eq. (12.106) gave results in accord with the rule.

Broad and Foster (*J. Chem. Soc.*, **1945,** 372) state that the S-shaped isothermals of vapors on ferric oxide gel indicate that after the adsorption of a layer of adsorbate one or two molecules thick, the remainder of the pore space fills up by capillary condensation (see Foster, *Proc. Roy. Soc.*, *A***147**, 128, 1934). On charcoals, in general, water is the only substance which gives these S-shaped isothermals, other liquids giving normal isothermals to which the Langmuir equation is usually applicable. McBain (*J. Am. Chem. Soc.*, **52,** 2198, 1930) suggests the term *presorption* to describe the case where the formation of a unimolecular layer leaves no room for further sorption of any kind. Thus the unimolecular layer would account for complete sorption. Broad and Foster found this to be the case for the adsorption of ethyl alcohol on charcoal.

Freundlich (*Colloid and Capillary Chemistry*, English Edition, New York, E. P. Dutton and Co., 1926) stated Traube's rule as follows: "The adsorption of organic substances from aqueous solutions increases strongly and regularly as we ascend the homologous series." This applied to adsorption, and according to King (*J. Chem. Soc.*, **1935,** 1975) is obeyed in the case of most charcoals. Yet some of the carbons adsorb quantities of fatty acids in the reverse order to that required by the rule. This King explains on the basis of the inaccessibility of small pores to large molecules. This idea of ultrapores was introduced by Herbst (*Biochem. Z.*, **115**, 204, 1921) and was termed *ultraporosity*. King concludes that Traube's rule is invariably obeyed if the ultrapores are sufficiently enlarged by oxidation. Linner and Gortner (*J. Phys. Chem.*, **39**, 35, 1935) found the ratio $\frac{a_{(n+1)}}{a_n}$ (where a is the amount adsorbed when the equilibrium concentration C is a maximum, and n is the number of carbon atoms), while indicating obedience to Traube's rule at various equilibrium concentrations of fatty acids on charcoal, yet yielded a more constant value as the equilibrium concentration approaches 0.25 molar. They further found that such a ratio was better than is the case of the equilibrium concentration, $\frac{C_n}{C_{(n+1)}}$, ratio.

RATE OF ADSORPTION

Swan and Urquhart (*J. Phys. Chem.*, **31**, 251, 1927) have given an extensive review of the equations used in adsorption. These include equations dealing with the rate of adsorption, and we shall follow their presentation rather closely.

Evidence indicates that equilibrium is reached in an adsorption system within a finite time, although times from a few seconds to a few years have been recorded. The amount of adsorbate adsorbed x, when plotted against time t, should have a slope $\frac{dx}{dt}$, which decreases with increasing time and which should become zero at a finite value of time.

Mills and Thompson (*J. Chem. Soc.*, **35**, 26, 1879) and Mills and Takamine (*J. Chem. Soc.*, **43**, 142, 1883) studied the rate of adsorption from solution by textile fibers. Their equations are perhaps the first proposed to express a rate of adsorption. Mills and Thompson found a logarithmic relation between the amounts of coloring matter remaining after successive intervals of time. This logarithmic relation is the sum of the separate and independent effects of the solvent and of the textile fiber. The equation they give is

$$y = A\alpha^t \pm B\beta^t \tag{12.107}$$

where y is the amount of coloring matter remaining after time, t, the total initial amount being $A \pm B$, and α and β being geometric factors, depending respectively upon the action of the textile, in this case silk, and of the solvent. These authors found that β equaled 1, 0, or a fraction so that Eq. (12.107) became in some instances

$$y = A\alpha^t + B \qquad\qquad (12.108)$$
$$y = A\alpha^t \qquad\qquad (12.109)$$

$(A \pm B)$ was always taken as 100. Thus 0.3791 gram of silk was immersed in a solution of 0.000825 gram of rosaniline hydrochloride (volume = 450 cubic centimeters) and allowed to stand at a temperature of 2.9° C. The equation used to calculate the amount of coloring matter remaining after time t was Eq. (12.108) written in the form

$$y = 83.77(0.7209)^t + 16.23 \qquad\qquad (12.110)$$

The relationships between calculated and observed values of y are given in Table II. The unit of time is 24 hours.

TABLE II Comparison of calculated and observed amounts of rosaniline hydrochloride remaining in solution

t	y observed	y calculated
0	100.00	100.00
1	76.54	76.62
2	59.79	59.77
3	47.60	47.61

Pickels (*Chem. News*, **121**, 25–7, 1920) studied the velocity of adsorption by charcoal dust of various substances in solution. Fifteen grams of charcoal dust per liter of solution were used. The amount adsorbed was measured by determining the decreased concentration of the solution. Solutions of benzoic acid, iodine and potassium permanganate of various concentrations were used. Pickels used the equation

$$k' = \frac{1}{t_2 - t_1}\left(\log\frac{a - x_1}{a - x_2} - 0.4343\,\frac{x_2 - x_1}{a}\right) \qquad (12.111)$$

to express the velocity of adsorption. In this equation a is the original amount of adsorbate and x is the amount of adsorbate at time t. k' is the adsorption velocity constant.

Freundlich and coworkers (*Z. physik. Chem.*, **85**, 641, 1913; *Z. physik. Chem.*, **89**, 417, 1915) have represented the rate function of adsorption reversal, i.e., of desorption of a dye from mercury sulfide by the *equations of negative autocatalysis*, either

$$\frac{dx}{dt} = 2k't(1 + bx)(1 - x)^2 \tag{12.112}$$

or

$$\frac{dx}{dt} = 2k't(1 + bx)(1 - x) \tag{12.113}$$

They have further found that the variation of k' with temperature is given by the Arrhenius' equation.

$$\log k' = -\frac{\Delta E}{2.3RT} + B \tag{12.114}$$

The value of ΔE is about 14,000 calories, and an increase of 10° C in the temperature quadruples the value of k'. In Eq. (12.112) and (12.113), k' and b are constants, t the time, and x the increase in concentration of the solution of a dye desorbed from amorphous mercury sulfide as the sulfide changes to the crystalline form.

Marc (*Z. Elektrochem.*, **20,** 515, 1914) assumed that the rate of adsorption in solution depends on the attractive force, the osmotic pressure of the solute, and the kinetic energy of the adsorbed molecules. He derived the rate equation

$$\frac{dx}{dt} = k_3 x^{-k_1} - k_3 + k_2(a - x) \tag{12.115}$$

where the first term represents the attractive force, the second term the kinetic energy of the adsorbed molecules, and the third term the osmotic pressure of the solute. An approximate solution of equation (12.115), for values of x not too near x_∞, is

$$\frac{x^{(k_1+1)}}{t} \left(2x_\infty^{k_1} + k_2 x^{k_1}\right) = k_3 \tag{12.116}$$

Gustaver (*Kolloidchem. Beihefte*, **15,** 185, 1922) set the amount of adsorption proportional to the free surface and also to the total amount of adsorbate in the gaseous or liquid phase. He obtained the equation

$$k' = \frac{1}{t(a - x_\infty)} \left(\log \frac{a - x}{x_\infty - x} \cdot \frac{x_\infty}{a}\right) \tag{12.117}$$

for adsorption from a liquid. A similar equation could be used for adsorption of a gas. The equations of Gustaver can be obtained from Langmuir's theory.

Solution of metals in aqueous and nonaqueous acid solutions

Among other heterogeneous reactions, the dissolution of metals both in aqueous and nonaqueous acid solutions have received considerable attention. Kilpatrick and Rushton (*J. Phys. Chem.*, **34,** 2181, 1930) investigated the rate of solution of magnesium in both strong and weak acids from the point of view of the extended theory of acids and bases developed by Brönsted (*Rec. Trav. chim.*, **42,** 718, 1923). Thus for hydrogen chloride in water we have the equilibrium

$$\underset{\text{acid}}{HCl} + \underset{\text{base}}{H_2O} \rightleftharpoons \underset{\text{acid}}{H_3O^+} + \underset{\text{base}}{Cl^-}$$

Since hydrogen chloride is such a strong acid, the above equilibrium is practically completely to the right. The acid present, therefore, in hydrogen chloride solution is the oxonium ion, H_3O^+. The concentration of proton H^+ is so small as to be insignificant kinetically. This would be the case for any strong acid dissolved in water, and explains why all strong acids appear to be of equal strength in aqueous solution.

For a weak acid in water two acids are present at appreciable concentrations, the oxonium ion and the weak acid molecule. Thus for formic acid we would have the equilibrium

$$HCOOH + H_2O \rightleftharpoons H_3O^+ + HCOO^-$$

and the two acids present are the formic acid molecule and the oxonium ion. If the concentration of the formate ion base $HCOO^-$ is increased by the addition of a salt of formic acid, the concentration of H_3O^+ is decreased and the solution is buffered with respect to the oxonium ion.

In aqueous solutions of strong acids, essentially the only acid present is H_3O^+ and magnesium dissolves according to the stoichiometric equation

$$\tfrac{1}{2}Mg + H_3O^+ \longrightarrow \tfrac{1}{2}Mg^{++} + H_2O + \tfrac{1}{2}H_2$$

A solution of weak acid, as well as a solution of weak acid-weak acid salt, contains two acids. For solutions of formic acid and formic acid-formate the two acids present are $HCOOH$ and H_3O^+. Kilpatrick and Rushton were interested in whether magnesium in these solutions reacted with the oxonium ion, with the formic acid molecule, or with both of these acids.

To test this point these investigators measured the rate of solution of magnesium in solutions of strong acid and in buffer solutions of various weak acids. The reaction was followed by measuring the volume of the gas evolved. The apparatus consisted of a florence flask fitted with a mercury-seal stirrer having an outlet attached to a gas burette. A cylinder of magnesium of measured surface was attached to the shaft of the stirrer. The solutions were stirred at a rate somewhat above 600 r.p.m. and the temperature was held at 25° C ± 0.01°.

In the case of strong acids, hydrochloric and perchloric, the rate of solution of magnesium was found to be proportional to the concentration of hydrogen ion. The effect of added electrolyte was small.

For the formate-formic acid buffer solutions it was observed that for over a four-fold change in oxonium ion concentration, the rate was proportional to the formic acid concentration. In a plot of the rate versus acid concentration the intercept on the axis of ordinates represents the part of the whole reaction due to the oxonium ion. For glycollate-glycollic acid buffers, acetate-acetic acid buffers, and chloracetate-chloracetic acid buffers, the rates were found to be proportional to the concentrations of the respective acids.

It was found that when the reactions were allowed to go to completion, the amounts of hydrogen evolved corresponded, within the experimental error of the measurements, to the initial concentrations of the acids.

The reaction followed the monomolecular law, and the specific reaction rate constant was calculated using the formula

$$k' = \frac{2.303V}{St} \log \frac{C_0}{C_t} \tag{12.118}$$

where V is the volume of the solution in cubic centimeters, S the surface of the magnesium in square centimeters, t the time in minutes, and C_0 and C_t are the initial and current concentrations of acid, respectively.

Expressing the customary dissociation constant of the acid A as

$$K_A = \frac{[B][H_3O^+]}{[A]} \tag{12.119}$$

the constant may be taken as a measure of the acid strength. Kilpatrick and Rushton observed that there was a proportionality between the logarithm of the reaction velocity constant and the logarithm of the acid strength. Brönsted and co-workers (see Chapter XI) had previously found such a relationship in certain cases of acid and basic catalysis.

Brönsted and Kane (*J. Am. Chem. Soc.*, **53**, 3624, 1931) studied the dissolution of sodium from sodium amalgam by various acids and buffers, using both aqueous and nonaqueous solvents. These authors also investigated the dissolution reaction using sodium hydroxide instead of acid. The chemical transformations upon which the equation for the total reaction depends was given by these investigators as

$$\underset{\text{(acid)}}{A} + \underset{\substack{\text{electron} \\ \text{(base)}}}{\theta} \longrightarrow \underset{\text{(base)}}{B} + \underset{\substack{\text{hydrogen} \\ \text{atom (acid)}}}{H}$$

and

$$2H \longrightarrow H_2$$

They point out that if the hydrogen atoms are in a normal state of energy, then, since these are not being accumulated, their formation must be slow compared to their combination to hydrogen molecules, and, disregarding *salt effects*, the velocity of the hydrogen evolution should be a first-order reaction as regards the concentration of acid molecule A. If, however, the hydrogen molecule is also formed by the collision of two hydrogen atoms only partly liberated from two A molecules, i.e., by two hydrogen atoms at low energy level, then the total reaction would be expressed by the formula

$$2A + 2\theta \longrightarrow 2B + H_2$$

and should be bimolecular as regards the A-concentration. Depending upon the degree of liberty required for the union of two hydrogen atoms, there might exist a transition between the two cases. Decreasing concentration of acid would favor the first reaction in relation to the second.

The first-order mechanism written above is clarified by using water solutions as an example. Let us remember that the hydrogen ion exists in aqueous solution as the oxonium ion, H_3O^+, and that the metal in a solid state probably consists of metallic ions and free electrons. Hence the H_3O^+ ion reacts as an acid with an electron as a base, and the resulting decrease in electrostatic forces on the sodium ion after the removal of the neighboring electron or electrons, allows the ion to dissolve from the metal. The governing steps in the reaction are the rate of reception of the electrons by the acid, and the formation of hydrogen molecules from hydrogen atoms.

Brönsted and Kane also point out that if the reaction of the acid with electrons is reversible, thus

$$A + \theta \rightleftharpoons B + H$$

and the formation of hydrogen molecules from hydrogen atoms is slow compared with both of these, then at constant C_B the concentration of H would be proportional to C_A, and the velocity of H_2 formation proportional to C_A^2. The reaction would thus be second-order with respect to the acid concentration.

The investigators found that the experiments agree fairly well with the assumption of a first-order reaction as regards the effect of the acid, and that the mechanism of the kinetic reaction is represented by the equation

$$A + \theta \longrightarrow B + H$$

the hydrogen atoms being liberated in the normal state and thereafter reacting with great velocity to form hydrogen molecules.

Brönsted and Kane found that an approximately linear relation existed between the velocity of the solution reaction and the square root of the sodium concentration in the amalgam. This relationship is expressed by

$$-\frac{dx}{dt} = k'\sqrt{x} \tag{12.120}$$

or

$$k't = 2(\sqrt{a} - \sqrt{x}) \tag{12.121}$$

where a is the initial concentration of the sodium in the amalgam and x is its concentration at time t. Thus plotting time against the square root of the sodium concentration, a straight line should be obtained the slope of which (namely, $-k'/2$) should be independent of the initial concentration of sodium. One can express the sodium concentration in terms of the hydrogen pressure, that is, $\sqrt{x}$ is proportional to $\sqrt{P_\infty - p}$, where P_∞ is the final pressure increase and p is pressure increase after time t. Then the relation given in Eq. (12.121) can be tested by plotting time against $\sqrt{P_\infty - p}$. The value of k' in all calculations was obtained by putting one centimeter of mercury equal to unit sodium concentration, and using for t the time in minutes. Thus if P_∞ equals 4 centimeters and after 10 minutes p equals 3 centimeters, the velocity constant k' equals 0.2.

These deductions were tested in solutions of 2.0 molar K_2HPO_4 in which the initial sodium concentration was varied in the ratio 1 to 4. Verification was also found for solutions of sodium glycocollate-glycocoll in which the initial sodium concentration varied from 1 to 8. In each solution a series of parallel lines was obtained from which k'

was determined and found to be independent of the sodium concentration as shown by the data in Table III.

TABLE III   Experimental data testing Eq. (12.121)

Solution	Initial Na concn. in arbitrary units	$k' \times 10^2$
2.0 molar K₂HPO₄	2	5.33
2.0 molar K₂HPO₄	4	5.20
2.0 molar K₂HPO₄	8	5.20
	Average	5.24
"9/1 glycocoll" buffer	1	6.06
"9/1 glycocoll" buffer	2	6.26
"9/1 glycocoll" buffer	4	6.06
"9/1 glycocoll" buffer	8	6.00
	Average	6.10

While the kinetic equation of a unimolecular reaction and reactions of higher orders require an infinitely long time for reactions to be completed, the dissolution of sodium amalgam described above requires a finite time for completion. Thus for $x = 0$ the reaction time for completion t is given by

$$t_\infty = \frac{2\sqrt{a}}{k'} \qquad (12.122)$$

This is a special case of the more general equation

$$k't = \frac{a^{(1-n)} - x^{(1-n)}}{1 - n} \qquad (12.123)$$

valid for a reaction of the nth order. For n less than unity, t will always be finite.

Other observations on this reaction and their interpretations are summarized below. Sodium amalgam would react with sodium hydroxide solutions slowly, but the results were not reproducible. With aqueous phosphate, glycocoll, and phenol buffers of constant hydrogen-ion concentration, the velocity showed a linear increase with increasing buffer concentration. Thus the dissolution of sodium is due to the reaction of the metal (electron) with the acid molecule. The molal reactivity constant of various acids showed a tendency to increase with the strength of the acid. The strength effect may be partly masked, however, by the effect of the charge of the acid, and other effects. The roseo cobaltic ion $[CoH_2O(NH_3)_5]^{+++}$ reacts very rapidly with sodium amalgam; this was explained as being due to the high positive charge and the resulting strong attraction for the electron. Corresponding to the high strength of the oxonium ion, this acid reacts with extreme speed. In strong acids, therefore, the rate of dissolution of sodium from sodium amalgam is governed chiefly by the rate of diffusion of the reacting substances into the surface of interaction. The $k'_{H_3O^+}$ value obtained by extrapolation of the velocity constant in solutions of high acidity to zero concentration of buffer was of the order of 10^7. This is merely the order of the velocity constant since experiments at lower acidity did not yield values compatible with this magnitude. The time of reaction calculated from Eq. (12.122) using $k'_{H_3O^+}$ as 10^7 and $\sqrt{a}$ as 3.5, corresponding to concentration of sodium amalgam used in these experiments, was 2.10×10^{-5} second. Thus, provided the H_3O^+ could be supplied by the diffusion process to the surface of the metal as fast as it could accept electrons, the reaction would be completed almost instantaneously.

In the experiment in which sodium amalgam reacted with phenol in dry benzene, the rate of the reaction was proportional to the phenol concentration.

King and Braverman (*J. Am. Chem. Soc.*, **54**, 1744, 1932) studied the reaction of zinc with acids and concluded that it was impossible to decide from available data whether acids other than H_3O^+ react directly with magnesium, zinc, cadmium, and marble, since previous experiments have measured rates controlled largely by diffusion rates.

Kilpatrick and Rushton (*J. Phys. Chem.*, **38**, 269, 1934) point out that these conclusions are based on facts accepted as criteria of the validity of the diffusion rate theory. They list these facts as:

(1) Different solids dissolve at nearly the same rate.

(2) Stirring has a marked effect upon the rate.

(3) The rate of solution is inversely proportional to the viscosity.

(4) The rates observed follow diffusion coefficients for comparable experimental conditions.

(5) The temperature coefficients are small compared to those of chemical reactions.

Kilpatrick and Rushton point out, however, that dissolution data on magnesium and zinc in acids do not bear out a diffusion-controlled process. With regard to the second point, these authors found that the effect of stirring could be expressed by the equation

$$k' = aR^n \qquad (12.124)$$

where k' is the reaction velocity constant, R is the surface speed in centimeters per minute, and n and a are constants. This relationship between the rate of dissolution and surface speed of the substance being dissolved is difficult to explain on the basis of any chemical rate theory. However, Kilpatrick and Rushton say that, owing to the temperature effects, it is not practicable to extend the measurements to such surface speeds that the thickness of the so-called diffusion layer would be such that the rate of the chemical reaction would be measured. They also found that the results of experiments to test the effect of change in viscosity were definitely contradictory to the diffusion theory in the case of salts, and for nonelectrolytes the inverse proportionality was at best qualitative.

These investigations give the order of decreasing velocity constants for the following acids as oxonium ion, formic acid, acetic acid, citric acid, tartaric acid, and phenol. The diffusion coefficients for these acids are given as oxonium ion, formic acid, acetic acid, phenol, tartaric acid, and citric acid. They point out that the exponents of the idea that oxonium ion is the only acid present might not consider it necessary for the acids other than the H_3O^+ to diffuse to the metal. However, this conclusion is not in accord with the experimental results. Also, if the diffusion process consists of a diffusion of an oxonium ion through a layer more dilute, and if this is the rate-controlling process, then what is the diffusion layer involved in the reaction of magnesium with water, which is independent of the oxonium ion concentration? The layer cannot be a film of hydrogen because the rate is unchanged by the addition of a depolarizer.

Kilpatrick and Rushton found the temperature coefficient for the reaction of magnesium with oxonium ion to be 1.7 for a 10-degree interval. Centnerszwer (Z. physik. Chem., **141**, 297, 1929) gave 1.2 for stirred and unstirred solutions. Bonsdorff (Medd. Ventenskapsakad. Nobelinst., **3**, 108, 1915) obtained a value which decreased markedly with increasing temperature. For the water reaction, Kilpatrick and Rushton reported a temperature coefficient of 1.34. These investigators point out, however, that a general criterion of the statement that chemical reactions generally have temperature coefficients greater than 2 for a 10-degree interval is that these temperature coefficients usually apply to reactions at an interface. They present the following arguments in favor of chemical processes controlling the rate:

(1) High temperature coefficient

(2) Proportionality of rate to concentration of acid present or, in general, for a number of acids

$$k' = k_1' C_{A_1} + k_2' C_{A_2} + k_3' C_{A_3} + \cdots \tag{12.125}$$

(3) Independence of the rate of the oxonium ion concentration in the case of weak acids

(4) A linear relationship between the logarithm of the velocity constant and the logarithm of the acid strength

Point (1) was discussed above. In the case of point (2), Kilpatrick and Rushton showed that when the oxonium ion was held constant, then the rate of reaction is proportional to the concentration of the other acid or concentrations of the other acids present.

Figure 8 taken from the paper by Kilpatrick and Rushton shows that the rate of reaction in the case of weak acids is independent of the hydrogen-ion concentration. Further these investigators found that the rate of dissolution of metals was practically independent of the acid-base ratio in buffer solutions.

Regarding point (4) it was found that the velocity constant was related to the strength of the reacting acid by an equation of the type

$$k_a' = G_1 K_A^x \tag{12.126}$$

where k_a' is the velocity constant, K_A the dissociation constant of the reacting acid, and G_1 and x are constants. x has a value greater than zero and less than one. Taking into account different charge types, as H_3O^+ and HSO_4^-, and also the statistical factor (see the Brönsted equation for acid base catalysis, Chapter XI) the more general equation is

$$k_a' = G_1 K_a^x q^x p^{1-x} \tag{12.127}$$

where q is the number of positions at which a proton can be attached to the molecule of the conjugate base, and p is the number of ionizable hydrogen atoms in the molecule. Kilpatrick and Rushton tested this equation for the dissolution reactions by putting it in the form

$$\log \frac{k_a'}{p} = \log G_1 + x \log K_A \frac{q}{p} \tag{12.128}$$

and plotting $\log \dfrac{k_a'}{p}$ as ordinates against $\log \dfrac{q}{p} K_A$ as abscissas. They found that while the agreement with the theory is not exceptional, that nevertheless there was a general relationship between the velocity constant and acid strength.

In brief, Kilpatrick and Rushton found that their experimental data were not in agreement with the older diffusion theory, but might be explained on the basis of a diffusion theory based upon the extended theory of acids, in which the diffusion of a molecular acid like acetic acid to the surface of the metal must be considered, as well as the

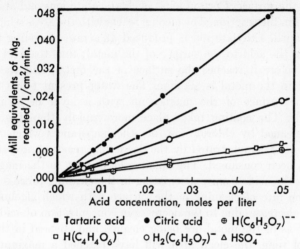

Figure 8 Rate of dissolution of magnesium as a function of acid concentration in solutions of various weak acids.

diffusion of the hydrogen ion. Subsequently two reactions would take place at the surface of the metal. These reactions can be typified thus:

$$H_3O^+ + e \longrightarrow H + H_2O$$
$$HA + e \longrightarrow H + A^-$$

Nevertheless, from their arguments, one would conclude that some chemical reaction could be the rate-controlling process. However, any modification must account for the water reaction.

Sclar and Kilpatrick (*J. Am. Chem. Soc.*, **59**, 584, 1937) found that for the reaction of magnesium with acids in ethyl alcohol, the magnesium could displace the hydrogen from the molecules of ethyl alcohol without the intermediate formation of a solvated proton; in fact, the predominant reaction was between the metal and the alcohol.

The production of ethylate ion was sufficiently rapid to prevent other acids from reaching the metal. In the reaction there was an induction period, followed by a period of accelerated reaction, after which the rate of reaction again decreased. The explanation given by Sclar and Kilpatrick is as follows: The induction period probably begins with acid reacting and removing a coating from the metal surface. Chloride ion or chlorine compounds, if present, aid the acid in cleaning the surface. Certain ions, as chloracetate ions, aid also when produced in the reaction. The alcohol reacts with the areas which have been cleaned. Ethylate ion is produced at a rate exceeding the approach of the acid to the surface of the metal; thus the acid is neutralized before it reaches the surface of the metal, and the region adjacent to the metal is alkaline. The water present tends to coat again the surface of the magnesium with a layer of magnesium hydroxide. The coating takes place more rapidly than the surface can be cleaned by chloride ion, or other substances which may be present, as is demonstrated by the decreasing reaction rate after the acid has been consumed. The alkaline layer next to the magnesium prevents the acids from participating in the cleaning process. Meanwhile, the rate of cleaning of the surface with which alcohol is not reacting decreases due to the decrease in concentration of acid. When equal areas of the metal are being cleaned and covered in the same period of time, the clean area will have reached a maximum and, consequently, the maximum rate of dissolution of the metal will be obtained. After the point of maximum rate of reaction is reached, the surface will be covered more rapidly than it is cleaned.

The measured rate of reaction at any time depends on the area of clean surface which, in turn, appears to be related to the concentration of ethylate ion adjacent to it. This should be so, since the concentration of ethylate ion depends on how much magnesium hydroxide has been formed on the surface of the metal due to the reaction

$$Mg + 2H_3O^+ + 2C_2H_5OH \longrightarrow Mg(OH)_2 + 2C_2H_5OH_2^+ + H_2$$

From the results of experiments to determine the effect of temperature and the rate of stirring upon the rate of dissolution of the metal, Sclar and Kilpatrick concluded that the rate of disappearance of the ethylate ion from the transport of acid and ethylate ion only partially determines the concentration of ethylate at the reaction surface. It also depends upon the rate of reaction of the metal with the alcohol molecules. In other words, the two rates do not differ sufficiently in magnitude for one to be the sole rate-determining factor.

Fletcher and Kilpatrick (*J. Phys. Chem.*, **42**, 113, 1938) and Dunning and Kilpatrick (*J. Phys. Chem.*, **42**, 215, 1938) have studied the rate of reactions of amalgams with acids. Their data confirmed the former work on the dissolution of amalgams. In general they reached the following conclusions:

(1) For strong acids and for certain weak acids, the rate of solution, under conditions such that the water reaction is negligible, is independent of the concentration of the alkali metal. The rate depends upon the stirring, is proportional to the surface, and is proportional to the concentration of strong acid above 1×10^{-4} moles per liter. For weak acids the increase in rate above the water reaction is proportional to the acid concentration.

(2) For the water reaction, and in the case of sodium amalgams, for the reaction with primary phosphate, the rate of reaction is proportional to the square root of the alkali metal concentration, to the acid concentration, and to the surface. The rate is independent of the oxonium-ion concentration.

(3) When oxygen is present, hydrogen peroxide is formed and reacts with the sodium amalgam. Thus might be explained in part, the lack of reproducibility in the rate of reaction of the amalgam with water.

An additional word might be said about the dependence of the rate upon the stirring. Dunning and Kilpatrick found that the equation of Roller (*J. Phys. Chem.*, **39**, 231, 1935), namely,

$$\frac{k'_{obs}}{s^{0.67}} = \text{constant} \tag{12.129}$$

where s is the rate of stirring, held fairly well for the dissolution of sodium from sodium amalgam in hydrochloric acid, and concluded that the controlling process in this reaction is the transport of the acid to the surface of the amalgam. The conclusion can be justified also by considering a mechanism similar to that proposed by Sclar and Kilpatrick (*loc. cit.*) for the dissolution of magnesium in alcoholic solutions of acids.

The catalytic decomposition of sodium hypochlorite solutions

Howell (*Proc. Roy. Soc.*, **104A**, 134, 1923) assumed that the rate of the catalytic decomposition of sodium hypochlorite solutions followed the unimolecular law; but indicated that the reaction rate constant k' increases as the reaction proceeds. He found that sodium ions increased the rate, whereas hydroxyl ions decreased the rate. Chirnoaga (*J. Chem. Soc.*, **1926**, 1693), however, found that the use of the equation

$$- \frac{dc}{dt} = k'c^{1/n} \qquad (12.130)$$

gave more concordant results. In this equation c is the concentration, t the time in minutes, and k' and n are constants. This equation was particularly applicable where the catalyst was very active, but in cases where the catalyst was less active the unimolecular law held.

The stoichiometrical equation for the decomposition is

$$NaClO \longrightarrow NaCl + \tfrac{1}{2}O_2$$

We shall deal in this section almost exclusively with the work of Lewis and co-workers (*J. Phys. Chem.*, **32**, 243 and 1808, 1928; *ibid.*, **35**, 915, 1931; *ibid.*, **37**, 917, 1933), who found in general that the mechanism can best be explained by use of either the equation for a zero-order reaction, which is

$$dC/dt = k' \qquad (12.131)$$

or the equation for the first-order reaction, namely,

$$- \frac{dC}{dt} = k_1'C \qquad (12.132)$$

For the zero-order reaction it was found that when the volume of evolved oxygen in cubic centimeters was plotted against time in minutes, a straight line was obtained in most cases over a range of from 10 to 20 per cent of the total reaction. Other examples of zero-order reactions are the hydrolysis of sugar solutions by enzymes studied by Armstrong and Hilditch (*Proc. Roy. Soc.*, **98A**, 27, 1920); the hydrogenation of certain unsaturated organic esters using nickel as catalyst also studied by Armstrong and Hilditch; the decomposition of hydrogen peroxide by colloidal platinum studied by Bredig and von Breneck (*Z. physik. Chem.*, **31**, 266, 1899); and the decomposition of certain gases at the surface of hot wires studied by Hinshelwood (*Kinetics of Chemical Change in Gaseous Systems*, Oxford, Clarendon Press, 1926, p. 148). Lewis (*J. Phys. Chem.*, **32**, 243, 1928) listed the conditions for a zero-order reaction as: (1) comparatively high concentration of the substance undergoing change; (2) the catalyst should maintain its activity; (3) there should be small quantities of catalyst in order that the active mass, i.e., the adsorbed reactant on the catalyst, is small compared with the bulk of reactant; (4) the decomposition of the reactant catalyst complex must be the slow reaction, thus insuring at all times a catalytic surface completely covered with reactant.

In studying the reaction rate, Lewis (*loc. cit.*) placed 25 cubic centimeters of sodium hypochlorite solution of the proper strength in an especially designed reaction flask. One cubic centimeter of a solution of copper sulfate, cobalt sulfate, or mixtures of copper and ferric sulfates to be used as a catalyst, was placed in a capsule in the neck of the flask until the desired moment, when it was allowed to fall into the hypochlorite solution; or pipetted directly into the reaction flask through a short neck which was immediately closed. At the instant the catalyst was added to the hypochlorite, a stop watch and shaker were started. The oxygen evolved was collected in a water-jacketed burette and its volume read at suitable intervals of time until the reaction was complete. The sulfate solutions in the alkaline hypochlorite solutions precipitated the oxides of the metals. These oxides were the actual catalysts. Sometimes the peroxides of the metals were used.

Calculations were made using the integrated forms of Eq. (12.131) and (12.132), namely,

$$k' = \frac{x}{t} \tag{12.133}$$

where x is the cubic centimeters of oxygen evolved in t minutes, and

$$k_1' = \frac{2.303}{t} \log \frac{C_0}{C_0 - C_t} \tag{12.134}$$

where t is the time in minutes, C_0 is the concentration of hypochlorite expressed in cubic centimeters of oxygen at zero time, and C_t is the concentration after time t. The equation

$$k_2' = \frac{1}{t} \left(\frac{C_0^{\frac{N-1}{N}} - C_t^{\frac{N-1}{N}}}{N-1} \right) N \tag{12.135}$$

which is the well-known Freundlich adsorption equation, was also used. In this equation C_0, C_t, and t are the same as in Eq. (12.134), and N is a constant.

From the data k' is found to remain fairly constant for a time but falls off after 20 to 30 per cent of the reaction is completed. On the other hand k_1' increases as the reaction proceeds. For mixed oxides of iron and copper, k_1' falls after an initial increase. Values of k_2' are more concordant than k_1' but increase or decrease, paralleling the k_1' values. See Table IV for an example of these data.

TABLE IV   Decomposition of sodium hypochlorite using copper oxide as a catalyst

Temp. $35°$ C; $C_0 = 35.8$; 1 cubic centimeter of $CuSO_4$ containing 0.6 gram of Cu per liter; $1/n = 0.8$ (See Eq. 12.130)

t (min.)	x	$k' \left(\dfrac{\text{cc. of } O_2}{\text{min.}}\right)$	k_1' (min.$^{-1}$)	$k_2' \left(\dfrac{\text{cc. of } O_2}{\text{min.}}\right)$
14	2.2	0.157	0.00452	0.0089
20	3.42	.171	.00512	.0100
30	5.46	.182	.00556	.0109
40	7.5	.187	.00588	.0116
55	10.1	.183	.00603	.0119
64	11.5	.180	.00605	.0118
75	13.1	.174	.00607	.0118
91	15.3	.160	.00609	.0116
125	18.9	.151	.00601	.0114
148	20.7	.140	.00584	.0110
194	24.1	.124	.00575	.0105

The mixed oxides showed a marked promoter effect on the decomposition rate.

The decomposition of sodium hypochlorite solutions when a constant fresh supply of hypochlorite was allowed to pass over a fixed amount of catalyst gave k' values which were practically constant over a wide range of concentration. It was found that the rate of the reaction was proportional to the concentration of the catalyst.

The normal temperature coefficient, $\dfrac{k_{40}'}{k_{30}'} = 2.0$ and $\dfrac{k_{45}'}{k_{35}'} = 2.02$, obtained for this reaction, indicates that the governing step in the catalytic decomposition of the hypochlorite is chemical in nature. Lewis pictures the reaction mechanism as being the combination of hypochlorite ions or molecules with the catalyst, forming the addition compound which immediately breaks down. As long as the concentration of the hypochlorite is such that when a catalyst-hypochlorite molecule breaks down another hypochlorite ion or molecule combines with the catalyst, there will be a steady rate of constant activity. In time, however, the rate will fall due to any one or a combination of the following causes: (1) change in the activity of the catalyst due to a change in its surface; (2) poisoning of the catalyst, in this case by hydroxyl ions; (3) a low concentration of reactant in the neighborhood of the catalyst. Data obtained under such conditions usually obey the unimolecular equation of Freundlich, Eq. (12.135).

Lewis (*J. Phys. Chem.*, **32**, 1808, 1928) studied further the promoter action of iron oxide in the copper oxide catalysis of the decomposition of sodium hypochlorite. He found as before that the reaction rate was proportional to the concentration of the catalyst. In the case of unpromoted catalyst the values of k' and k_1' fell off rapidly after the first 4 or 5 per cent of the reaction had taken place. By increasing the amount of promoter for a given quantity of catalyst, the values of k' and k_1' fell off less rapidly until satisfactory results were obtained for k_1', as shown in Table V. On the other hand, when small quantities of catalyst were added to an excess of promoter, the values of k' were constant, whereas the values of k_1' increased. The data given graphically in Fig. 9 show that the most effective mixture of catalyst and promoter is about one milligram atom of copper to one milligram atom

TABLE V **Iron oxide promoted decomposition of sodium hypochlorite using copper oxide catalyst**

Temp. 35° C; $C_0 = 89.3$; catalyst: 0.003504 gram of Fe used with 0.00578 gram of Cu

t (min.)	x	$k' \left(\dfrac{\text{cc. of } O_2}{\text{min.}} \right)$	k_1' (min.$^{-1}$)
2	2.7	1.35	0.01541
3	5.4	1.8	.02077
4	7.7	1.92	.02254
5	10.0	2.0	.02373
6	12.5	2.1	.02528
7	14.56	2.08	.02570
8	16.5	2.06	.02560
9	18.3	2.03	.02560
10	20.2	2.02	.02570
11	21.9	1.99	.0256
12	23.2	1.94	.02522
14	26.8	1.915	.0255
16	30.1	1.88	.0257
18	32.5	1.8	.0252
20	34.9	1.75	.0249
22	38.7	1.75	.0258
23	39.8	1.73	.0257

of iron. The values for the temperature coefficient for the unpromoted reaction were low, falling between 2.1 and 1.2 over the temperature range 25° C to 45° C. For the promoted reaction the values of the temperature coefficient were normal, being 2.3 over the range 25° C to 35° C, but fell off to 1.7 for the range 35° C to 45° C.

The rapid fall in the reaction rate was attributed by Lewis to changes on the catalytic surface. The active points are decreased by

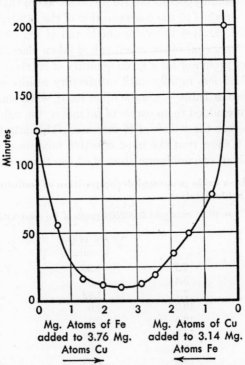

Figure 9 Effect of ratio of promotor (iron oxide) and catalyst (copper oxide) upon the time for the decomposition of sodium hypochlorite.

coagulation, dehydration, and similar phenomena. The low temperature coefficient of the unpromoted reaction is accounted for on the same basis. Thus the normal increase in the reaction rate with increasing temperature is offset by the increased rate of decay of active catalyst at the higher temperatures. The promoter stabilizes the catalyst, for when the promoter is present, all of the initial active centers are preserved over (at least) 20 to 30 per cent of the reaction. Thus the promoted reaction should give a normal temperature coefficient, at least over a narrow temperature range.

The normal temperature coefficient obtained with the promoted reaction suggests that the reaction might be taking place in the homogeneous phase. Lewis, however, gave four reasons why this was improbable. These reasons are: (1) the rate of reaction is directly proportional to the concentration of catalyst present; (2) the rate falls off with certain physical treatment of the catalyst, such as letting the catalyst age, grinding the catalyst in a colloidal mill, bubbling oxygen through a suspension of the catalyst, and heating the catalyst in a closed tube; each of the above mentioned treatments lowered the effectiveness of the catalyst; (3) the catalyst can be poisoned by the addition of certain salts; (4) the presence of the oxides is essential to the decomposition of the hypochlorites even though sufficient copper and iron are in the solution to give positive tests.

Studying the promoter action of hydrated magnesium oxide in the hydrated copper oxide catalysis of sodium hypochlorite, Lewis (*J. Phys. Chem.*, **35,** 915, 1931) found that the maximum promotion of copper catalyst, under experimental conditions used by him, was reached when the ratio of copper atoms to magnesium atoms was one to three or four. When the ratio of copper to magnesium was one atom to eight atoms, the promoter effect practically disappeared.

The suitably promoted catalyst retained its activity by aiding in the formation and preservation of active centers on the catalyst particles by preventing the agglomeration of the particles. That agglomeration was prevented was evidenced by the promoted catalyst retaining its blue color, while the unpromoted hydrated copper oxide catalyst was blue when first precipitated but turned soon to dark brown or black. Weiser (*The Hydrous Oxides*, New York, McGraw-Hill Book Company, Inc., 1926) states that large particles of copper oxide are black whilst the hydrous oxide consists of very much more highly dispersed, gelatinous particles which are blue. Lewis believes that it is not unreasonable to suppose that the ideally promoted hydrated copper oxide catalyst is one in which each molecule is separated from its neighbors by a definite number of molecules of the promoter. Lewis and Seegmiller (*J. Phys. Chem.*, **37,** 917, 1933), studying the promoter effect of various metallic oxides upon the copper oxide catalyzed decomposition of sodium hypochlorite conclude, however, that there is no apparent simple relation between the crystal structure of the promoters and their activity. Lewis (*loc. cit.*) had previously believed that oxides or hydroxides whose crystal structures are the same as those of the catalyst oxides should have the property of separating the catalyst molecules from each other in a definite manner, for example, by forming mixed crystals, and thus prove to be the best promoters.

Lewis and Seegmiller found for different promoters maximum promotion was obtained, not at a definite ratio of promoter to catalyst atoms, but rather at various ratios, depending upon the promoter used. With each promoter its effect became negligible as the ratio of promoter to catalyst became high. This was explained by assuming that the active centers were covered at the higher ratios. The fact that maximum promotion came at various ratios of catalyst to promoter indicated, according to Lewis and Seegmiller, a physical spreading out of the catalyst (perhaps on a foundation of promoter molecules) rather than to any definite arrangement (crystal pattern).

Index

327

LIBRARY
R.A.E., R.P.D.

No..........................

WESTCOTT

LIBRARY
R.A.E., R.P.D.

No.............................

WESTCOTT